Modern Radar Techniques

Modern Radar Techniques

Editor: M.J.B. Scanlan

COLLINS
8 Grafton Street, London W1

Collins Professional Books
William Collins Sons & Co. Ltd
8 Grafton Street, London W1X 3LA

First published in Great Britain by
Collins Professional Books 1987

British Library Cataloguing in Publication Data
Modern radar techniques.
1. Radar
I. Scanlan, M.J.B.
621.3848   TK6575

ISBN 0-00-383190-6

Typeset by Katerprint Typesetting Services, Oxford
Printed and bound in Great Britain by
Mackays of Chatham, Kent

Contents

Preface

The six chapters of this book each contain a coherent account of an important radar topic, dealt with at review paper length and including a good bibliography. The topics have been chosen as having present-day relevance and future growth: Chapters 1 and 2 deal with important sub-systems, 3 and 4 with general topics important to every radar system designer and 5 and 6, by way of illustration, with two radar systems which seem to have been somewhat neglected elsewhere.

None of these topics is new; indeed, many of them have been foreshadowed or known for years, or even decades. Nor are they claimed to be comprehensive, since a number of other topics came to mind in the planning of this book. These particular six chapters were chosen to cover matters which are at least vaguely familiar to most radar engineers, but where more detailed knowledge in one place, written by an international authority, would be of most value. The treatment is designed to be readable, descriptive and informative, rather than rigorously mathematical.

It may help the reader to put the topics of this book in context if we look back more than 40 years to the earliest operational radar system, the British CH (Chain Home) system. CH used very roughly the same frequencies as the over-the-horizon radars of Chapter 5: it had a number of manually operated antijamming devices (Chapter 4 calls them ECCMs) including a measure of frequency agility; it had an electromechanical calculator which processed readings taken by an operator; and, being a flood-lit system, it avoided the problem of a fluctuating target cross section (Chapter 3) by having a long (virtually infinite) integration time. (At such a low frequency, we were blessedly ignorant of target statistics!)

Today's descendents of these facilities, as discussed in this book, are almost infinitely faster, more powerful and more adaptable. Over-the-horizon radar, using high-resolution Doppler processing, extracts valuable information from what was clutter to CH radar. Frequency agility is available on a pulse-to-pulse basis, if necessary, the new frequency being selected as free from jamming: ECMs are now more varied and sophisticated, and so are the ECCMs, as discussed in Chapter 4. A modern data processor (Chapter 1), allied to a phased array radar (Chapter 2), can search for, and track, hundreds of targets simultaneously: the system can null itself on jamming sources. With modern high frequency, narrow beamwidth radars, target fluctuation (Chapter 3) is a real problem, only alleviated by frequent searches of the target space, and by frequency agility and diversity. Chapter 3 makes it quite clear that radar detection is something of a statistical gamble: we can only calculate the odds and then bend them as far as possible in our favour.

To sum up then, this book deals with two major radar problems (Chapters 3 and 4); shows two ways in which modern electronic techniques can help (Chapters 1 and 2); and describes two radar systems (Chapters 5 and 6) which would have been unthinkable a decade or two ago.

Finally, it is my pleasant duty to express my warmest thanks to those who have contributed to this book. First in the list must be the authors, who have made time in their crowded schedules to write their chapters, and who have dealt with my nit-picking queries with patience and courtesy. Next must come Bernard Watson and Janet Murphy of Collins Professional Books, who have cajoled, chivvied and consoled authors and editor alike, as occasion required. I am also indebted to my secretaries, Sheila French and Pamela Betts, and to Louise Titford and Tracy Cooch of the M.R.C. drawing office, who have drawn most of the artwork. I have also to thank David Speake and John Williams, successive Directors of the Marconi Research Centre, for allowing me to use some of the facilities of M.R.C. in the preparation of this book. Last of all, I owe a debt to some dozens, or even hundreds, of individuals through the years who have contributed to the unconscious osmotic process by which I have acquired most of what I know about radar. Editing this book has crystallised for me many ideas which were vague and amorphous: I hope the book will do the same for many readers.

M.J.B.

Authors' Biographies

Billetter, D. R.

Mr Billetter is presently a consultant in Woodland Hills, Ca. He was employed by ITT-Gilfillan prior to becoming a consultant, involved with advanced programs. He was previously at RCA where he was responsible for advanced aspects of the Aegis Weapon System and the AN/SPY-1 radar; he was also involved with several forward-looking programs for Air Defence and Ballistic Missile Defence. He was at SEMCOR Inc. for 3½ years working on advanced techniques for the use and control of phased array radars, primarily the SPY-1. Mr Billetter was initially at RCA for 18 years where he functioned as Program Manager, System Manager and in a broad spectrum of engineering roles.

Mr Billetter graduated from Lehigh University, Bethlehem, Pennsylvania in 1954 with a BSME degree. He completed most of the requirements toward an MSEE degree at Villanova University in Philadelphia, Pennsylvania.

Cole, H. W.

H. W. Cole, after service in the Royal Corps of Signals, worked for A. C. Cossor Ltd as a development, and later as a field commissioning, engineer. He joined Marconi Radar Systems Ltd in 1960 as a radar systems engineer, specialising in secondary radar. He was Development Programme Manager for Marconi's monopulse secondary surveillance radar system 'Messenger'. Author of many papers on radar and air traffic control, he represents Marconi on several professional bodies concerned with air traffic control. His book *Understanding Radar* was published by Collins in 1985.

Forrest, J. R.

J. R. Forrest graduated at Cambridge University in 1964 and then carried out research at Oxford University until 1967, and at Stanford University, Ca., until 1970. Between 1970 and 1984 he was at University College London, first as Lecturer, then Reader and finally Professor of Electronic Engineering. He built up a research group active in the topics of phased array radar, satellite communications and microwave opto-electronics. He has acted as a consultant to a number of organisations in Europe and the USA and has also worked on a number of government committees dealing with electronics, radar, telecommunications and professional engineering training. In 1984 he joined Marconi Defence Systems as Technical Director and was elected to the Fellowship of Engineering in 1985. In 1986, he was appointed Director of Engineering to the Independent Broadcasting Authority.

Johnston, Stephen L.
Stephen L. Johnston received the BEE degree with Honours in 1948 and the MSEE degree in 1949 from the Georgia Institute of Technology, Atlanta, Georgia. He was a research assistant at the Engineering Experiment Station at Georgia Tech from 1947 to 1950, entered Federal Civil Service in 1950 at the Joint Long Range Proving Ground, Patrick AFB, Florida, and was employed by the US Army Missile Command at Redstone Arsenal, Alabama from 1951 to 1980. He is now the Editor-in-Chief of the International Radar Directory and also a lecturer for George Washington University Continuing Engineering Education. Currently he is conducting short courses on his first book, *Radar Electronic Counter-Countermeasures*, and his second book, *Millimeter Wave Radar*. He is a Senior Member of the IEEE, and a past Associate Fellow of the AIAA. He has published and presented over 50 papers at numerous international technical symposia, both professional and government.

Olin, Irwin D.
Irwin Olin received a BSEE from the Newark College of Engineering and an MS from Rutgers University in the USA. His professional experience includes development of microwave components and antennas, radar systems design, and backscatter measurements and statistical analyses of radar targets and the sea. He has actively participated in an international committee on radar technology and served briefly as a Project Officer with the Ballistic Research Laboratory in Aberdeen, Maryland, and as an exchange scientist with the Royal Signals and Radar Establishment in Malvern, UK. Presently, Mr Olin is Associate Superintendent of the Radar Division of the Naval Research Laboratory in the USA.

Proof: **Shearman, E. D. R.**
E. D. R. Shearman, after early work on HF communication in the Admiralty Signal Establishment, joined the DSIR Radio Research Station (now the SERC Rutherford-Appleton Labora-

tory), where he carried out research in ionospheric sounding, HF backscatter radar investigations and satellite instrumentation. In 1962 he joined the University of Birmingham, Department of Electronic and Electrical Engineering, where he led a research team active in radar, satellite communication and, more recently, remote sensing by radar. Until recently Head of the Postgraduate School, he is now a Research Professor, active in HF radar oceanography and microwave radar studies. In 1985 he was awarded the Faraday Medal of the IEE for contributions to the understanding of radio wave propagation and sea state sensing.

CHAPTER 1
Computers and Data Processing in Radar

DALE R. BILLETTER

The application of digital computers to radar has evolved from providing simple throughput processing of output data, to performing many of the classical radar functions as well as new functions. Computers (control processors) intimately control the operation of most modern radars.

While the control processor uses disciplines not historically associated with radar design, i.e. those of computer program design, it has become an inherent part of the radar, and is now the focal point of effective radar system operation.

1.1 Radar control

The radar control processor, as considered here, provides not only the control of radar operation but also tracking and automatic test and exercising. These functions may be allocated to different sets of programs and even to different hardware. In larger systems, of which the radar is only a part, the testing and exercising may be system functions which are supported by the radar control processor. Tracking may also be a system function. All of these functions will be considered to be resident in the radar control processor, but the three functions will be treated independently. The control processor allows the radar to function efficiently, coordinating the operation of the radar within restrictive constraints. Figure 1.1 presents an epitomised version of this function.

The radar control design as discussed here relates to a 3D search and tracking radar. The radar may employ a mechanically rotated antenna with electronic beam steering in only elevation or in both azimuth and elevation, or it may use fixed antennas with

1

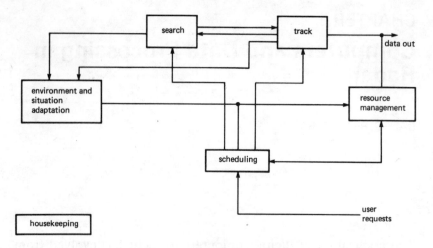

Fig. 1.1   Functional control.

electronic beam steering in both dimensions. It is assumed that
the radar generates separate beams for search and track[1]. The
concepts presented here are also applicable to 2D search radars,
but to a lesser degree.

The radar control design will not be constrained by the size of
the radar processor. Recent advances in the state of the processing art provide relief in the form of faster and smaller computers.
Historically, some of the very early phased array radars were
restricted in terms of processor size and, therefore, in the ability
to control the radar effectively and efficiently. In several cases,
the advent of phased arrays has been the driving impetus for the
development of larger and faster processors.

The control processor is involved in all aspects of the radar's
operation[2,3]. Figure 1.2 is a simplification of the radar control
process. The discussion in this chapter cannot delve into all
aspects of the radar control process. Several volumes would be
required to define adequately and thoroughly the control process
design, which is far more complex and interrelated than is shown
in either Fig. 1.1 or Fig. 1.2. The computer operation must deal
with issues as they develop in real time, so that the programs
cannot just start and run until complete. Interrupts will occur
constantly and must be dealt with on a priority basis. The control
design must be both adaptive and reactive.

Much of the control design centres around the establishment of
priorities. Many different sets of priorities must be developed and
they will rarely be either compatible or static. Priorities must be

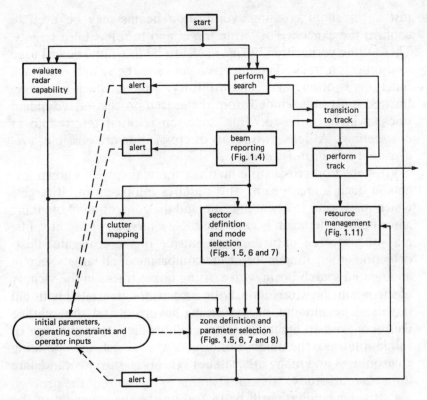

Fig. 1.2 The control process.

established for spatially distributed radar functions, for targets being tracked, for control functions, and for interrupts. The list continues. An early establishment of the various priorities facilitates and simplifies the control design process. These initial priorities must be established as functions of prior events. Section 1.1.7 describes the use of priorities and the relationship to other events and timing. Some of the priorities must have dual values: the value of starting the event and the value of continuing the event once started. The initial priority of a burnthrough, for example, may be low but once started the priority of continuing may be very high.

The interrelationships of the functions are far more extensive than is shown in the example and are the subject of many tradeoffs. An example of this is the connections shown between the search and track functions in Fig. 1.1 and Fig. 1.2. The track function starts with a detection of a target in the search function. The detection is usually a complex operation involving more than just a threshold crossing; verification beams may be used to confirm the existence of a true target and to reject false targets. These same verification beams may also be the initial beams used to establish a track. The interface between the search and track functions is often vague and arbitrary. Targets which are being tracked must be excluded from the search process or redundant tracks will be initiated. This exclusion is often referred to as *crossgating*[2]. At least two forms of crossgating are possible, *pre-detection* and *post-detection*.

Pre-detection crossgating involves the blanking of known targets in each search beam. This requires a look-up of all targets which may occur in a search beam and the generation of blanking gates before the beam is generated. New targets, or target splits, may be obscured until they are outside of the crossgate. Post-detection crossgating involves the comparing of all targets seen in an ungated search beam with existing target tracks in the vicinity of the beam. New targets may be incorrectly associated with old targets. The amount of processing involved and the relative merits of the two techniques varies, depending upon the type of validation used, the number of targets which exist, the operating environment and many other issues. This is an obvious candidate for a tradeoff study.

Particular emphasis will be placed on the management of the radar's operation throughout this chapter. Attention will be paid to environmental adaptation in selecting radar parameters to optimise the performance of the radar under a given set of environmental conditions. Considerable attention must be paid to the resource management of the radar throughout the determination of the radar's parameters. The particular aspects of radar control design covered in this chapter are indicated by the references in Fig. 1.2 to other figures in this chapter. It will be assumed that the radar has the ability to perform its basic functions of search and track.

The control design set forth does not represent an actual control design; it is certainly not a complete design. The discussions which follow will highlight certain aspects of the control design and illustrate how the control design is to be implemented.

1.1.1 UTILISING THE OPERATOR

The role chosen for the operator will, to a very high degree, dictate the control design. Computers are far more capable of making routine decisions than are human beings. The human being, however, is far superior when reasoning is required. The degree of superiority of the operator depends on his abilities and his training. The role of the operator may be considerably different for different radar applications as well as for different levels of manpower available to operate the radar. Where decisions are to be highly automated, proper decision criteria have to be defined and provisions made to obtain the necessary data to allow the computer to make the proper decision. The same statement applies to decisions made by an operator, but the decision criteria and the information provided need not be as explicit. The human being is capable of resolving conflicts or areas of indecision, although often arbitrarily and not always properly. The human being knows the type of information required and can seek more information from superiors or by drawing upon past experience. The computer is certainly capable of determining when it does not have adequate information or criteria for making a decision; it can then only request assistance.

Radars designed for scientific or information gathering applications will usually be operated by a higher skill level of personnel than tactical radars which are used in a hostile environment. The information gathering radar can benefit from the use of the operator, in that unforeseen situations or sources of data may arise in which the operator is called upon to use his inherent intelligence, his background and his training to optimise the radar. While the tactical radar could benefit from such training and high level skilled personnel, these are usually not available. The tactical radar must, therefore, be designed to impose the minimum requirements on the operator associated with his skill level. The fully automated radar eliminates the need for operators and is desirable in that human beings need not be put in threatening or inhospitable locations. This is possible for relatively simple radars such as early warning radars, with the processing now available. The tactical radar, on the other hand, which experiences continually changing environments and situations, is far more difficult to automate fully in that the decision criteria are more difficult to specify and obtaining the information required to facilitate fully automated decisions can consume a large amount of the available radar resources. In this case, the operator's role may be one of providing rules of operation, monitoring the operation of the radar and resolving conflicts which occur. In designing a fully or highly automated radar, it is exceedingly important that a situation not be allowed to occur where a conflict or decision point is reached which will result in the radar ceasing to operate. This is true whether an operator is available to resolve such difficulties or not. Certainly, when the operator is available he should be used; but it should not be necessary that the operator make a decision for the radar to continue to operate and provide at least some level of performance.

The role assumed for the operator throughout this discussion will be one of monitoring the control process of the radar, providing inputs to define how the control processor should function, and resolving conflicts. The control program will request assistance from the operator but will not cease to function if the operator does not intervene.

1.1.2 IMPLEMENTING OPERATING DOCTRINE

The constraints on the operation of the radar control processor are provided through the insertion of operating doctrine. The operating doctrine will not necessarily always be the same. Dependent upon the preferences of the user or higher echelons of command, different degrees of automation and flexibility may be allowed within the control processor. Some users will recognise the need for, and prefer, a high degree of automation; other users will not have the same degree of faith in the computer. The situation may change with time as the situation or capabilities of operating personnel change. A good control design must be capable of providing different levels of automation and flexibility as dictated by the user. Provisions must be included for the insertion of operating doctrine which can change the manner in which the control program will work. Changes may also be brought about by changes in the status of the equipment, either the classical radar equipments or the control processor itself. Varying degrees of automation are possible. The control processor may sense changes in the status of the equipment and adapt to them, or it may be preferable to have the status of the equipment displayed to an operator who will then make decisions as to how the control processor should operate. The operator should be able to override any automated decisions made by the control processor. Varying levels of displayed information may be desired, depending upon how active a role the operator is to have.

Higher level doctrine may play a significant role in defining the operation of the radar. Varying levels of coordination or constraints on the operation of the radar may be imposed for a variety of reasons and change with time. Doctrine must be an allowable input to the control program, both initially and during operation. Changes in the situation, or the overall status, may change the role of the radar. The radar may be called upon to provide a lower level of performance if all other aspects of the system are functioning at their peak. The radar may be required to provide more performance and, in fact, over-tax itself for a brief period of time, perhaps to the point of damage, if other parts of the system go down, either through inherent unreliability or damage.

In the example which follows, the operating doctrine will be assumed to be an initial input to the control program, thus initialising the operation of the radar. It has been assumed that operating doctrine will be inserted by the operator. At various times, because of conflicts which arise, the operator will be called upon to reassess or modify the operating doctrine.

1.1.3 ADAPTING TO THE ENVIRONMENT[3,4,5]

Figure 1.3 is a simplified flow diagram of the process of adapting the radar's performance to changes in the environment. Foremost is sensing the environment or in some manner, perhaps through other sensors, determining the environment and, more importantly, changes in the environment. It is equally important that the radar be advised of both an improvement and a degradation in the environment. The radar control must be provided with decision criteria so that it can take advantage of the inherent flexibility built into the radar. The control program must have knowledge of the performance capabilities of the radar and against what environmental state the different capabilities are best utilised. The radar must develop an evaluation of the environment to utilise these capabilities fully. The control program must also be aware of the operating status of the radar, not only in terms of what modes and parameters are available to it but in terms of the resource budgets. Much of the control of the radar is involved with utilising the proper parameters in the radar both to optimise its performance and to optimise the resource budgets. In order to minimise the control program, the radar must be capable of defining sectors or zones so that a different set

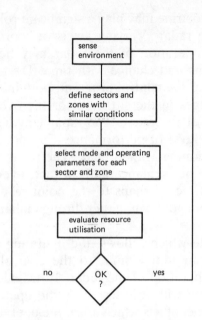

Fig. 1.3   Environment adaptation.

of parameters or modes is not utilised for every beam position. The control program would become unmanageably large and require too much parallel processing if a different set of parameters were used for each beam position.

While some inputs on the situation and the environment may be available from external sources, most of the information needed to determine how the radar should operate is best obtained by the radar itself. This process is defined here as 'beam reporting', which is that function within the radar's operation which evaluates the environmental situation existing in each beam position. Figure 1.4 is a simplified flow diagram of a possible logic for determining the environmental situation existing in a beam. The process depicted is broken into two major subfunctions: the beam position and time report, and the radar return processing. The beam position and time report is a simple matter of filing the statistics associated with the beam in terms of its position in space and the time at which the beam was generated. The radar return processing is a far more complicated process.

The radar return processing, as shown here, is a matter of separating the returns and segregating them according to targets, clutter and interference. The flow diagram of Fig. 1.4 does not

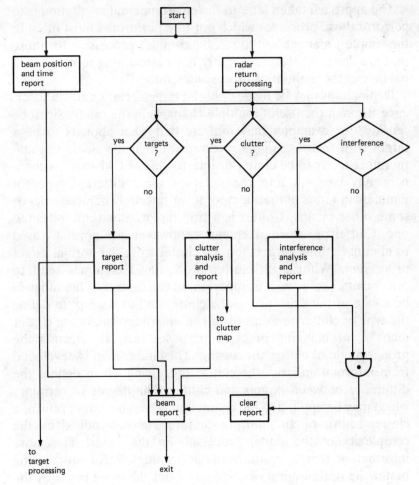

Fig. 1.4 Beam reporting.

assume that a return can be declared unambiguously as a target, clutter or interference; the same signal return can conceivably be denoted as all three. The beam report specifies the location and time of the beam and whether or not that beam contains targets, clutter or interference, and the type of clutter and interference when possible.

In the event that neither clutter nor interference are present, a 'Clear Report' is tagged; note that this allows for the presence of targets. Target reports are also separated and passed to other parts of the radar processor which do the normal target processing – thresholding, tracking, etc.

The approach taken here to the environmental adaptation is to perform those processes which must be performed most often in the simplest manner and to reserve complex processing for those that are done the least frequently, thus attempting to maintain a balance in the amount of processing required.

Distinctions may be made between targets, clutter and interference through the use of multiple channels in the radar. Sidelobe sensing, for example, may indicate that what appears to be a target is in reality a signal received through the sidelobes, and therefore likely to be clutter or interference. ECM analysis channels may be built into the radar to sense different types of jammers in terms of their temporal and spectral characteristics or some other means. Clutter is a true target, albeit an undesired one. Clutter processing techniques, however, are normally used to eliminate those targets termed clutter from the normal target processing. While such clutter processing techniques tend to reject clutter returns, it is important in the control of the radar to be aware of the existence of the clutter and to attempt to define the type of clutter present. Most contemporary radars use clutter maps[4,5] for blanking or other purposes such as selecting the proper mode of clutter processing. The clutter map is developed from information from the clutter processing which defines the difference between targets and clutter. The degree of certainty which may be applied to the distinction between a target return, a clutter return or an interference return is determined by the complexity of the signal processing in the radar. The more information that is made available to the control process the better the optimisation of the control but the more complex the radar processing and the control processing.

The degree of flexibility required in the radar and, hence, the amount of information which the radar must gather to utilise the inherent flexibility must be defined. Given that a decision has been made as to the amount of information which is to be included in each beam report and how much processing is required to support these beam reports, decisions must then be made as to how best to utilise them. The approach taken here is to develop a means of grouping together beam reports with like characteristics.

1.1.4 DEVELOPING SECTORS AND ZONES[2]

Efficient control of the radar requires that the variations in its operating parameters be held to a manageable level. Angle sectors and range zones are therefore established to define areas or volumes within which a given mode of operation and set of operating parameters will be used. Sectors and zones may overlap, although this is not a desirable situation. A reasonable case where zones or sectors would overlap, and create a third sector or zone, is the overlapping of sectors requiring clutter processing in one and ECM processing in the other. The overlapping sector would then require both clutter and ECCM processing. This may be accommodated either by creating a third sector or by allowing sectors to overlap.

Size constraints must be placed on sectors and zones, particularly on their minimum size. The larger the number of allowable sectors or zones, and hence the smaller their size, the higher the degree of operational flexibility in the radar. Large numbers of zones, or very small zones, impose a larger burden on the control processor. The thresholds on both the parameter variations that are desirable and the environmental measurements which are possible must be determined. The relationship between the degree of parameter variation and the size of sectors and zones is not a fixed relationship, however. Fine levels of parameter and mode variations may still be desirable even if the minimum allowable size of a sector or zone is quite large. This may be necessary to ensure that the proper type of operation can be brought to bear, even though very fine changes from one beam to another, or from one sector to another, may not be desirable from a control viewpoint. The degree to which changes in the environment can be sensed has a direct bearing on both the degree of parameter variation desirable and the size constraints on sectors and zones. If only gross changes in the environment can be sensed, then there is little point in having very small sectors and zones and very fine changes in the radar's operating parameters.

There are three distinct phases involved in the developing of sectors and zones for the radar's operation. First, the sectors and zones must be established based on operating constraints and on information on the environment. Second, the number of zones and sectors, which results from the initialising of the sectors and zones, must then be reduced to provide efficient operation of the radar. Third, the sectors and zones must be maintained after the set of zones and sectors has been initiated and reduced to a manageable number. Maintaining the sectors and zones involves sensing changes in the environment, changes in the radar's operational capabilities and changes in the operating constraints, imposed upon the radar. In summary, the zones must be initiated, then reduced and then maintained.

Figures 1.5(a), (b) and (c) show the process for initialising sectors and zones. The beam reports, which resulted from the beam reporting function previously shown in Fig. 1.4, are sorted and collected. The individual beam reports are then further sorted, if clutter or interference exists, according to the type of clutter and interference present. This assumes that the radar is capable of differentiating between clutter and interference and the different types of each. Contiguous beams which have the same type of signal returns are grouped together to form a sector, the operator providing the parameter thresholds. Clutter, being a range function, is amenable to the establishment of range zones. Once the individual beam reports have been collated and combined into sectors and zones, they are further combined. The output at the bottom of Fig. 1.5(a) is the initial environmental sectors and zones. This output is fed to Fig. 1.5(b) and combined with any operating parameter inputs. These parameters may involve the level of performance required from the radar as well as restrictions imposed upon the operation of the radar. Table 1.1 shows a typical set of input operating parameters which can be

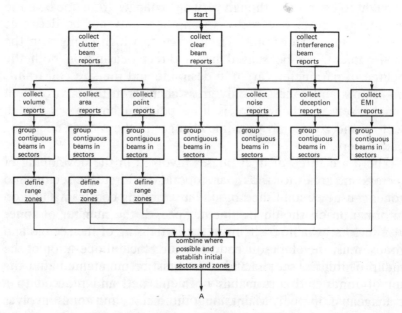

Fig. 1.5(a)   Sector and zone initialisation.

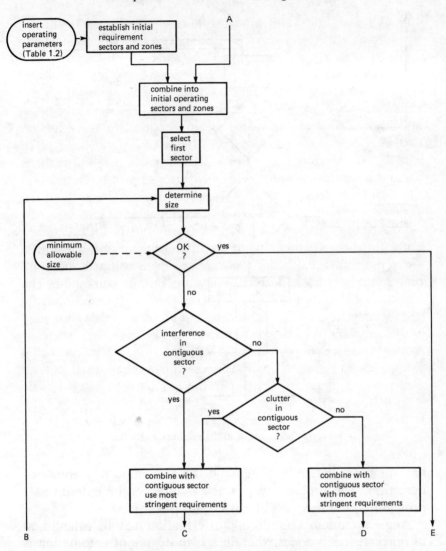

Fig. 1.5(b) Sector and zone initialisation.

used to control the radar's operation. The input parameters on minimum detection range and the associated probability of detection and track should be derived parameters starting with the minimum allowable track initiation range. The control program is more easily developed if it deals with probabilities of detection and probabilities of track. The conversion from a minimum track initiation range to a probability of detection and a probability of track may be done by a separate routine in the control program or by the operator who then, having made the conversion, inserts

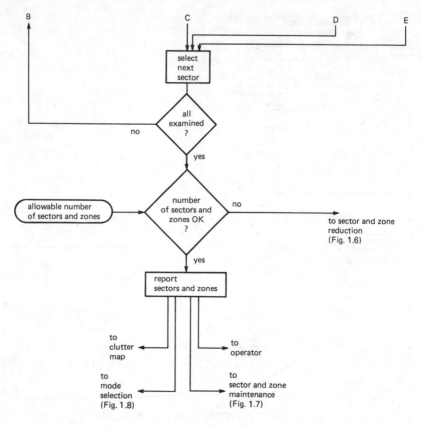

Fig. 1.5(c) Sector and zone initialisation.

the minimum detection range and the associated probability of detection. The probability of track would then be entered as a probability of a successful transition-to-track.

Angle sectors in azimuth and/or elevation may be established as quick reaction zones wherein a high degree of automation is required. There may be radar silence sectors wherein the radar should be forbidden to transmit, either totally or with selected frequencies or waveforms. Range zones may be established wherein the system should not process detections. Any other constraints desired on the part of the operator in terms of controlling the radar as a function of azimuth, elevation and/or range, are provided at this point. These inputs are combined to provide the initial requirement sectors and zones which are then combined with the environmental sectors and zones to establish the initial set of sectors and zones. The individual sectors are then evaluated to determine if their size is above the minimum allow-

Table 1.1   Input operating parameters

Radiation restrictions
Minimum search rates
Minimum ranges
   Detection
   Track initiation
   Firm track
P_d
P_{fa}
Expected target size
Transition-to-track priorities
Operating restrictions
   Radiation
   Track-while-scan
   Group tracking
   ECCM techniques
Minimum acceptable zone size
Minimum acceptable sector size
Minimum acceptable zone separation
Minimum acceptable sector separation
Allowable number of zones and sectors
Search/Track loss ratio

---

able size. If the operator constraint on minimum allowable size of a sector has not been met, the characteristics of the sector under investigation are evaluated as shown in Fig. 1.5(b) to determine in what manner they should be combined with an adjacent sector and what parameters should be used. Note that jamming always takes precedence, followed by clutter, to determine which operating parameters should be used in both cases. If zones or sectors are combined, the resultant parameters are the most stringent combination of the parameters in the combined two sectors or zones.

This process is iterated until all of the sectors are above the minimum allowable size. An evaluation is then made of the total number of sectors and zones to determine whether or not it is acceptable, based on an operator input. If the total number of sectors and zones is acceptable, they are reported to the using sections as shown at the bottom of Fig. 1.5(c). Note that the outputs include in forming the clutter map of all of the clutter zones and sectors. The operator is provided with the results of the initialisation of sectors and zones and the data is forwarded to 'mode selection' and to 'sector and zone maintenance' for the selection of the appropriate modes and parameters to be used and to maintain and adjust the sectors and zones as required. If the number of sectors and/or zones exceeds the allowable number, the 'sector and zone reduction', as shown in Fig. 1.6, is employed. Note that the output of 'sector and zone reduction', as shown at the bottom of Fig. 1.6(c), is the same as the output of the sector and zone initialisation function shown at the bottom of Fig. 1.5(c).

The sector and zone reduction function shown in Fig. 1.6 may receive inputs from either the 'sector and zone initialisation' function or the 'sector and zone maintenance' function. The

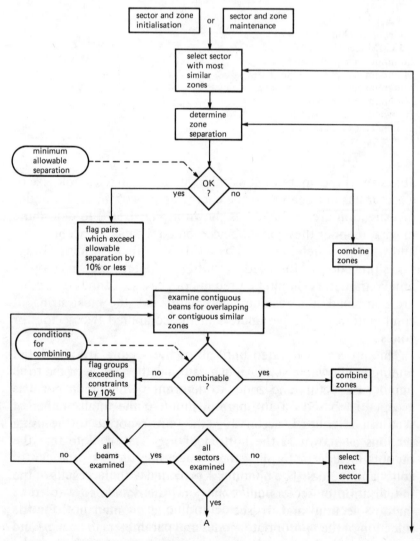

Fig. 1.6(a)   Sector and zone reduction.

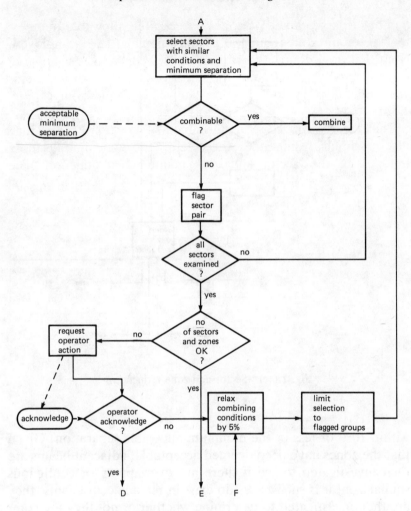

Fig. 1.6(b) Sector and zone reduction.

sector and zone reduction function is called upon whenever the number of sectors and zones requested by the radar control program has exceeded the allowable number as established by the operator. The function starts by selecting a sector and investigating the zones within the sector. It is likely that the zones may be separated by as little as a few range cells in the presence of clutter. The process, as outlined here, picks the sector that has the largest number of similar zones. The separation between the zones is then investigated to determine whether or not it meets the criteria of minimum allowable separation. The beams are flagged for further investigation if the separation of the zones is

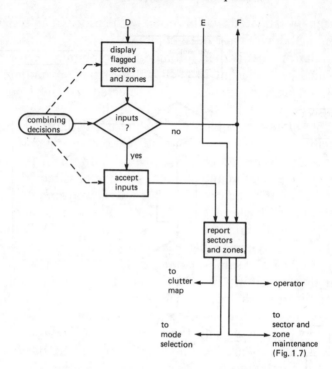

Fig. 1.6(c)   Sector and zone reduction.

within 10% or less of the minimum allowable separation. Given that the zones have been deemed acceptable, adjacent beams are then investigated to see if there are overlapping or contiguous similar zones. If such zones do exist in the adjacent beams, they are then investigated to determine whether or not they are combinable within the sector. (One beam may show a very small separation in clutter and range, whereas the adjacent beams may not show such a separation.) While the separation may be real, and allowable in terms of the minimum allowable separation, it is not a desirable situation to maintain. Even if a target does appear in this small separation, it would quickly be masked by the clutter in the adjacent zones and be lost. The conditions for combining are shown in Fig. 1.6(a) as an operator input but may be an inherent part of the control program. In the event that the zones are not combinable, they are passed on with those which are within 10% of the limiting constraints and flagged for further investigation. This process is reiterated for all of the zones in the selected sector. The process is then iterated until all of the sectors have been investigated. At this point in the process, all zones that are combinable will have been combined.

A similar process is then initiated for combining sectors. Sectors, which are adjacent to each other or have a minimal separation and similar parameters, are selected and investigated to determine their combinability based, in the case shown, on the acceptable minimum separation. In the event that they are not combinable, they are flagged and the next sector or pair of sectors is investigated. This process is repeated until all of the sectors have been investigated and combined where possible.

Once all of the sectors have been reviewed and zones and sectors combined where possible, an evaluation is made as to whether or not the number of sectors and zones is now within the allowable limit. If the limit is acceptable, the sectors and zones are reported in the same manner as from the sector and zone initialisation function. If there is still too large a number of sectors and zones, the computer will request the operator to take action. If the operator acknowledges the request for action, the computer will then display those sectors and zones previously flagged as being near the minimal constraints. If the operator provides a combining decision input, i.e. whether or not such zones and sectors should be combined, the operator's inputs are accepted and the resulting beams and sectors reported to the users. If the operator does not acknowledge the computer's request for assistance, the computer will automatically raise the minimum allowable separation by 10%. The computer would then go back and select those groups previously flagged and evaluate and combine where possible. If the operator acknowledged the request for action but did not provide the necessary decisions on whether or not to combine the beams and zones, the computer would take two courses of action. First, it would report the beams and sectors as they presently existed even though the number exceeded the constraints set into the program. It would also relax the combining conditions by 5% and go back and combine as necessary. If the relaxing of the combining conditions did not yet provide an acceptable number of sectors and zones, the process would repeat, starting with the decision point 'Number of Sectors and Zones O.K.?' In any case, the interruption of the radar because of lack of operator action is not a concern. The radar will continue to function even though the number of sectors and zones is excessive, while continually re-evaluating both the combining criteria and the number of sectors and zones until such time as their number has been reduced to the acceptable number or the operator takes action.

Note that changing the combining conditions by 5% will change those pairs of sectors and zones which are flagged by each successive iteration. The process cannot end up an endless loop. It will iterate as many times as necessary to meet the fundamental criterion on the allowable number of sectors and zones. The operator has a continuing control over this function in terms of inputs on allowable separations and the conditions for combining, as well as by responding to computer requests for assistance.

Given that a set of sectors and zones has been developed, either as a result of the sector and zone initialisation function or the sector and zone reduction function, the computer must then continually perform a sector and zone maintenance function as shown in Fig. 1.7. The control program must continually compare the outputs of the beam reporting function with the parameters of the sector and/or zone that exists for that beam to determine whether or not the zones and sectors as presently established are appropriate for the sensed environment. The process selects a sector as shown in Fig. 1.7(a) to determine whether or not zones are present. If zones are present, the beam report is compared with the conditions previously established for that zone. If the parameters are compatible, an evaluation is made as to whether or not the zone size should be changed. If the variations are not acceptable (based on an operator input of acceptability), contiguous beams are examined to determine whether or not a comparable situation exists in those beams. If the situation is unique to this beam, a decision must be made as to whether or not a new zone is required or the zone should be deleted. A new zone will be created if necessary and the operator advised. If it is determined that the contiguous beams give rise to the need for the creation of a new zone or the modification of a zone, the zones are adjusted as required and again the operator is advised that a change has been made. Note that the determination of what should be done to the zone determines the next step of the function, as shown in Fig. 1.7(b). The operator has the right to intervene in the establishment of a new zone. If he chooses not to intervene, the new zone will be created and the number of sectors and zones re-evaluated to determine whether or not sector and zone reduction is required.

Sectors are investigated after all of the zones have been reviewed. If a beam report and a sector are not compatible, the

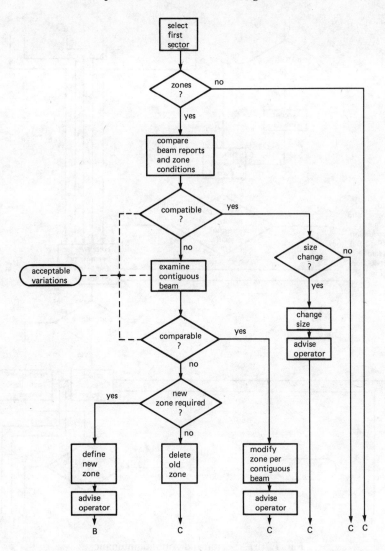

Fig. 1.7(a) Sector and zone maintenance.

contiguous beams within the sector are investigated to determine
the degree of variation that exists within the sector. If all beams
are comparable, the adjacent sector is evaluated, as shown in Fig.
1.7(c), to determine whether or not combining sectors is possible.
If the contiguous beams are not comparable, a unique beam
situation exists and the operator is requested to approve the
creation of a single beam sector for one transmission only. When
approved, the beam is flagged for the next time through the total

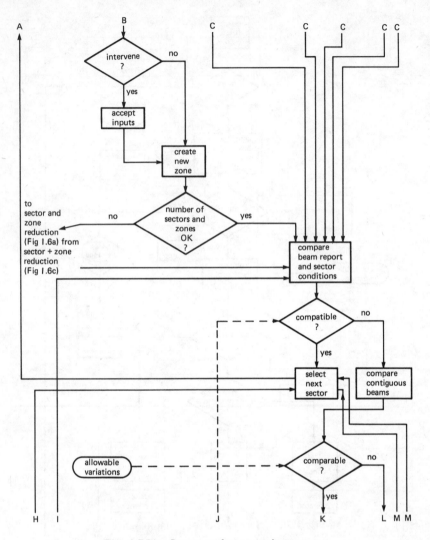

Fig. 1.7(b) Sector and zone maintenance.

control process; if he ignores or rejects the request the beam is left in the sector. If the comparison results in a condition which indicates that a new sector is required, the operator is advised and requested to provide the operating parameters for that sector. The sector is created and any operator inputs included. If the operator does not provide the operating parameters then the new sector will be created using the most severe parameters from the adjacent sectors. The number of sectors and zones will then be re-evaluated with the new sector to determine if it is still within the

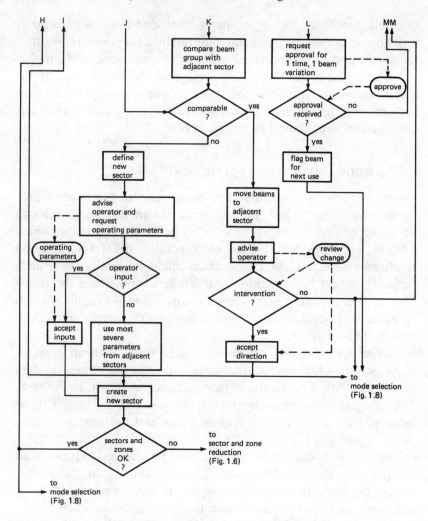

Fig. 1.7(c) Sector and zone maintenance.

acceptable limits. The sector and zone reduction function will be called upon as required. A corrected sector will be passed on to Mode Selection and the process will be reiterated, constantly evaluating all of the zones and sectors.

The process for establishing, reducing and maintaining sectors and zones set forth in Figs. 1.5, 1.6 and 1.7 provides a means for continually controlling the operational characteristics of the radar as a function of the operating environment. The sector and zone initialisation functions only occur once, when the radar is turned on. The sector and zone reduction function is used whenever deemed necessary by either the sector and zone initialisation function or the sector and zone maintenance function. How often the sector and zone maintenance function must be used is a major decision to be made during the design of the radar. The application and deployment of the radar will have a major effect on determining the frequency with which the sector and zone maintenance function should be called upon.

1.1.5 MODE AND PARAMETER SELECTION[2,4,5]

Once the zones and sectors have been defined, the control program proceeds to select the operating parameters and modes to be implemented in the sectors and zones. The discussion which follows will consider the search function; the track function requires a similar type of operation but it is usually done on a target-by-target basis within a particular sector. Since the range of a track is known *a priori*, more information is available which allows a more optimal set of operating modes and parameters to be selected for track.

The selection of the operating modes starts with an examination of the detection requirements and the environmental data associated with a particular sector or zone, as shown in Fig. 1.8. The program may exit directly to the selection of search parameters if the performance requirements and the environmental data are compatible within the given sector. If the requirements are not compatible, a special mode must be selected to provide an adequate level of performance. The selection of special modes should be made based on the use of the environmental data. A criterion, such as the radar resources consumed by each mode, must be established for selecting these modes, as several may be useful. Once a mode has been selected, the performance must be estimated to determine whether or not it is adequate but not excessive. The program exits to the search parameter selection as shown if the performance is deemed adequate. Another mode must be selected if the performance is not deemed adequate and the process iterated, until either an adequate level of performance is achieved or all of the different modes have been tried.

The operator must be alerted that a conflict exists when the radar cannot provide the level of performance required; the operator is then requested to select a mode as shown in the lower part of Fig. 1.8. The control program will select that mode which provided the best level of performance and then proceed to the

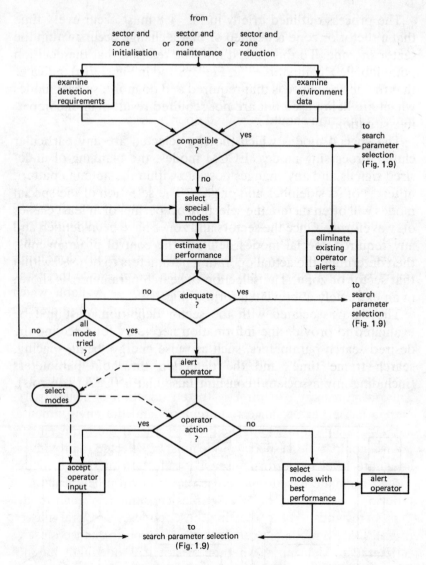

Fig. 1.8 Parameter selection.

search parameter selection if the operator does not respond. It will also flag the operator that a conflict continues to exist and make available the information for the particular sector and zone, the problem that exists and the action taken. The computer program will proceed, however, to select the search parameters and to control the radar. The operator has the option, once presented with this data, to override the program and call up a particular sector and determine its operating parameters.

The process outlined briefly in Fig. 1.8 must occur every time that a sector or zone is defined or that a change occurs within the sector or zone. To this end, it must be realised that the decision point labelled 'compatible?' in Fig. 1.8 and in Fig. 1.7(a) indicates that the performance is that required and no more; special modes which are being used but are not required result in an incompatible situation.

The special modes which may be selected are any particular clutter processing modes, ECCM modes, the blanking of undesired signals and any changes possible within the antenna pattern in terms of its sidelobes and/or gain. The selection of the special modes will often dictate the selection of specific, or at least classes of, waveforms. Once the sectors and zones have been defined and any required special modes defined, the control program must then determine the actual operating parameters to be used within that sector or zone. The selection of search parameters is shown in an extremely abbreviated form in Fig. 1.9.

The data associated with the sector definition must first be evaluated to provide the information necessary for selecting the desired search parameters, such as pulse energy, beam spacing, search frame time, and the detection threshold parameters (including any associated constant false alarm (CFA) controls).

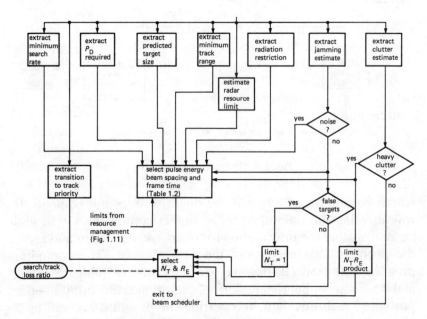

Fig. 1.9 Search parameter selection.

The presence of noise jamming or clutter will also affect the selection of search energy and the type of CFAR. Given the case where noise jamming and clutter exist simultaneously, there is an effective limit on the maximum useful energy. The detection requirements, in terms of the noise jamming level, dictate an increase in the pulse energy used; increasing the pulse energy results in an increase in the apparent clutter. Figure 1.10 shows the effect on overall probability of detection given a one square metre target in the presence of rain clutter and noise jamming. It is apparent that there is a maximum probability of detection that can be achieved under these circumstances and that increasing the pulse energy beyond a given level will have no appreciable effect. This is brought about by the fact that the radar must deal with the combined thermal noise, clutter noise, and jamming noise, as expressed by Equation 1.

$$S/N_T = \frac{S}{(N^2 + C^2 + J^2)^{1/2}} \tag{1}$$

where S = signal level
N_T = combined noise level
N = thermal noise
C = clutter signal
J = jammer signal.

As the transmitter power is increased, the clutter return will also increase, and the signal-to-average noise ratio will approach the signal-to-clutter ratio as expressed in Equation 1a. Selection of the maximum effective pulse energy must consider the impact of any clutter processing techniques employed to reduce the clutter return.

$$S/N_T = S/C \tag{1a}$$

The selection of the search parameters can be accomplished by using a look-up table based on the requirements for detection translated to pulse energy, constrained as just discussed, and an indication of the resource budgets of the radar. Different combinations of pulse energy, frame time and beam spacing can provide the same level of detection of performance[1,3], but have different effects on the resource budgets of the radar, as shown by Table 1.2. The selection of the particular search parameters requires an input from the resource management process, as shown in Fig. 1.9. Given the initial search operating parameters,

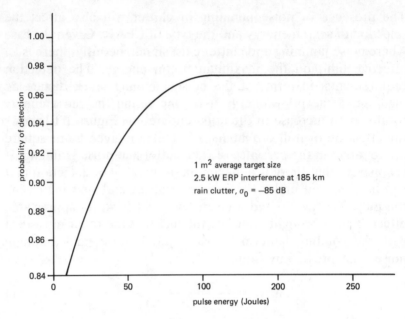

Fig. 1.10   Maximum useful energy.

the process must then evaluate and determine the parameters to
be used, once a threshold crossing occurs to change a true target
into track and to reject a false alarm.

The selection of these parameters is influenced by the relative
losses in search and track which have a direct influence on the
ratio of the energy used in search to that used in transition-to-

Table 1.2   Parameter selection matrix

Joules per beam	*Beams per 90° azimuth*	*Frame time (s)*	*Relative energy consumed*	*Relative time consumed*
100	490	5	0.99	0.28
80	510	4	0.99	0.37
60	650	3	1.00	0.52
40	560	3	0.85	0.63
20	840	3	0.85	0.82
10	1200	4	0.38	1.00

Provides $P_d = 0.99$ on a high velocity target in clutter by 55.6 km.
Search/track energy ratio = 1.00.
Only one attempt to transition allowed.

track. Either an operator input is required, or such information should be built into the program. An optimum threshold exists which minimises the total energy required to establish tracks.

The energy required to achieve an initial detection is reduced if a lower threshold level is used. This lower threshold occasions increased false alarms, which in turn require added energy to reject them. A balance exists between the energy used to achieve the initial detection and the energy used to reject false targets due to noise. Equation 2 presents this relationship for an individual beam.

$$E_{total} = E_{detect} + E_{reject} \qquad (2)$$

or

$$E_{total} = E_{detect} (1 + RNCP_{fa})$$

where R = the ratio of energy used in transition to track to the search energy
N = the number of transition attempts allowed
C = the number of resolution cells
P_{fa} = the probability of false alarm.

Figure 1.11 presents plots of the relative energy as a function of P_{fa} for some representative cases.

The existence of false targets provides a constraint on the allowable number of attempts that should be used. If false targets are deemed to be likely and several attempts to change the initial detection into a valid track are allowed, they can consume a very

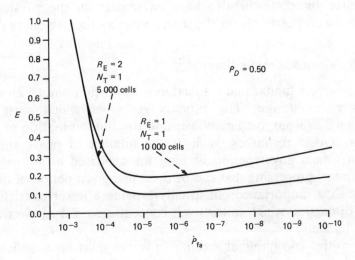

Fig. 1.11 Track energy optimisation.

large amount of radar resources. The number of attempts is limited to one in Fig. 1.9. This is an arbitrary value chosen for the illustrative example and must be evaluated in terms of the radar's application and the resource budgets. Similarly, the presence of heavy clutter will probably result in residual point clutter after clutter processing. An effective clutter map will largely reduce such signals[4,5] but some large clutter returns from point sources will inevitably appear in the radar processing. Heavy clutter residuals can consume large amounts of radar resources. Increasing the pulse energy will not improve the situation; allowing a large number of attempts will consume both radar time and power. A limit should be imposed both on the number of attempts allowed and the energy ratio in sectors where there is a large amount of clutter present.

The search parameter selection is completed by selecting the number of attempts to upgrade the threshold crossing into a valid track and the energy ratio used in the upgrading process relative to the search process. This selection is influenced by the operating requirement on the priority of upgrading targets to track. The priority of upgrading targets to track will often be a function of the range of the detection. Having selected the parameters to be used in search, the program then exits and the beam scheduler will program the search function.

Concurrent with the performance of the search function and the track function, the control program must continually maintain the resource budgets associated with the radar. Maintaining these resource budgets will also have an impact on the parameter selection and certainly on the search rates and search energies.

1.1.6 RESOURCE MANAGEMENT[1,2,3,6,7,8]

The resource management function is the focal point of an efficient radar design. The primary resources which must be managed are the average power and the time utilisation of the radar. Other resources, such as the number of phase shifter settings in a given period of time for a phased array, or the amount of processing that can be done in a given period of time, are also of importance but usually provide a lesser restriction. The discussion which follows will concentrate on the power and time budgets.

Priorities and minimal acceptable values must be established, in addition to the inherent limits on the available power and time, to manage the radar's operation. Search priorities for the different sectors are required to select the energy and the search rate. Which targets are the most important must be established in order to control tracking. Minimal acceptable values have to be established so that, if the management of the resources attempts to degrade the radar below given levels, flags will be raised and other actions taken. The minimal acceptable search volume and/ or range must be specified, usually as a function of the environment and situation. Minimum acceptable search rates for different conditions must be defined. Minimum acceptable track rates, as a function of the target or track priority and perhaps in terms of given sectors and zones, are required. The track capacity can also be a variable in terms of controlling resources and a minimal acceptable value, usually related to categories of target priority, needs to be established. All of these priorities and minimal acceptable values are part of the operational parameters which are provided as inputs into the sector and zone initialisation function, as was shown in Fig. 1.5(b) and outlined in Table 1.1.

Given the constraints discussed above, a resource management control program can be developed. A simplified version of such a program is illustrated in Fig. 1.12. The resource management function is an iterative function. The starting point of the resource management function can be either a regularly scheduled evaluation or a continual monitoring of the resource consumption. In either case, the resource management function must start from a determination of the resource status. If the available resources are adequate, then an evaluation must be made as to whether or not additional performance is desired. If additional performance is required, those requirements can be added. The processor is then advised of the changes about to be made, but not yet implemented, and the process recycled, as shown in the upper right-hand part of Fig. 1.12(a). The operator is provided with the opportunity to review and modify the changes, to allow them to occur, to reject them or to modify them.

If adequate resources are not available, the first and simplest action taken to resolve the problem is to attempt to change the search parameters of Table 1.2. This does not change the performance of the radar, but shifts the burden between the time budget and the power budget. If changing the search parameters does not provide a solution to the problem, then other means must be investigated. In the example shown in Fig. 1.12(a), the

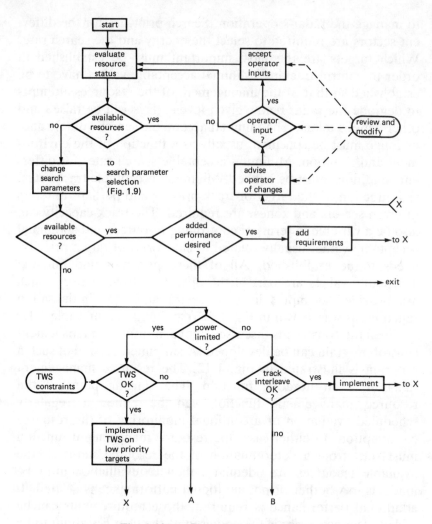

Fig. 1.12(a) Resource management.

first area of the resource budget to be investigated is whether or not adequate power is available. Whether power or time should be investigated first depends largely upon the characteristics of the radar being controlled. For example, there may be more means available to satisfy a time budget problem than a power budget problem if the radar uses multiple beams. In a single-beam radar, time may be more constraining and therefore a more difficult problem to solve. If power is not the limiting item or the power restriction is alleviated, the time constraints are investigated as shown in Figs. 1.12(a) and 1.12(b). Those techniques

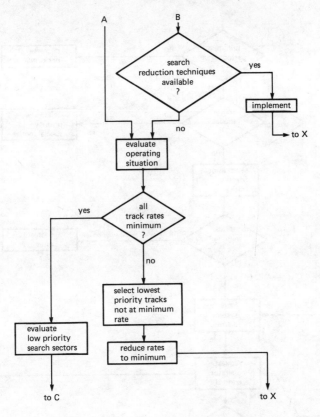

Fig. 1.12(b) Resource management.

which can alleviate the time budget without alleviating power budgets, and which in fact may increase the power consumed, are subsequently investigated in some predetermined sequence (the sequence shown here being largely arbitrary) to determine whether or not they are in use and whether or not their use is suitable. In the event that techniques which can provide significant relief in the time budget are available, they are implemented and the process is recycled. Thus, if introducing the time budget relief solutions creates a power budget problem, it will be quickly accommodated.

If a power budget constraint has been found rather than a time budget constraint, the example shown in Fig. 1.12 will consider the use of track-while-scan, on the assumption that dedicated track beams are being used (see Section 1.2); the use of smoothed search data rather than dedicated track beams. The use of track-while-scan will alleviate both time and power budget problems in

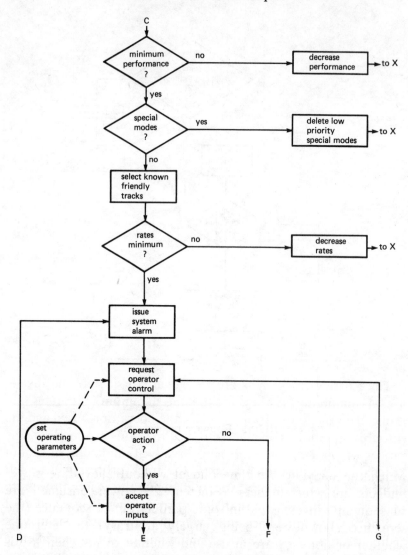

Fig. 1.12(c) Resource management.

that it will drop specific dedicated tracks on certain classes of targets. If track-while-scan is acceptable, the operator is advised and a reassessment of the resource status is made.

If applying either the time or power budget techniques shown does not provide a solution to the resource problem, then the operating situation must be reviewed to determine what further actions are acceptable, as shown in Fig. 1.12(b) and 1.12(c).

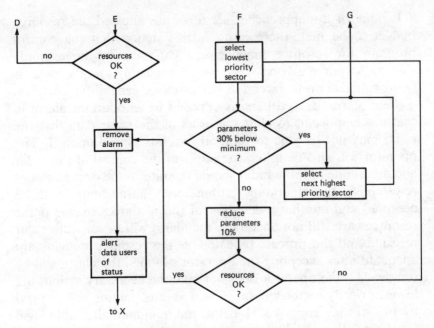

Fig. 1.12(d) Resource management.

The existing track rates are investigated to determine if they are at minimum. If they are not at minimum, the rates are reduced on the lower priority tracks, the operator advised and the resource situation re-evaluated. Once the rates are reduced, the process reiterates. If the rates are already at minimum, or cannot be changed because of priorities, the track process will be left alone and a second look taken at changing the search process to conserve resources. The search performance will be decreased if it is not at its minimal acceptable level. The performance may be either decreased totally to a minimum, or some incremental decrease may be specified in the program. If a decrease is possible, the change is made and the resource status re-evaluated. If no further reduction is tolerable, an investigation is made as to whether or not special modes have been called for. If special modes are in use, those with lowest priority will be deleted, the operator advised and another evaluation made of the resource status. Priorities must be associated with the special modes to facilitate their deletion. If the performance cannot be degraded or special modes cannot be removed, no further action can be taken to reduce the resources consumed in the search function, and track must be looked at again as shown in Fig. 1.12(c).

If none of the approaches set forth has allowed the resource budget to be met, there is no further action that the control program for resource management can take in the example shown. A system alarm will be issued indicating that the radar is being called upon to exceed its performance capability. The term 'system alarm' is used here as opposed to an operator alarm in that it is important to alert the users of the radar data that the radar may not be able to fulfil all requests placed upon it. The operator will also be asked to take over the control of the radar and determine how the radar should operate. If the operator does re-establish the operating parameters, these inputs will be accepted and another evaluation of the resources made. If the resources are still not adequate, the alarm will be maintained or reissued and the process repeated. If the resource budgets are adequate after accepting the operator's inputs, the alarm will be removed. If the operator does not take the necessary action, the lowest priority sector will be chosen and its parameters reduced by 10% if they are not 30% below the minimum allowable level (note that 10% and 30% are arbitrary values chosen for the sake of the example). If the resources are adequate, the alarm is removed but the users are notified of abnormal operation. If the resources are still not acceptable, a further reduction of 10% will be made. If the parameters have been reduced so that performance has been reduced by 30% in that sector, then the next lowest priority sector will be chosen. A second request for operator invervention will be made and the new sector's parameters will be reduced as required. In the event that the operator never takes action, the resource management function will continue to select sectors, starting with the lowest priority sector, and reduce their performance down to some level, in this case 30% below the minimum allowed performance level, until such time as a resource balance is achieved.

The illustrative example shown covers only a small part of the total radar control process. The radar control must provide functions such as the ones described as well as maintaining the track function and the total operation of the radar, including the computers which, in turn, operate the radar.

1.1.7 RADAR SCHEDULING

Scheduling varies in complexity with the type of radar involved. A 3D radar using fixed antennas with electronic beam steering in two dimensions provides a high degree of flexibility which permits a much more versatile and complex control function. A 2D radar with a mechanically rotated antenna provides virtually no flexibility for scheduling. The 3D radar with a mechanically rotated antenna and electronic beam steering in one or two dimensions provides an intermediate degree of flexibility.

The purpose of the scheduling function is to satisfy as many of the coverage requirements as possible while emphasising the higher priority requirements. Both search and track requirements must be satisfied.

Typically, a scheduling time window is defined in keeping with the highest data rate required. The relationship between the window and the data rate varies with the processing design. Processing is usually done in 'time slices' during which a group of events are processed. If three slices are required to complete an event (one slice to schedule, one slice to transmit and receive and one slice to process the results) then the scheduling window must be no greater than one third of the minimum allowable data interval. The scheduling process must select the radar events which must occur in each of these windows.

The relative priorities established during the design of the control must be modified by the radar controller to account for preceding events and the conflict of events which are desired concurrently. There is an optimum time for each event to occur. The optimum timing is a combination of the design process and the result of preceding events. Search timing is typically designed into the radar but it may be modified as a result of the resource management function. There is a penalty associated with performing an event either earlier or later than the optimum time. The value of an event occurring at any time can generally be described by S-shaped curves about the optimum time (inverse S-curves are included)[3]. There is rarely symmetry about the desired time. Defining relative priorities of different events includes a definition of such a value function, including the peak value.

The function will change as events occur or do not occur but it does not change because of the actual time of the event. The individual values for multiple events can be determined for any time when an event can be scheduled. The ordering of a group of events can be evaluated by summing their value functions for the different possible combinations of events. Maximising the sum provides the optimum schedule. Such a process involves a large amount of iterative, but simple, analysis; an excellent task to assign to a computer.

1.2 Tracking

The subject of tracking is diverse and well documented[9-20]. A separate chapter or book could be devoted to the subject. The subject encompasses mechanical servo-controlled single-target tracking radars, the scanning track-while-scan (TWS) radar, the multi-purpose phased array radar and many combinations of the three. Tracking can be 2-, 3- or 4-dimensional involving azimuth, elevation, range and/or Doppler. Another dimension of tracking can be added for polarisation[9]. Doppler tracking is important in some classes of radar, particularly airborne radars, and can be implemented via filter banks and Fast Fourier Transforms (FFT)[10,11,12,13]. Three-dimensional tracking in terms of azimuth, elevation and range will be considered here.

Two different forms of tracking will be considered. The first form uses data derived from the search process to develop tracks, the track-while-scan (TWS) process. The second form uses dedicated track beams directed towards specific targets. The second form when coupled with search in the same radar is termed track-and-search (TAS)[1]. The two forms will be compared in terms of the impact on the radar's computer and performance.

Track-while-scan radars are predominantly search radars which operate at a search rate dictated by the tracking requirements[1]. Tracks are developed by open loop smoothing of detections developed in the search process. These are typically low data rate trackers (seconds between samples). A dominant characteristic of this type of tracker is the association-correlation process[6,14,15]. The association-correlation process involves selecting a single radar return from many and declaring that return as belonging to the target being tracked. This is a simple process when only a few non-manoeuvring targets exist, but becomes very difficult in a dense environment with manoeuvring targets. Typically, a gate is generated which will include the desired return and exclude as many of the undesired returns as possible. The data samples are typically so separated in time that a high degree of imprecision exists in predicting the location of the target at the next sample. The imprecision results in having to place a large gate around the target; the gate will then usually contain two or more returns, from which the proper return must be selected. A variety of algorithms exist for this process, ranging from simply selecting the target nearest the centre of the gate to minimising the composite error of all the tracks which may be involved with the returns in the gate[6]. Selecting the wrong return for association will generate track noise and errors and can, in the extreme, generate 'ghost tracks'. The selected return is combined with prior returns deemed to be associated with the particular track by filtering. Usually a Kalman[15,16,17] or an α-β[18,19] filter is used to provide a high degree of 'smoothing', retaining a large amount of past data and providing a very narrow bandpass tracker commensurate with the low sample rate involved. The association-correlation process can require very large amounts of computation. It will usually dominate the tracking computer requirements.

The dedicated track beam approach (TAS) can employ a variable data rate as required by individual targets. The data rate is limited by the rotation rate in a simple radar. A rotating radar with azimuth beam agility can provide a very high data rate over a time window determined by the azimuth beam scanning extent and the rotation rate. The fixed phased array radar can provide a very high data rate limited only by duty cycle, phase shifter cycle time and target loading. The availability of a high data rate changes the nature of the tracking problem and a different approach to processing the data is possible. The use of a high data rate can greatly improve the prediction precision due both to an improvement in the measurement accuracy of manoeuvring targets and to a decrease in the prediction interval. The improvement in prediction accuracy permits a much smaller association-correlation gate to be used and can virtually eliminate the association-correlation processing. It is unlikely that more than one target will be in the gate. The gate can be small enough, if more than one target is present, for the target nearest to the centre of the gate or the average position to be used. The higher data rate permits the tracker to follow target manoeuvres, which changes the desired filter characteristics. 'Window' trackers which use comparatively few data points become more useful and wider bandwidth filters are more attractive and possible.

Most track filters associated with TWS are based, at least to some degree, on the assumptions of low signal-to-noise, low data rate and little or no target manoeuvres (note that the Kalman uses a zero-mean acceleration noise assumption). Only the low data rate is a true and necessary assumption and then only for certain classes of radars. Most radars will detect targets at long ranges and then develop tracks. Tracks of interest will typically have decreasing range and associated increasing signal-to-noise. The assumption of little or no manoeuvres fits the low data rate.

Considerable work has been documented about adapting TWS filters to handle manoeuvring targets[16,18,19]. Higher data rate, when available, obviates these assumptions and a different approach should be used.

Track data rate can be the basis for two tradeoffs in the design of a radar. The first tradeoff is between the amount of processing required for the low data rate association-correlation processing versus the processing required for processing tracks more often with a higher data rate. The higher data rate filter can be a much simpler filter, using only a few data points, but the process must be done more often. The selection depends on the target density and the expected target dynamics. The second tradeoff involves the measurement error, or signal-to-noise, and the data rate on the assumption that target manoeuvres exist. The average power required for a track can be minimised by balancing the measurement error and the lag error[3]. The total energy available can also be shared among the targets being tracked in a manner that optimises the tracking of all of the targets[21].

Tracking is a complex issue and no single approach can be recommended. The advent of electronic beam steering with the attendant beam agility can provide higher data rates which brings the problem closer to control theory issues and farther away from the filter theory issues associated with most TWS trackers.

1.3 Other processing functions

The radar control and tracking are the two major computer processing issues but not the only ones. The computer must also perform 'housekeeping' and in some cases built-in testing, fault isolation and system exercising.

1.3.1 HOUSEKEEPING[22,23]

The example shown in this chapter has separated the functions that were illustrated to a fairly large degree and yet there remained considerable interaction between the functions. Each function, in itself, is highly complex with many interactions, branch points and loops. The radar control process, in doing its housekeeping, must manage all of the iterations, interconnections, interrupts and loops involved. It must maintain the timeliness of operation when faced with many interrupts, both internal and external. It must also maintain the operation of the control program itself.

The amount of housekeeping involved depends not only on the complexity of the control program and the type of tracking but also on the implementation and architecture used. The housekeeping for control implemented in a single, central computer is far different from that for a distributed system. The amount of parallel processing which is possible changes the amount of housekeeping required.

1.3.2 BUILT-IN TESTING

The control program must continually evaluate the performance of the radar and implement at least a large degree of the automatic testing or BITE (built-in test equipment) built into the radar. It must perform a similar function upon itself, evaluating its own computer operation and its own programs. It must be prepared to reconfigure the system and maintain some level of operation in a 'fall-back' mode if something malfunctions or is damaged.

The complexity of BITE depends on the application and type of radar involved. The phased array radar can involve very complex BITE if the individual elements are evaluated[24].

The availability of a computer as a part of the radar also provides a means for exercising the radar, the operator and any system of which the radar is a part. Simulation programs can be written to run on the radar's computer which can test the radar and the operator under a variety of situations and environments[25].

1.4 Conclusion

The ability to develop a useful radar control program which performs all of the housekeeping as well as all of the functions required of it is dependent, to a large degree, on being able to keep the functions or sub-functions at a manageable level so that they do not interact too much with each other. The choice of both the computer and program architecture becomes very important and is a major tradeoff or decision point in the design. It is further important that the architecture be selected and its modules, or sub-functions, be defined so that changes can be made when required and only affect the area of concern and not have a major impact on all of the other areas. This is also an important aspect in being able to reconfigure the system after failures or damage.

Information was given to the operator and operator action requested many times in the example. The example is limited and the operator interface is far more extensive than indicated. Considerable effort must be expended in defining the interface with the operator. Too much information is as damaging as too little in this interface. The operator must be able to assimilate and use the information. Informing the operator of every change in the operation of the radar (as was implied in the example) may interrupt more important aspects of the interface, may overload the operator and/or may simply lead to boredom and resultant inattention.

The example given may appear to be extensive, but is closer to being trivial. The effective design of the control of a radar is an extensive task. The system engineering involved in the control design is at least equivalent to all of the system engineering involved in all of the other aspects of the radar design; it will usually be much larger. The hardware and software (firmware) designs are usually equivalent. An error or oversight in the control design can be costly in many ways. Correcting an error can, dependent upon the architecture chosen, be either simple or complex.

Computer control of radars, even the simplest radar, introduces a new dimension to radar design. New disciplines are brought to radar design, and far more performance can be made available.

References

1. Billetter, D. R. 'Efficient 3-D Radar Design', *Radar-85 Int. Conf.* May (1985).
2. Baugh, R. *Computer Control of Modern Radar*, RCA (1973).
3. Billetter, D. R. 'Efficient Radar Control', *Microwave J.*, Jan. (1986).
4. Cantrell, B. H. 'Preliminary Results of Environmental Mapping', *Naval Res. Lab. (Rep. 8400)*, April 28 (1980).
5. Tunnicliffe R. J. 'A Simple Automatic Radar Track Extraction System', *Radar-77 Int. Conf.*, Oct. (1977).
6. Binias, G. 'Computer Controlled Tracking in Dense Target Environment Using a Phased Array Antenna', *Radar-77 Int. Conf.*, Oct. (1977).
7. Sarig, M. J. and Bowser, D. S. 'Implementation of a Distributed Node of Radar Control', *Rec. IEEE 1980 Int. Radar Conf.*, April (1980).

8. Salinger, S. N. and Wangsness, D. 'Target-Handling Capacity of a Phased Array Tracking Radar', *Trans. AES-8*, 1, Jan. (1972).
9. Guili, D., Fossi, F. and Gheradelli, M. 'A Technique for Adaptive Polarization Filtering in Radars', *Radar-85 Int. Conf.*, May (1985).
10. Roberts, J. B. G., Eames, R., McGaughan, D. V. and Butler, M. B. N. 'A New Approach to Pulse Doppler Processing', *Radar-77 Int. Conf.*, Oct. (1977).
11. Taylor, R. G., Durrani, T. S. and Goutis, C. 'Block Processing in Pulse Doppler Radar', *Radar-77 Int. Conf.*, Oct. (1977).
12. Holborn, P. E. 'Performance Analysis of Airborne Pulse Doppler Radar', *Radar-85 Int. Radar Conf.*, May (1985).
13. Irabu, T., Kiuchi, E., Higisawa, T. and Tomita, Y. 'Range-Azimuth Correlation Processor in the Frequency Domain for a Primary Radar', *Radar-77 Int. Conf.*, Oct. (1977).
14. Maged, Y. A. 'Critical Probabilities for Optimum Tracking System', *IEEE 1980 Int. Radar Conf.*, April (1980).

CHAPTER 2
Phased Arrays

J. R. FORREST

In 1986, the following statement was made by a Working Party in the USA given the remit to look at future radar needs:

'Electronically steerable phased array techniques are the only possibility becoming available which promise the flexibility and capability of coping with the new space age environment'.

The phased array is essentially just the special case of an antenna which, instead of having a continuous aperture, has an aperture composed of a number of individual radiating elements. The number of such radiating elements in the overall aperture may range from just a few to many thousands, depending on the application. Constructing an aperture out of many radiating elements involves an increase in electronic and mechanical complexity as compared to a single continuous aperture, but does bring the most important advantage that the amplitude and phase of the aperture illumination may be prescribed both flexibly and accurately. This permits the realisation of a considerable variety of beam patterns that might be defined from the system requirement. The precise control of the aperture illumination also allows the attainment of low sidelobe levels, a feature becoming more and more important in modern radar systems to reduce their vulnerability to ECM.

The flexibility to control the aperture illumination distribution confers another vital advantage to phased arrays, in that the illumination function may be controlled electronically, and thus rapidly, by changing the phase and amplitude of signals to or from the individual array elements. This is significant in allowing the antenna to operate in a multi-function way, for example, in performing interlaced surveillance and tracking of a variety of

44

targets. Changing the phase slope dynamically across the array aperture produces electronic steering of the antenna pattern, thereby reducing or removing the need for mechanical scanning of the antenna. Changing both phase and amplitude in pre-scribed, but complex, ways produces beam steering and also changes in the antenna pattern; this can be particularly useful in adapting the antenna pattern so that pattern nulls are placed in the direction of interference sources.

Access to each element in the array aperture means that mul-tiple beams may be formed by connecting separate phase and amplitude control networks in parallel to the elements. This may be done as an electronic circuit matrix, a so-called beam-forming matrix, the connections to which form the individual simul-taneous beams in space in different directions or different patterns from the same aperture.

Clearly, a phased array approach offers the ultimate in flexi-bility of use of an antenna aperture. Though it is possible to realise scanning antennas without mechanical motion and thereby reduce some complexity, this has been outweighed in most cases by the increase in complexity associated with signal distribution, control and processing for all the individual array elements.

The emergence of phased array radar systems has, therefore, been slower than originally predicted. The flexibility they offered was only really justified for the most demanding defence tasks, such as ICBM surveillance and tracking. Hence for many years, apart from experimental test beds, the only electronically scanned phased arrays of significance were of the type character-ised by the Cobra Dane or Pave Paws[1,2] installations. Two fac-tors, however, are now leading to a rapid acceleration in implementation of phased array radars. The first is that the increased complexity of electronic countermeasures and target concentrations now makes phased array radars essential for a wider range of applications in air, sea and land environments. The second is that the development of monolithic microwave integrated circuits (MMICs) and silicon very large scale inte-grated circuits (VLSI) enable array elements to be manufactured in modular form with relatively few semiconductor chips; pro-vided applications for large quantities of these modules can be found, the potential for phased arrays without the high cost penalties of the past is now here.

There is every chance that the prediction quoted at the start of this introduction can now be quickly fulfilled provided carefully worked out strategies are evolved to support the initial very large investments in the new integrated semiconductor technologies.

2.1 Basic theory of phased arrays

The radiation pattern of any antenna is a plot of the relative strength of the radiation field as a function of the angles θ and ϕ for a given distance τ from the antenna in spherical geometry. Unless otherwise specified, the field is taken to be that in the so-called 'far-field' region at distances greater than $2D^2/\lambda$ from the antenna; D here is the antenna aperture dimension and λ is the radiation wavelength. Antenna directional response is usually expressed through the directivity $G_D(\theta,\phi)$:

$$G_D(\theta,\phi)=4\pi\,\frac{\text{Power radiated per unit solid angle in direction }\theta,\phi}{\text{Total radiated power}}$$

This is the power density in any given direction relative to that which an isotropic radiator would produce. The maximum directivity G_{DM}, frequently abbreviated just as 'directivity', is strictly the value of the directivity in the direction of maximum antenna response.

The gain, or more strictly, the power gain $G(\theta,\phi)$ differs from the directivity in that it takes into account the inefficiencies of the antenna through dissipative losses in conductors and dielectrics:

$$G(\theta,\phi)=4\pi\,\frac{\text{Power density radiated per unit solid angle in direction }\theta,\phi}{\text{Total input power to the antenna}}$$

The maximum gain, also often abbreviated just as the 'gain', is the value of $G(\theta,\phi)$ in the direction of maximum antenna response.

Since losses may easily be lumped into a single efficiency parameter, η:

$$G(\theta,\phi) = \eta G_D(\theta,\phi) \tag{1}$$

The directional pattern of the antenna is the Fourier transform of the electric field distribution across the aperture. In the case of an array of elements, the pattern may be obtained by a summation. This can be easily illustrated for the simple case of the uniformly spaced one-dimensional line array of N isotropic elements shown in Fig. 2.1. The pattern in the plane of the array in direction θ is given by:

$$E_a(\theta) = \sum_{n=1}^{N} E_n \exp\left[j \frac{2\pi}{\lambda} nd \sin \theta\right] \quad (2)$$

d is the separation between the elements; the total aperture $D = (n - 1)d$, and E_n is the complex excitation coefficient (amplitude and phase) at element n.

For a uniformly excited array with all signals in phase, the E_n are identical and may be denoted E_o. The pattern is then:

$$E_a(\theta) = E_o \frac{\sin[N\pi d \sin \theta/\lambda]}{N \sin[\pi d \sin \theta/\lambda]} \quad (3)$$

This pattern is shown in Fig. 2.2.

When the individual array elements are not isotropic (omni-directional), but have a radiation pattern $E_e(\theta)$ themselves, this can be included to give the overall array pattern:

$$E(\theta) = E_a(\theta) \cdot E_e(\theta) \quad (4)$$

$E_a(\theta)$ is known as the array factor and $E_e(\theta)$ the element factor. In many cases, such as those of dipoles, slots and waveguide apertures, $E_e(\theta)$ may be approximated by a simple $\sqrt{(\cos \theta)}$ function.

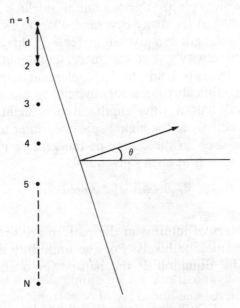

Fig. 2.1 Line array configuration.

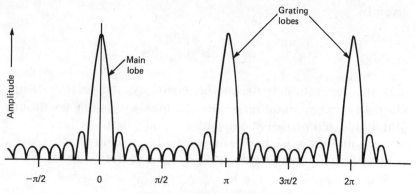

Fig. 2.2 Array factor.

The relationships $P(\theta) = E(\theta)^2$, $P_a(\theta) = E_a(\theta)^2$ and $P_e(\theta) = E_e(\theta)^2$ relate the electric field expressions to the power expressions used in the directivity and gain formulae.

It may be seen that the pattern of Fig. 2.2 is repetitive, consisting of a maximum response at $\theta = 0°$ (main lobe or main beam), others of equal response (grating lobes), and subsidiary maxima (sidelobes). The grating lobe spacing is a function of element spacing and, by making $D < \lambda$, it can be ensured that under normal circumstances the grating lobes do not enter the real space region. The usual array element spacing is close to half a wavelength, which places the minimum sidelobe level at the edges ($\theta = \pm 90°$) of the array coverage. Placing elements closer than half a wavelength can give an increase in directivity, or so-called 'superdirectivity'[3], but the increase in mutual coupling between the elements leads to large element impedance mismatch which is difficult to control. Increasing the inter-element spacing beyond half a wavelength gives a slight progressive decrease in directivity as the higher sidelobes enter real space and then a sudden drop in directivity as the grating lobes appear. Grating lobes appear at angles given by[4]:

$$\theta_{GL} = \sin^{-1}(\pm m\,\lambda/d) \qquad (5)$$

where m is an integer.

Key parameters of interest in the pattern are the main beam width and the sidelobe levels. For the uniformly excited array characterised by Equation 3, the half-power beamwidth θ_B is given by:

$$\theta_B = 0.886\lambda/D \text{ or } \theta°_B \approx 51\lambda/D \qquad (6)$$

and the first sidelobe level is at -13.2 dB relative to the main beam[4].

For non-uniformly excited arrays, numerical computation methods are generally used to evaluate the beam width and sidelobe levels. Tapering of the excitation across the aperture so that elements towards the edges of the array are more weakly excited has a beneficial effect in reducing the sidelobe levels, but also reduces directivity and gain together with an increase in beamwidth. A variety of common tapering or weighting functions such as cosine or Taylor functions are used to specify element excitation amplitudes. Useful design tables have been produced by Hansen[5] and a summary is given in Table 2.1.

Electronic beam steering in the phased array is produced by imposing a phase difference between adjacent elements of the array to create a linear phase slope across the aperture. This can be visualised as a sideways translation on the patterns in Fig. 2.2. A phase difference ϕ between adjacent elements produces a beam steering angle:

$$\theta_o = \sin^{-1}(\lambda\phi/2\pi d) \tag{7}$$

Steering of the pattern means that grating lobes may appear for inter-element spacings less than one wavelength. The maximum

Table 2.1 Far field radiation pattern characteristics of various aperture illumination functions

Aperture illumination function with axis z	Relative maximum directivity	Half-power beamwidth, deg	Intensity of first sidelobe, db below maximum intensity
Uniform; $A(z) = 1$	1	$51\lambda/d$	31.2
Cosine; $A(z) = \cos(\pi z/2)$:			
$n = 0$	1	$51\lambda/d$	13.2
$n = 1$	0.810	$69\lambda/d$	23
$n = 2$	0.667	$83\lambda/d$	32
$n = 3$	0.575	$95\lambda/d$	40
$n = 4$	0.515	$111\lambda/d$	48
Parabolic; $A(z) = 1 - (1 - \Delta)z^2$:			
$\Delta = 1.0$	1	$51\lambda/d$	13.2
$\Delta = 0.8$	0.994	$53\lambda/d$	15.8
$\Delta = 0.5$	0.970	$56\lambda/d$	17.1
$\Delta = 0$	0.833	$66\lambda/d$	20.6
Triangular; $A(z) = 1 - |z|$	0.75	$73\lambda/d$	26.4
Circular; $A(z) = \sqrt{(1 - z^2)}$	0.865	$58.5\lambda/d$	17.6

element spacing allowed for an array with maximum electronic beam steering angle θ_{max}, if grating lobes are to be avoided, is[4]:

$$d < \lambda/(1 + |\sin \theta_{max}|)$$

Radford[6] goes into more detail on these aspects. As the pattern of a phased array is scanned electronically, the presented aperture in the direction of the beam decreases. This effect becomes significant at large angles away from the normal to the array aperture and Equation 3 has to be modified[4] by the so-called 'obliquity factor' $(1 + \cos \theta)/2$.

In practice, the array pattern variation with electronic scan can be quite complex and is the resultant of the array factor, the obliquity factor, the element factor and the effects of varying array element impedance mismatch[4].

A difficulty with phased arrays is the large number of individual elements required if narrow beams are to be obtained. The maximum directivity of a uniformly excited aperture of area A is given by[7]:

$$G_{DM} = 4\pi A/\lambda^2 \qquad (8)$$

For the simple case of a rectangular aperture of dimensions D_1, D_2, this directivity can also be expressed using Equation 6 as:

$$G_{DM} = 4\pi D_1 D_2/\lambda^2 \approx 32\,000/\theta^\circ_A \phi^\circ_B \qquad (9)$$

where θ°_A and ϕ°_B are the beamwidths in orthogonal planes associated with the dimensions D_1 and D_2. This expression becomes even simpler if put in terms of the number of elements in the array.

For half-wavelength element spacing in an $N \times M$ element array,

$$D_1 = (N - 1)d = (N - 1)\lambda/2$$
$$D_2 = (M - 1)d = (M - 1)\lambda/2$$

Thus, for $N, M \gg 1$,

$$G_{DM} \approx \pi NM \qquad (10)$$

Taking account of aperture excitation taper, array efficiency and other factors, a useful rule of thumb is that the array gain is of the same order as the number of elements for simple non-directive elements.

So far, it has been assumed that the phase and amplitude of the aperture excitation at each array element may be achieved exactly as specified. Errors in amplitude and phase from element to element modify the radiation pattern, the effect being most noticeable in the detailed structure of the sidelobes. Calculation of the effects of errors is complicated and is usually best represented statistically in terms of mean square values[8].

Errors which have the most effect are those which are periodic across the aperture. An example of this is the discrete stepping of the phase front from element to element. This can be represented as a linear phase slope with a superimposed phase ripple. The phase ripple gives rise to 'quantisation' sidelobes having an rms value relative to the main beam[9]:

$$(G_{SL})_{rms} \approx 5/(2)^{2p}N \qquad (11)$$

where p is the number of control bits for the phase shifter (phase step $= 2\pi/2^p$) and N is the number of elements in the array. There is also a small associated loss in array directivity[9]:

$$\Delta G \approx \pi^2/3.(2)^{2p} \qquad (12)$$

A useful guide to the effect of various systematic phase and amplitude errors has been given by Milne and is shown in Fig. 2.3. An understanding of these effects if often useful in aiding pattern error diagnostics in antennas.

2.2 Phased array configurations

The various configurations for phased arrays may be classified in different ways. A logical distinction may be made between systems in which the array occupies the antenna aperture (aperture arrays) and those in which the array feeds another structure acting as the radiating aperture, typically a reflector or lens (hybrid arrays).

Figure 2.4 shows some variants of aperture arrays. They all have the advantage of wide angle scanning capability (typically up to ±60°), but require a large number of array elements. Figure 2.4(a) shows a phased array of simple phase control or phase/amplitude control elements used as a lens to shape and steer the broad beam from a waveguide horn. A variant of this format, using an offset-fed reflector to collimate the beam first, is shown in Fig. 2.4(b). A relatively popular arrangement[10] also has been the 'reflectarray' shown in Fig. 2.4(c), which involves the RF energy passing in and out of the phase or phase/amplitude control elements terminated in short circuits. An offset-fed arrangement

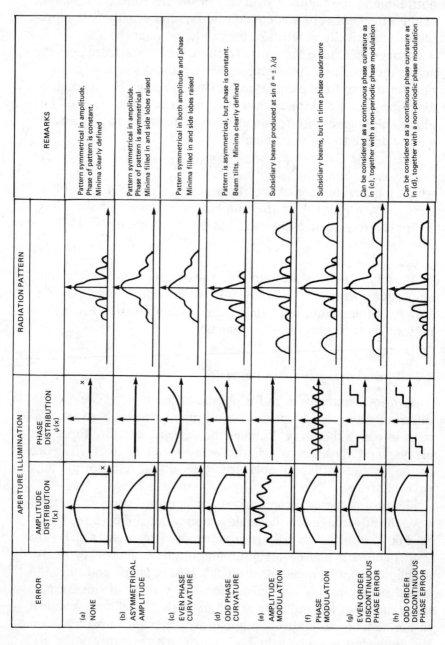

Fig. 2.3 Effects of illumination errors on the radiation pattern.

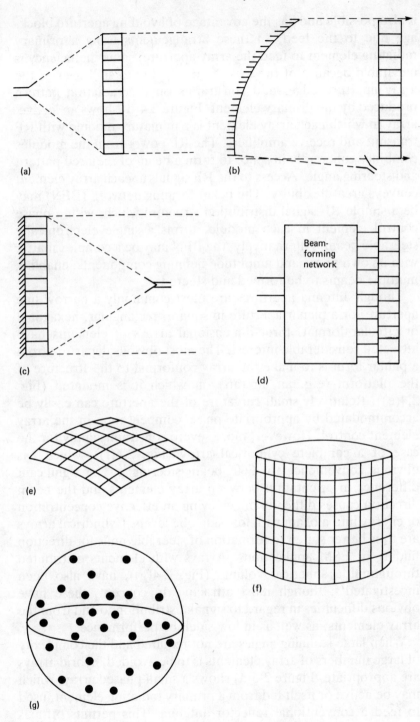

Fig. 2.4 Variants of aperture arrays.

is also possible and has the advantage of avoiding aperture block-age due to the feed. In these arrangements using a primary radiating element to feed the array aperture, some inefficiency is inevitable because of the loss of energy due to spill-over at the array aperture edges and constraints on the radiation pattern produced by the primary element. Figure 2.4(d) shows an 'active' array in which each array element is a miniature module with RF transmit and receive amplifiers. The RF power from the modules combines coherently in space to form a beam of required pattern and steering angle. Access to the RF signals at each array element conveys great flexibility. The beam-forming network (BFN) may be a simple RF signal distribution structure which, with a phase control element in each module, forms a single electronically steerable beam. Alternatively, the BFN may be a complex matrix with its own phase and amplitude defining components, enabling multiple beams to be formed and steered.

Though antenna apertures are most commonly a narrow line aperture, or a planar aperture in square, rectangular, hexagonal or circular format, three-dimensional arrays of elements have attracted considerable interest. The most obvious departure from a planar form is to make the array conformal to the structure of the platform (e.g. an aircraft) on which it is mounted (Fig. 2.4(e)). Relatively small curvature of the aperture can easily be accommodated by appropriate phase compensation in the array element control. However, more severe constraints apply for the case of a complete cylindrical array (Fig. 2.4(f)), which has obvious convenience for 360° beam steering[11]. The significant difference in orientation between array elements and the beam direction causes difficulty in achieving an effective concentration of energy into a beam with low sidelobe levels. Cylindrical arrays are thus better suited to formation of steerable nulls for direction finding or ESM applications. Arrays with elements distributed throughout a spherical volume (Fig. 2.4(g)), have also been investigated[12]; though most attractive in concept, these have obvious difficulties in regard to signal distribution to and from the array elements, as well as in low sidelobe performance.

When large scanning angles are not required and the complexity of large numbers of array elements is to be avoided, hybrid arrays are appropriate. Figure 2.5(a) shows a small phased array, which may be active or itself fed from a primary radiating element, used to feed a conventional reflector antenna. This permits off-axis scanning of the reflector antenna beam, but the angle of steering away from boresight is limited to a few beamwidths if degradation of the beam pattern is to be avoided[13]. An array may also be used to feed a passive lens structure, as in Fig. 2.5(b), with limitations similar to those of the array-fed reflector. One of the most interesting array-fed lens structures is the 'dome' antenna, shown in Fig. 2.5(c), which allows a planar array to achieve beam scanning over a hemispherical volume[14]. The major application of hybrid array systems is currently to the next generation of satellite-borne communications antennas rather than to radar. The narrow beams, and hence large antenna apertures, together

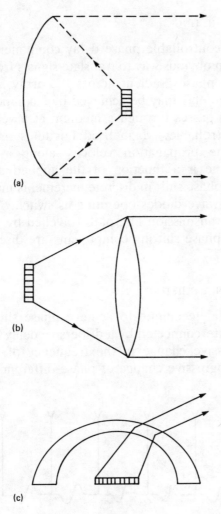

Fig. 2.5 Hybrid arrays.

with the limited beam steering needed to cover the Earth's surface from geostationary orbit, make a hybrid array solution the
best approach[15].

2.3   Electronic beam steering

There are a variety of ways of changing electronically the direction of the phase front radiated from an array, or equivalently,
coherently combining the signals received by array elements from a
given direction. These ways involve either phase shifting, frequency shifting, or time delay.

2.3.1   PHASE SHIFTING

Electronically controllable phase delay components at all array
elements are an obvious way to translate signals from an in-phase
condition to a phase gradient across the array and *vice versa*.
Variable phase delay may be achieved by a component in which
the RF energy passes through a medium at a velocity which is
externally controllable. Magnetised ferrite is most commonly
used, since the propagation velocity along a ferrite-loaded
transmission line is a function of the applied magnetic field.
Alternatively, phase shift in discrete increments may be achieved
by using microwave diodes operating as switches to change the
length of the transmission line path travelled by the RF signal.
Both of these phase shifting components are discussed in more
detail later.

2.3.2   FREQUENCY SHIFTING

This is a special technique to achieve phase shifting. If array
elements are interconnected by a dispersive delay line (Fig. 2.6),
then a progressive change in the frequency of the RF signal
results in a progressive change of phase difference between the

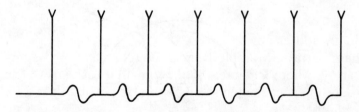

Fig. 2.6   Dispensive delay line.

array elements. The beam from such an array will, therefore, point in a given direction for a given frequency. A frequency ramp waveform thus produces a scanning motion of the beam. While this is simple and highly convenient, it has the disadvantage that it does not allow for frequency agility — a vital ECCM need in military radar.

2.3.3 TIME DELAY

For systems which must operate over wide bandwidths, the distinction between phase delay and time delay is important. True time delay beam steering techniques are relatively rarely used since most current radars do not operate over much more than 10% bandwidths and the radiating elements themselves are bandwidth constrained. However, future systems may have to operate over much larger bandwidths or with large bandwidth waveforms, so time delay techniques could increase in importance. In a true time delay system, array elements are fed through switched non-dispersive delay lines. In this case, the beam steering angle θ is given by[6]:

$$\theta = \sin^{-1}(c\tau/d) \tag{13}$$

where τ is the time delay between adjacent array elements, d is the inter-element spacing, and c is the RF signal velocity on the delay line. In large arrays, the total length of each delay line will be many wavelengths, similar to the array dimensions; this introduces significant losses and may also be physically inconvenient.

2.4 Beamforming networks and multiple beams

A single agile beam has clearly great flexibility in that it can interlace a variety of surveillance and tracking functions. However, there can be serious time penalties involved in the use of a single beam if long-range detection is required, since the beam must dwell for a time sufficient to receive the return signals from the longest range. The formation of multiple simultaneous, independently addressable beams is therefore a significant capability of phased arrays. Multiple beams, though, may only be formed with arrays where RF access to the signals at each array element or groups of array elements (sub-arrays) is possible.

Beamforming is basically a simple process, involving collecting the signals received at an antenna aperture, weighting these signals in amplitude and phase and then summing the weighted samples; beamforming on transmit is the reverse of this process, frequently possible with the same beamforming network provided the network components are reciprocal. Beamforming may be carried out at RF, or alternatively signals may be converted to IF or to baseband for the beamforming operation to be carried out. Beamforming at IF or baseband involves the added complexity of coherent frequency conversion of all the RF signals by a common local oscillator, but allows the beamformer to operate at lower frequencies, where tolerances are not so critical, or digitally with great accuracy and flexibility.

2.4.1 RF BEAMFORMERS

The simplest beamforming network, which forms a single beam, fixed in space, is an in-phase combining network (Fig. 2.7(a)). Such a network clearly operates reciprocally and is suited to both transmit and receive operation. It may be realised in a variety of transmission line media; waveguide would typically be used where loss is critical, but space and weight are less important constraints; microstrip or stripline would be used where space, weight and cost are key factors, stripline generally being preferred because of its lower loss characteristics. A given amplitude taper across the array can be provided by appropriate fixed power division ratios at the nodes of the network. In most cases the path lengths to each element are equalised (the 'squintless' network[16]), to give a stable beam position over a wide frequency range; the exception to this is where path lengths are made deliberately different to allow beam steering to be achieved by change of frequency, as discussed earlier.

To allow electronic beam steering of a single beam, the normal method is to introduce an electronically controllable phase shifter at each array element port (Fig. 2.7(b)). A fixed amplitude taper to set the desired beam pattern may still be incorporated in the beamforming network itself. The most versatile system of all for a single beam involves the introduction of both amplitude and phase control elements at each array element port. These can be realised as entirely separate components, but most interest now centres on achieving amplitude and phase control together in a component known as a *vector modulator*. The need for both amplitude and phase control in phased arrays, particularly in receive mode, is increasing rapidly because of the need to have not only control of beam position, but also beam pattern for the placement of nulls on sources of interference. However, such amplitude and phase control may introduce very significant losses and it will in general be preferable to carry out this more complex weighting by means of IF or baseband digital systems.

In beamformers to form multiple beams, the beam set may be one occupying the full radar field of view, one involving a beam

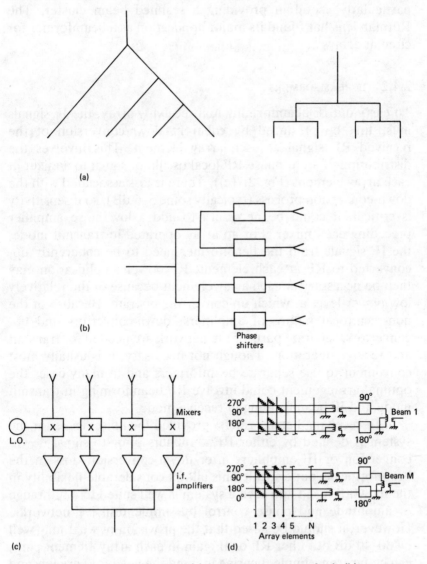

Fig. 2.7 Beamforming networks; (a) in phase, corporate feed; (b) corporate feed with phase shifters; (c) IF beamforming; (d) IF resistive beamformer.

cluster, steerable or fixed, or one involving several independent beams. Many varieties of RF network have been used to provide multiple fixed beams, the best known being the Butler matrix, the Maxon–Blass matrix, and the Rotman lens[4,17]. These networks all become complex, susceptible to tolerance problems and losses, and thus expensive if large numbers of beams are required. They are best suited to systems requiring a small number of beams and, with the addition of phase shifters, can be particularly useful in providing a scanned beam cluster. The Rotman lens has found its major application as a beamformer for circular arrays[18].

2.4.2 IF BEAMFORMERS

To carry out IF beamforming in a receiving array, the IF signals must first be produced by coherent down-conversion of the received RF signal at each array element. This involves the distribution of an in-phase RF local oscillator signal to a mixer at each array element (Fig. 2.7(c)). There is loss associated with the down-conversion process (typically some 5–6 dB), so if sensitivity is critical, it could be necessary to add a low noise amplifier preceding each mixer. For an array operated in transmit mode, the IF signals from the beamformer need to be coherently up-converted to RF at each element; RF power amplification may then be necessary at each array element because of the relatively low power level at which up-convertors operate. Because of the non-reciprocal nature of amplifiers, down-convertors and up-convertors, separate parts of the network are needed for transmit and receive operation. Though not necessary, it is usually most convenient to use separate beamformers and in many cases the optimal arrangement could involve RF beamforming in transmit mode and IF beamforming in receive mode.

In IF receiving beamformers, provided the noise figure for the system is defined by either RF amplifiers prior to signal down-conversion or IF amplifiers after down-conversion, loss in the beamformer is not critical. This allows considerable flexibility in the networks used and such a system is well suited to a full range of amplitude and phase control by simple resistive networks. However, it should be noted that the provision of what may well be 30–40 dB of either RF or IF gain in each array element path, can be far from simple, bearing in mind the need for very low and stable differential gain and phase between the parallel signal paths. In general, therefore, a calibration signal injection scheme will be required and provision made for phase and gain adjustments on a regular basis.

Because of these complexities, an IF beamformer would be unlikely to be used for the formation of a single beam. It is, however, well suited to the formation of many beams over the full radar surveillance volume and also to the formation of many independently agile beams.

There are many technologies available for the construction of IF beamformers[19]. Amplitude weighting can be carried out by fixed resistor networks or by PIN diodes; phase control or time delay can be achieved using PIN diodes, surface acoustic wave delay lines, or optical fibre delay lines[20]. A most satisfactory type of IF beamformer for multiple fixed beams is that based on the resistive matrix (Fig. 2.7(d)). The operation of the matrix is most easily visualised as follows: if, from an IF signal, four equal components referenced 0°, 90°, 180° and 270° are synthesised, then any amplitude and phase version of that signal may be created by simple summation of those components after appropriate amplitude weighting; the weighting can be carried out using a simple resistor network. Such networks can be realised in printed thick film resistor form on alumina substrate and will operate satisfactorily up to about 100 MHz[17].

Another promising IF beamformer is based on the vector modulator approach, discussed later and shown in Fig. 2.10. Though more complex, this allows complete electronic control of the amplitude and phase weighting; it is therefore suited to electronically steerable multiple beams or adaptive beamforming involving null steering.

2.4.3 DIGITAL BEAMFORMERS

The principle of digital beamforming is that the received signal at each array is down-converted, after RF amplification if necessary, into in-phase (I) and quadrature (Q) components at a very low IF or at baseband[21]. After suitable amplification, involving very high gain to bring the signals into the conversion range of analogue-to-digital (A/D) convertors, the signals are sampled and converted into I and Q digital words, I_n and Q_n for array element n. These two digital words for each array element channel may then be multiplied digitally by appropriate weighting factors (a_n and b_n), digitally summed, and the modulus taken. Mathematically, the operations are as follows:

1. Form: $a_n I_n$ (Weighted components
          $b_n Q_n$ – provides amplitude
                                           taper and phase shift)

2. Sum:
$$I_s = \sum_1^n a_n I_n; \quad Q_s = \sum_1^n b_n Q_n$$

3. Modulus: $(I_s^2 + Q_s^2)^{\frac{1}{2}}$ (Forms beam output,
                                           converted back to
                                           analogue form by D/A
                                           convertor if necessary)

Digital beamforming is thus in essence very simple. Following A/D conversion, all operations are carried out in a computer. It follows that an infinite variety of beams could be synthesised simultaneously given adequate parallel processor power. Practical implementation of digital beamformers is not so simple, however, and they are still very much at the experimental stage. The coherent down-conversion process (probably a double down-conversion) is complex in terms of components and signal distribution; the large signal gain in each array element channel, typically in excess of 50 dB, causes problems in phase and amplitude stability; the large amount of digital circuitry operating at high clock rates requires very close attention to data bus structures and circuit interactions. Also, with current semiconductor technology the primary power consumption of this type of beamformer is very high.

Nevertheless, digital beamforming will clearly be a very important technique in the future. Its great advantage lies in its flexibility and ease of calibration or modification through software rather than hardware. The pace of its development will be related to the growth in need for highly adaptive multiple beam patterns[22] and the progress with VLSI realisations of parallel computer processing architectures.

2.4.4 BEAMFORMER SUMMARY

The tradeoffs involved in selecting a type and architecture of beamformer are difficult to generalise. Wallington[23] has given a most useful summary of the options, reproduced in Table 2.2.

Table 2.2 Beamformer choices (after Wallington)

		Fixed	Steered	Adaptive
Single Beam		RF	RF	Digital or beam/beam S/L cancel (RF or IF)
Multiple beams	Complete set	RF (orthogonal) IF (non-orthog)	N/A	Digital
	Small set	RF	RF or IF with RF steering	Digital or beam/beam S/L cancel (RF or IF)
	Independent	RF (orthogonal) IF (non-orthog)	Digital or IF	Digital

2.5 Amplitude and phase control

2.5.1 AMPLITUDE CONTROL

The PIN diode may be used either as an attenuator or as a switch at IF or microwave frequencies. Figure 2.8(a) shows a simple configuration using one PIN diode in shunt so that when zero-biased the signal is transmitted; when the diode is forward biased, the RF resistance decreases and the output signal is attenuated. This is the basic reflective attenuator. The disadvantage of such a circuit is that some of the input signal will be reflected back to the input port, resulting in a poor VSWR that increases as the current is increased. In addition, the attenuation range available is limited to about 20 dB.

The attenuation range may be improved by the construction of a distributed circuit using a number of shunt PIN diodes, as shown in Fig. 2.8(b). At microwave frequencies each diode is separated by a quarter-wave transmission line to yield a high attenuation range with good attenuation flatness over a substantial bandwidth. The phase characteristics of this attenuator are poor as the transforming effect of the quarter-wave lines will vary with frequency; as the attenuation level is changed the phase variation becomes non-linear over the frequency range. Typically, attenuators have been designed with ±30° phase variation for an attenuation range of about 40 dB and a bandwidth of 20%. These characteristics may be improved by optimising the inter-diode spacing rather than using simple quarter-wave lines.

The absorbtive attenuator shown in Fig. 2.8(c) provides a correctly matched circuit. The input power is split in quadrature

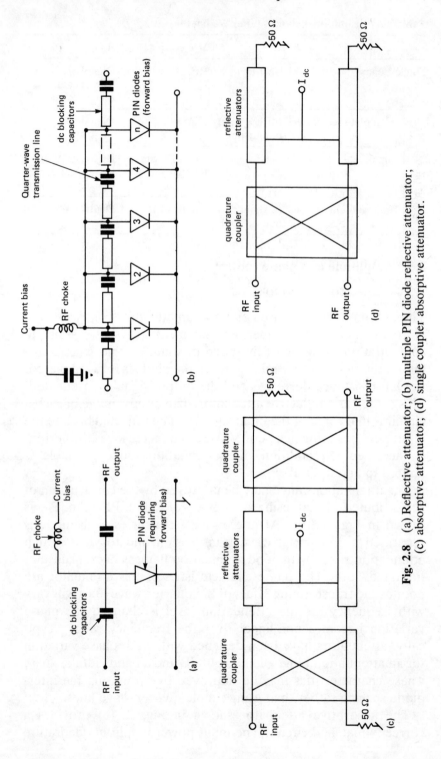

Fig. 2.8 (a) Reflective attenuator; (b) multiple PIN diode reflective attenuator; (c) absorptive attenuator; (d) single coupler absorptive attenuator.

and the signals are attenuated by the reflective attenuators before again being combined. When the diodes are matched and biased identically, the reflected signals are the same, thus cancelling at the input port and combining in the load of the hybrid. This gives a low input VSWR independent of the attenuation setting. As a result the absorbtive attenuator is used in preference to the simple reflective attenuator. Problems with phase variation as a function of frequency are still not eliminated, however.

Figure 2.8(d) shows another absorbtive attenuator configured with just one quadrature coupler. The signal input at one port is divided in quadrature and attenuated in the same way as above and the reflected signal from each reflective attenuator is then recombined in the quadrature coupler. With such a circuit, attenuation ripple over the band is observed because of coupling between the input and output ports. The higher the attenuation setting, the more the attenuation flatness will degrade. Typical figures show as much as 10 dB of ripple for such attenuators with an attenuation range of 25 dB and octave bandwidth.

2.5.2 PHASE CONTROL

Most phase shifters employ PIN diodes as switches to give phase control in discrete increments by switching lengths of line in and out of circuit. The PIN diode is well suited to switching applications as the time to change between 'on' (high forward bias) and 'off' (zero/reverse bias) states is very short (typically 100 ns or less). Also, the on/off states represent low and high impedances of approximately 1Ω and 1000Ω respectively. There are two different types of phase shifter, based on transmission and reflection.

Figure 2.9(a) shows the switched line phase shifter. PIN diodes are used to switch the RF signal between lengths of line that represent the specified phase states at a given frequency. The phase change in switching between the lines is $2\pi.\delta l/\lambda$ where λ is the wavelength. The device has limited bandwidth but with careful design the bandwidth can be improved by coupling techniques as in the Schiffman phase shifter[24].

Another common type of transmission phase shifter uses a loaded line as shown in Fig. 2.9(b). The phase change on switching between the PIN diode states is:

$$\phi = 2.\tan^{-1}\left\{\frac{2Z_N}{2 - Z_N^2}\right\}$$

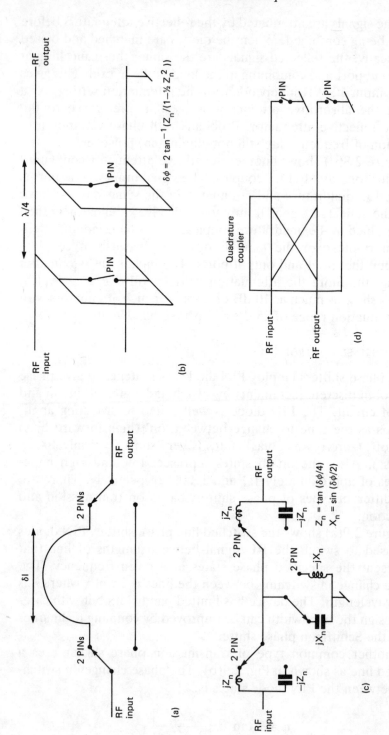

Fig. 2.9 (a) Switched line phase shifter; (b) loaded line phase shifter; (c) hi-pass, lo-pass phase shifter; (d) reflective phase shifter.

where the load impedance with the diodes off is jZ_N and the load impedance with the diodes on is $-jZ_N$[25]. The quarter-wave line between each line loading is used to give the best possible bandwidth, but must be modified in the cases of large phase shifts. For a phase shift greater than 45° it is found that the VSWR increases substantially when the quarter-wave line is used. Some tradeoff between bandwidth and return loss is thus required.

The hi-pass, lo-pass phase shifter is configured with shunt capacitors and series inductors (Fig. 2.9(c)). Switching in the high pass filter increases the phase by $+\phi/2$ and switching in the low pass filter changes the phase by $-\phi/2$. Although the design is complex, this type of phase shifter may be fabricated in a compact form as it does not require distributed circuitry. The bandwidth of the device is also larger than that available with either the switched line or the loaded line phase shifter. Typically, a 180° phase shifter is operational over a 10–20% bandwidth and a 45° phase shifter is operational over an octave.

The reflection type phase shifter uses either a circulator or a 3 dB quadrature coupler in conjunction with shunt diodes. Figure 2.9(d) shows the configuration of a 180° phase shifter. When the diodes are 'off', ideally they appear as an open circuit to the input signal and the phase delay is 0°. When the diodes are 'on', ideally they appear as a short circuit and the phase delay is −180°. The coupler can be designed to have broad bandwidth and the bandwidth of the phase shifter is largely dominated by this coupler. If a smaller phase shift between the diode states is required, a small line length is inserted. A major advantage of this form of phase shifter is that only two diodes are used per bit.

All the phase shifters mentioned above are digitally controlled diode phase shifters. In addition, the varactor diode is often used as an analogue control phase shifter, but is limited to low power applications, since harmonics are generated at powers greater than about 1 dBm.

An alternative to the PIN diode phase shifter is the ferrite phase shifter. A full comparison of these two generic types has been made[4]; for applications up to 15 GHz, the PIN diode phase shifter is preferred. A basic problem with diode phase shifters is that there are fundamental limitations on the insertion loss, which increases as more diodes are used. For this reason, reflection phase shifters offer the lowest insertion loss with the lowest number of PIN diodes. The insertion loss becomes a significant problem in the design of high resolution phase shifters as more diodes are required to achieve the high resolution. A typical value of loss usually allowed is in the region of 0.5–1 dB per bit of phase control.

2.5.3 VECTOR MODULATORS

Rather than using independent phase and amplitude control devices, another approach is to use a vector modulator which allows phase and amplitude control in a single unit. The vector modulator is configured with a 3 dB in-phase combiner, two current-controlled attenuators, and a 3 dB quadrature coupler. The bandwidth is principally restricted by the attenuators and it is usually possible to realise an octave range. The signal input is split into quadrature components by the quadrature coupler. Each component is individually attenuated, and the resultant vectors are summed using a Wilkinson divider (Fig. 2.10). The device is capable, in theory, of setting vectors over a phase range of 0–90°, and an attenuation range of between 6 dB and some maximum attenuation value determined by the diode attenuators. The vector modulator is perfectly reciprocal, provided its component parts are reciprocal, and thus a single unit could be used in both transmit and receive operation. Full 360° control can be achieved using a coarse digital PIN diode phase shifter in conjunction with a single vector modulator to provide fine control.

Another type of vector modulator can more conveniently cover the full 360° phase range. It has previously been described[26] for use at IF or low RF, but is equally applicable at microwave frequencies. As shown in Fig. 2.11, it consists of simple absorptive attenuators used in the two branches of a conventional vector modulator. However, the PIN diodes are used as RF variable

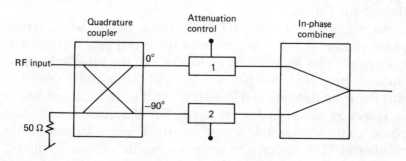

Fig. 2.10 90° vector modulator.

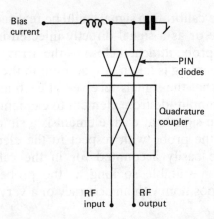

Fig. 2.11 Absorptive attenuator with gain −1 to +1.

resistors rather than as switches, giving the attenuators a range in gain from −1 to +1.

2.6 Calibration and monitoring of arrays

Following assembly of a phased array, initial test and calibration will be required. Adjustments may be made to bring the array performance within the required specification. During subsequent operation, some form of performance monitoring or built-in test equipment (BITE) is required to ensure that the array remains within specification.

There are two approaches to achieving stable performance. The array can use high precision or compensated components, the parameters of which vary little with time or environmental conditions; this involves little monitoring equipment, but is a costly approach. The alternative is to use components with less stringent tolerances and provide an overall open-loop or closed-loop correction system. The decreasing cost of digital electronic circuitry makes the latter approach increasingly attractive.

Any calibration or monitoring system must involve a means for measuring the performance, and a means for deriving any necessary corrections. The most critical part of any calibration or monitoring system is the way in which the array element signals are sampled or test signals injected. Because of tighter error tolerances on a receiving array, associated with low sidelobe levels and control of nulls, receive channel calibration is the more important.

In this case the calibration signal could be realised either from a near-field source or as a signal directly injected into each array element from a probe attached close to the array. An advantage is that mutual coupling is taken into account in the calibration. A disadvantage is that the signals received at each module differ in both phase and amplitude from element to element. The relationship between the signals at each element is a simple function of the position of the probe with respect to the element position, and this can be easily accounted for in the calibration. This technique is then suitable so long as the probe can be fixed permanently in position with an accuracy of a very small fraction of a wavelength.

The signal could alternatively be injected into each array element individually by directional couplers. In this way the calibration is simpler to perform, though the effects of mutual coupling are no longer accounted for. The problem is that the signals would be provided by a n-way splitter, where n is the number of array elements. This splitter will then have its own errors associated with it and these cannot be incorporated into the calibration procedure. This imposes strict requirements for the splitter, given the requisite module accuracy on receive. The use of optical fibres carrying a reference signal modulation has been suggested as a way of overcoming this difficulty[27,28].

Likewise, in a transmitting array, near-field receiving probes may be used to sample the radiated field, but to obtain diagnostics adequate for individual element corrections to be made, sampling would be required at each element. Some systems[1] have used a single probe in the near field to receive the signal from elements excited singly and successively over many radar dead times or to detect the signal from one particular element in the presence of the others energised through a characteristic modulation on that element.

2.7 Active arrays

The term 'active array' is applied to a phased array having some active signal processing, such as gain, at each array element. In a receiving array, a low noise amplifier (LNA) immediately after each array element aperture defines the system noise figure, making subsequent losses in signal combining and down-conversion networks of insignificant effect. Figure 2.12 shows typical noise figures for low noise amplifiers at the present time. These

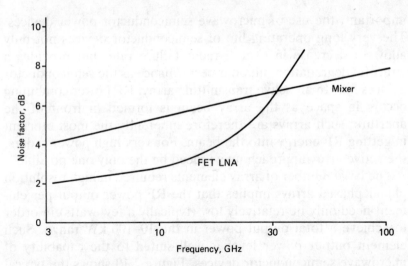

Fig. 2.12 Receiver low noise amplifier (LNA) noise figures.

amplifiers make use of GaAs field-effect transistors and noise figure improvements are still occurring as the technology allows further reductions in FET gate width[29]. It is anticipated that gate widths may be reduced to as low as 0.1 μm from the present 0.3–0.5 μm, allowing improvements of at least 0.5 dB at the higher radar frequencies. The narrower gate width and the use of new high electron mobility FET structures (HEMT structures) will almost certainly extend the operation of low noise FET amplifiers up to 100 GHz. The impact of FET LNAs has been substantial in terms of overall radar performance. As compared to a system without low noise RF amplification, the improvement of some 3 dB in noise figure is equivalent in radar performance to doubling the transmitter power. The active array with an LNA at each element thus offers the best possible sensitivity for an antenna system.

Active transmitting arrays are now attracting increasing interest. Conventionally, radar transmitters have used a single high power microwave valve. Though there are advantages to this approach, a disadvantage is that such valves have a limited life and failure results in complete radar system failure. Also, considerable power is lost in the distribution network to the array elements. A natural step therefore is to provide RF power amplification at each array element rather than centrally. This allows the use of smaller, less stressed, microwave valves or, more important, the use of microwave semiconductor power devices. The very long operating life of semiconductor devices not only allows a decrease in overall radar failure rate, but provides a 'graceful degradation' in radar performance as the semiconductor devices fail. In an active transmitting array, RF power combining occurs in space as the array beam is formed in front of the aperture; such arrays are therefore inherently the most efficient in getting RF energy into the beam. For very high power radars, the active array approach may indeed be the only one possible.

The large number of array elements required in high resolution planar phased arrays implies that the RF power output per element need only be relatively low (typically a few watts) in order to achieve a total output power in the 10–100 kW range. Such element output power level is well suited to the capability of microwave semiconductor devices. Figure 2.13 shows the typical current performance of RF semiconductor high power amplifying (HPA) devices. At up to about 4 GHz, the highest power outputs are obtained from Si bipolar transistors; between 4 GHz and 20 GHz, the GaAs power FET is the preferred source. At frequencies above 20 GHz, there is currently no very satisfactory microwave semiconductor power source, but Si IMPATT diodes offer a limited capability.

The cost of active arrays, associated with the considerable electronic complexity of low noise amplification, power amplifi-

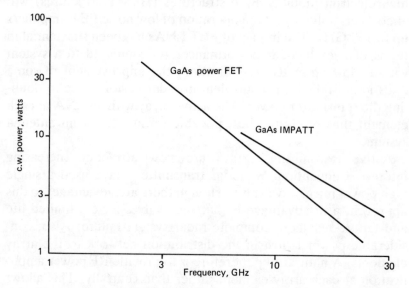

Fig. 2.13   RF Output power of semiconductor devices.

cation and phase shifting at each array element, has limited their development. With conventional hybrid microwave integrated circuit technology using discrete semiconductor devices, it is difficult to achieve a unit cost much below £1000 ($1500) for an active transmit/receive array element. Much of this cost is associated with the achievement of tight phase/gain performance criteria and the individual test and alignment. The rapid improvements in monolithic microwave integrated circuits (MMICs), whereby complete functional blocks (LNA, HPA, phase shifters) may be realised on a single GaAs chip, are dramatically altering this situation[29,30]. A modular concept may now be adopted to an active array element (Fig. 2.14), allowing mass production of common modules with associated cost reduction. Recently, mass-produced MMIC functional blocks have been marketed at a cost of the order of £10 ($15), which indicates the feasibility of achieving active phased array element unit costs in the region of £100 ($150).

A number of different approaches to active phased array element design have been adopted (Fig. 2.15). Most interest centres on parallel receiving and transmitting amplifier chains isolated by RF switches (Fig. 2.15(a)); isolation using circulators is possible in low power systems, but the higher isolation provided by switches is usually necessary. PIN diode switches are the most usual, though FET switches[29] may have some advantages in MMIC technology compatibility. The phase shifter, if a reciprocal device, may be placed in the common branch of the element; separate transmit and receive phase shifters are required if they are non-reciprocal devices. An important element configuration for the future, with the flexibility for adaptive and multiple beam

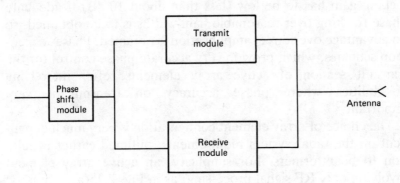

Fig. 2.14 Modular concept of active array elements.

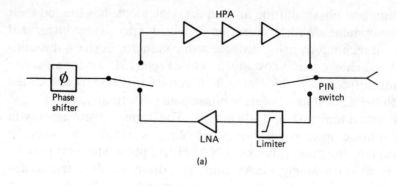

(a)

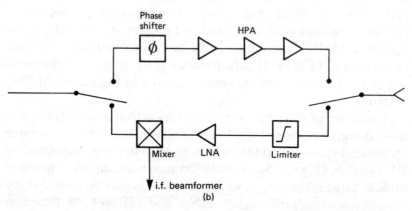

(b)

Fig. 2.15 (a) RF T/R module; (b) T/R module with IF beamforming.

forming, involves down-conversion to IF for the receive channel
and the use of a separate IF beamformer (Fig. 2.15(b)).
Approaches other than direct amplification have been proposed
for the transmit chain[31]; locked oscillators may be used, but the
locking gain has to be low (less than about 10 dB) if adequate
phase tracking over reasonable bandwidths is to be obtained, so
no advantage over direct amplification is obtained. Phase-locked-
loop schemes, which provide very accurate phase control for the
transmit section of active array elements, offer interesting
possibilities where phase accuracy on transmit is very
important[32].

The choice of array element configuration is very much dependent on the radar system requirements, outlined earlier in rela-
tion to beamformers. For simplicity, an active array element
involving only RF signal processing, as in Fig. 2.15(a), would be
preferred. More complex system demands will, however, dictate

more interest in the future in configurations which allow IF and digital beamforming.

2.8 Phased array radar systems

The earliest phased array radars operationally deployed are still the most impressive. These are the very large, high power, high resolution, electronically scanned radars constructed at enormous cost on the US continent for ICBM defence. COBRA DANE[1,2] is a 30 m diameter, 15 MW peak power (1 MW mean power) single-face phased array which can provide 1 m range resolution on targets at ranges up to 1500 km. The aperture is divided into approximately 100 sub-arrays, each having 160 active array elements. Each sub-array is fed by a 160 kW peak power travelling wave tube. The array makes use of element thinning; towards the edges of the array an increasing number of elements are dummy elements, so RF power is concentrated towards the centre, providing an amplitude taper (approximately 35 dB Taylor) to reduce the sidelobes. Some 19 000 elements out of a total of 35 000 are dummy elements. The PAVE PAWS radar[2], of which two have been built, is a radar of similar function, but operating at 450 MHz with 600 kW peak output power (150 kW mean). It uses transmit/receive modules of the type shown in Fig. 2.15 (a), employing silicon bipolar transistors. There are two faces to the array, each providing 120° azimuth cover. A 23 m diameter face consists of 56 sub-arrays, each having 32 active array elements; again, array thinning is used with 885 dummy elements in addition to the 1792 active ones. A detection range of some 4500 km is obtained for a 10 m^2 cross section target.

The first example of a mass produced phased array system is the Raytheon AN/TPN-25 precision approach radar. Many tens of these were built for precision landing approach guidance of aircraft over a limited 15° × 20° sector. For electronic scanning over this limited angular coverage, it was possible to use a hybrid array technique with a phased array illuminating a reflector antenna, as shown in Fig. 2.5. The phased array is an array of 824 phase shifters, itself space-fed by a horn. The system can track up to six aircraft simultaneously on final approach.

One-dimensional electronic scanning arrays have also been taken through to considerable levels of mass production. One of the first was the Plessey AR3-D radar[33] which operated in the 3 GHz band and used a single high power microwave valve

feeding a slow wave structure and line array at the focus of a
cylindrical parabolic antenna. This provided frequency scanning
in elevation combined with mechanical scanning in azimuth. The
elevation scanning could be carried out within one radar pulse,
but had restrictions in frequency agility. The AR320 series
radar[34], shown in Fig. 2.16, is a planar array version of the AR3-D
which uses the same elevation frequency scanning principle and
mechanical scanning in azimuth; the use of the planar array,
comprising 76 horizontal linear arrays 4.3 m long stacked vertically, each having 80 slot radiating elements, allows excellent
aperture illumination control, thereby achieving better than
−30 dB sidelobe levels. A 150 kW peak (6 kW mean) TWT

Fig. 2.16 Plessey/ITT AR 320.

amplifier fed by a solid state driver provides the RF power, adequate for detection of 1 m^2 targets out to 250 km range over a 28° elevation coverage.

The first mass production all solid state phased array was the General Electric AN/TPS-59 (or GE 592)[35]. This is a 1 GHz band planar array for shorter range air defence purposes which uses phase scanning of a single narrow beam in elevation and mechanical scanning in azimuth. The array aperture is approximately 10 × 5 m and consists of 54 line arrays stacked vertically, each fed from a 1 kW solid state power amplifier. PIN diode phase shifters are used and considerable emphasis is placed on low cost technology in the subsystems and stripline distribution networks. The

Fig. 2.17 Martello.

Marconi Martello[36] radar is also a planar phased array with similar applications and has been developed to use either a high power microwave valve or solid state power modules (Fig. 2.17). A special feature of this radar is that it uses a broad elevation transmitting beam mechanically scanned in azimuth, with IF receive beamforming to produce 8 simultaneous narrow elevation beams over the full elevation coverage. Each of the 60 line arrays, stacked vertically, has its own low conversion loss down-converter feeding the IF beamformer.

Other phased array radars for air defence applications which have reached quantity production are the Raytheon PATRIOT system[2], which is a space-fed single-face radar using some 5000 ferrite phase shifters, and the Hughes FIRE FINDER (AN/TPQ-37) mortar location radar[38]. The latter radar, shown in Fig. 2.18, is particularly interesting for the development which has gone into mass production techniques for the sub-array assemblies containing the printed antenna elements, PIN diode phase shifters and the integrated circuit diode control chips.

A novel approach to achieving hemispherical coverage from a single-face array has been adopted in the Sperry DOME antenna[14]. The planar array is placed with its boresight vertical and a lens structure is placed over it, as shown in Fig. 2.4. The lens then has the effect of magnifying the scan angle from the array. The lens structure used in a development model was fabricated from a honeycomb of fixed phase shifters. Though most elegant in concept, the scheme has the problem that the dome is cumbersome and heavy; also the beam shape and polarisation change with beam steering angle, which creates difficulty. The best application of this technique may be to much higher frequencies where the dome may be moulded from dielectric material in the same format as an optical lens.

Naval applications have always attracted interest for phased arrays. The ship is a high value platform with limited space for a multiplicity of radars, but a need for multifunction capability is surveillance, tracking and weapon control. The most ambitious programme has been the US Navy AEGIS programme to fit a number of ships with the RCA AN/SPY-1 radar[37]. This system comprises four phased array faces mounted on the ship superstructure (Fig. 2.19) to provide complete electronic beam steering over all azimuth angles. Each array has 4350 radiating elements (Fig. 2.20); early versions used 64-element sub-arrays, but later versions use 2 element sub-arrays. Careful design of the aperture

Fig. 2.18 AN/TPQ37 mortar location radar.

illumination taper and the use of very fine resolution 7-bit phase shifters gives good low sidelobe performance. Sixteen crossed-field amplifier tubes are used to feed each array through wave-guide distribution networks with ferrite phase shifters.

Another major programme for a naval phased array (MESAR) has involved the development in the UK of transmit/receive modules for the 3 GHz band[30,38]. The configuration is that of Fig. 2.15(a), the receive section having a noise figure of 3.5 dB and the transmit section having a power output of 2.5 W. Individual GaAs MMIC chips, including a digitally controlled FET phase shifter, are all assembled on an alumina substrate, this technique providing the optimum in cost and yield with the current state of GaAs technology.

Fig. 2.19   AEGIS AN/SPY-1.

Fig. 2.20   One of the four phased arrays of the AEGIS AN/SPY-1.

Phased arrays have been slow to appear in airborne applications despite the need for a multi-function radar. The major development programme is for the Rockwell B-1B bomber aircraft and the F-16 fighter aircraft; the radar is the Westinghouse AN/APQ-164 phased array[40], evolved from the EAR demonstrator. This planar array employs 1526 ferrite phase shifters in plug-in module form. The latest developments involve complete plug-in GaAs transmit/receive modules.

References

1. Coraine, R. T. 'Cobra Dane (AN/FPS-108) Radar System', *Signal*, May/June (1977).
2. Brookner, E. (Ed) *Radar Technology*, Artech House (1977).
3. Newman, E. H., Richmond, J. H. and Walker, C. H. 'Superdirective Receiving Arrays, *IEEE Trans. AP-26*, 629–635 (1978).
4. Skolnik, M. I. *Radar Handbook*, McGraw-Hill Book Co, New York, Chapter 11 (1970).
5. Hansen, R. C. 'Tables of Taylor Distribution for Circular Aperture Antennas', *IRE Trans. AP-8*, 23–26 (1960).
6. Radford, M. F. 'Electronically Scanned Antenna Systems', *Proc. IEE*, **125**, IIR, 100–112 (1978).
7. Elliott, R. S. *Antenna Theory and Design*, Prentice Hall, New Jersey (1981).
8. Ruze, J. 'Antenna Tolerance Theory – A Review', *Proc. IEEE*, 54, 633–640 (1966).
9. Mailoux, R. J. 'Phased Array Theory and Technology', *Proc. IEEE*, 70, 246–291 (1982).
10. Mohr, M. C. and Lewis, L. R. 'A Reflective Phased Array Antenna using Circularly Polarised Phase Shifters', *IEEE AP-S Digest*, 447–453 (1966).
11. Rudge, A. W. and Olver, A. D. (Eds) *Handbook of Antenna Design*, Peter Peregrinus (1984).
12. Ender, J. and Wilden, H. 'The Crow's Nest Antenna – A Spatial Array in Theory and Experiment', *Proc. 2nd International Conference on Antennas and Propagation, IEE*, Vol. **1**, 25–27 (1981).
13. Mrstik, A. V. and Smith, P. G. 'Scanning Capabilities of Large Parabolic Cylinder Reflector Antennas with Phased Array Feeds', *IEEE Trans AP-29*, 455–462 (1981).
14. Schwartzmann, L. and Liebman, P. M. 'A Report on the Sperry Dome Radar', *Proc. Military Microwave Conf.*, London, 167–176 (1978).
15. Roederer, A. G. 'Multibeam Satellite Antenna Concepts for Mobile Communications', *IEEE Conf. Publ. No. 222*, 83–9, (1983).
16. Rodgers, A. 'Wide Band Squintless Linear Array', *Marconi Rev.*, **35**, 221–243 (1972).
17. Wallington, J. R. 'The Role of Analogue Beamforming in Radar', *GEC J. Res.*, **3**, 1, 25–33 (1985).
18. Rotman, W. and Turner, R. F. 'Wide Angle Microwave Lens for Line Source Applications', *IEEE Trans AP-11*, 623–632 (1963)
19. Hansen, R. C. *Microwave Scanning Antennas*, Vol. 3, Ch. 3, Academic Press (1966).
20. Sheehan, P. G. and Forrest, J. R. 'The Use of Optical Techniques for Beamforming in Phased Arrays', *Proc. SPIE*, **477**, 82–89 (1984).

21. Wardrop, B. 'The Role of Digital Processing in Radar Beamforming', *GEC J. Res.*, **3**, 1, 34–35 (1985).
22. Steyskal, H. 'Synthesis of Antenna Patterns with Prescribed Nulls', *IEEE Trans. AP-30*, 273–279 (1982).
23. Wallington, J. R. 'Beamforming Options for Phased Array Radar', *Proc. 4th Military Microwaves Conf.*, MEPL, Brighton, UK (1986).
24. White, J. F. 'Review of Semiconductor Microwave Phase Shifters', *Proc. IEEE*, 72, 697–708 (1984).
25. Garver, R. V. *Microwave Diode Control Devices*, Artech House (1976).
26. Windram, M. D. and Brunt, L. 'Theory and Operation of and Adaptive Array for Broadcasting', *Proc. IEE Conf. on Radio Receivers and Assoc. Sys.*, Publ No. 44, (1978).
27. Wallington, J. R. and Griffin, J. M. 'Optical Techniques for Signal Distribution in Phased Arrays', *GEC J. Res.*, **2**, 2, 66–75 (1984).
28. Forrest, J. R. *et al.* 'Optical Fibre Networks for Signal Distribution and Control in Phased Array Radars', *Radar 82, IEE Comp. Publ. No. 216*, 408–412 (1982).
29. Pengelly, R. S. *Microwave Field Effect Transistors and their Applications*, Research Studies Press (1984).
30. Pengelly, R. S. *et al.* 'An Integrated Transmit/Receive Module Employing GaAs Monolithic Integrated Circuits', *Proc. Mil. Microwaves Conf.*, MEPL, London, 449–456 (1984).
31. Austin, J. and Forrest, J. R. 'Design Concepts for Active Phased Array Modules', *Proc. IEE, pt. F*, **127**, 4, 290–300 (1980).
32. Ward, C. J. *et al.* 'High Phase Accuracy Active Phased Array Module for Multi-function Radars', *IEEE MTT-S Digest*, 179–181 (1982).
33. Bradsell, P. 'Microwave Radar', *IEE Journal Electronics and Power*, **27**, 367–370 (1981).
34. Pfister, G. 'The Series 320 Radar: Three-dimensional Air Surveillance for the 1980's, *IEEE Trans. AES-16*, 626–638 (1980).
35. King, I. E., Albanese, A. A. and Burris, H. A. 'The AN/TPS-59 and GE592 – A Family of Solid-State Radars', *Proc. IEE Conf. 'Radar 77'*, 12–16 (1977).
36. Latham, C. 'Martello – A Long Range 3D Radar', *Proc. Mil. Microwaves Conf.*, MEPL, London, 79–84 (1984).
37. Britton, R. L. *et al.* 'AN/SPY-1 Planned Improvements', *IEEE Eascon 82 Record*, 379–386 (1982).
38. Mailloux, R. J. 'Phased Array Theory and Technology', *Proc. IEEE*, **70**, 246–291 (1982).
39. Billam, E. R. 'Phased Array Radar and the Royal Navy', *J.N.S.*, **12**, 2, 91–103 (1986).
40. Klass, P. J. 'B-1 Pioneers Airborne Phased Array', *Av. Week & Space Tech.*, 84, 9 Apr. (1984).

CHAPTER 3
Target Characteristics

IRWIN D. OLIN

3.1 Radar cross section

When a radar illuminates a target, the power that is backscattered or reflected back to the radar is defined in terms of a measurable quantity, the target radar cross section. But since there is substantial variation of the reflected power about the target for any given illumination angle, an equivalent hypothetical target, which reradiates isotropically, is used as the basis for measurement. The equivalence is based on requiring the isotropic target to be sized so that the power density backscattered to the radar receiving antenna is the same as that for the actual target. Thus, if P_i is the effective incident (transmitted) power, including the antenna gain, then the power density incident on the target at range, R, is:

$$p_i = \frac{P_i}{4\pi R^2} \tag{1}$$

If σ is the equivalent area of that target, it will intercept and isotropically scatter a power $P_s = p_i \sigma$. Then back at the radar, assuming monostatic operation, the power density is:

$$p_s = \frac{P_s}{4\pi R^2} = \frac{P_i}{4\pi R^2} \cdot \frac{\sigma}{4\pi R^2} \tag{2}$$

therefore

$$\sigma = 4\pi R^2 \frac{P_s}{P_i} \tag{3}$$

Note that P_s is the backscattered power at the target and P_i is the incident or transmitted power measured at the radar. To assure plane wave propagation, so that σ is independent of range, R is made arbitrarily large. Then from Equation 3:

$$\sigma = 4\pi \lim_{R \to \infty} R^2 \frac{P_s}{P_i} \qquad (4)$$

An equivalent definition, expressed in terms of the electric and magnetic field components, $\mathbf{E}$ and $\mathbf{H}$, is given by Ruck[1]:

$$\sigma = 4\pi \lim_{R \to \infty} R^2 \frac{(\mathbf{E}^s \cdot \mathbf{E}^{s*})}{(\mathbf{E}^i \cdot \mathbf{E}^{i*})} = 4\pi \lim_{R \to \infty} R^2 \frac{(\mathbf{H}^2 \cdot \mathbf{H}^{s*})}{(\mathbf{H}^i \cdot \mathbf{H}^{i*})} \qquad (5)$$

where * denotes the complex conjugate.

For the analysis presented here, the fields $\mathbf{E}^i$, $\mathbf{E}^s$, $\mathbf{H}^i$, $\mathbf{H}^s$ will be assumed completely polarised, i.e. all amplitudes and phase angles are deterministic functions of time. Moreover, since $|\mathbf{E}| = \sqrt{(\mu/\varepsilon)}|\mathbf{H}|$, where $\sqrt{(\mu/\varepsilon)}$ is the intrinsic impedance of the medium (377 Ω for free space), only the $\mathbf{E}$ field component need be considered.

3.1.1 WAVE POLARISATION

The definition of radar cross section in terms of the incident and scattered fields, $\mathbf{E}^i$ and $\mathbf{E}^s$, requires further definition in terms of the polarisation of these fields. In general the observed radar cross section characteristics of a target using vertical polarisation, for example, will be different from that when using horizontal polarisation. But vertical and horizontal are only two, albeit the most often used, polarisations. Moreover, the target itself will always exhibit characteristics for which one radar transmitter and receiver polarisation is optimised in terms of its radar cross section. Alternatively, different polarisations for the same target can be found for which no return is theoretically possible.

To develop these concepts further, consider the generalised form for the complex electric field vector of a propagating wave, as described by Kales[2]:

$$\mathbf{E} = (\mathbf{E} \cdot \mathbf{a}_1^*)\mathbf{a}_1 + (\mathbf{E} \cdot \mathbf{a}_2^*)\mathbf{a}_2 \qquad (6)$$

where $\mathbf{a}_1$ and $\mathbf{a}_2$ are a pair of unit length orthogonal base vectors, and $(\mathbf{E} \cdot \mathbf{a}_1^*)$ and $(\mathbf{E} \cdot \mathbf{a}_2^*)$ are the scalars representing the projection of $\mathbf{E}$ along the directions of the unit vectors $\mathbf{a}_1$ and $\mathbf{a}_2$. For the familiar case of vertical and horizontal polarisations, this becomes:

$$\mathbf{E} = E_X\mathbf{a}_X + E_Y\mathbf{a}_Y) \qquad (7)$$

in which $\mathbf{a}_X$ and $\mathbf{a}_Y$ correspond to unit vertically and horizontally polarised vectors.

For convenience, the sinusoidal time dependence of the R.F. wave has been omitted, but in the case of Equation 7 this can be represented by:

$$\mathbf{E} = \mathscr{R}\{[E_X\mathbf{a}_X + E_Y\mathbf{a}_Y]e^{j\omega t}\} \qquad (8)$$

If $E_X = E_Y = E$, this becomes: $\mathbf{E} = E(\mathbf{a}_X + \mathbf{a}_Y) \cos \omega t$, which describes a linearly polarised wave with equal amplitudes along the horizontal and vertical axes, i.e. 45° polarisation.

In general, however, the signal components E_X and E_Y are unequal and not in phase and must be represented by complex numbers (scalars). Figure 3.1 depicts a right-hand coordinate system with unit vectors $\mathbf{a}_X$, $\mathbf{a}_Y$ and a wave travelling in the $+z$ direction, away from the origin. Including the propagation factor β ($= 2\pi/\lambda$, where λ is the radar wavelength and βz accounts for the phase change in the wave with z), Equation 8 becomes:

$$\mathbf{E} = \mathscr{R}\{[E'_X\mathbf{a}_X + E'_Y\mathbf{a}_Y]e^{j(\omega t - \beta z)}\} \qquad (9)$$

where E'_X and E'_Y are complex scalars. But since only the phase difference between these components, represented by ϕ, is important, without loss in generality Equation 9 can be rewritten as:

$$\mathbf{E} = \mathbf{a}_X E_X \cos(\omega t - \beta z) + \mathbf{a}_Y E_Y \cos(\omega t + \phi - \beta z) \qquad (10)$$

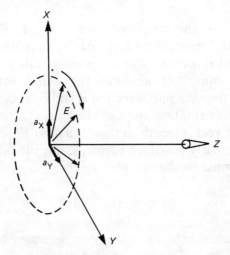

Fig. 3.1 Right-hand coordinate system for a wave propagating in the $+ Z$ direction. $\mathbf{a}_X$, $\mathbf{a}_Y$ are unit length vectors. $\mathbf{E}$ vector positions indicated for right circularly polarised wave as projected in the plane $\mathbf{Z} = 0$.

At any fixed z, the locus of $\mathbf{E}$ projected in the $X - Y$ plane can be determined. For convenience let $z = 0$, and let the amplitudes in the X and Y directions be denoted by x and y, then

$$x = E_X \cos \omega t \tag{11a}$$

$$y = E_Y \cos(\omega t + \phi) \tag{11b}$$

If these equations are solved parametrically, eliminating ωt, the result is:

$$ax^2 - bxy + cy^2 = 1 \tag{12}$$

where

$$a = \left(\frac{1}{E_X \sin \phi}\right)^2, \quad b = \frac{2 \cos \phi}{E_X E_Y \sin^2 \phi}, \quad c = \left(\frac{1}{E_Y \sin \phi}\right)^2$$

This is recognised as the general equation for an ellipse centred on the coordinate origin. The ellipticity (ratio of major to minor axes), tilt angle and direction of rotation of the equivalent R.F. vector are all functions of E_X, E_Y and ϕ.

For example, let $\phi = -\pi/2$ and $E_X = E_Y = E$. Then from Equation 12, the ellipse becomes a circle. Moreover, if $E = 1/\sqrt{2}$, then from Equation 10 with $z = 0$:

$$\mathbf{E} = \frac{1}{\sqrt{2}}(\mathbf{a}_X \cos \omega t + \mathbf{a}_Y \sin \omega t) \tag{13}$$

With reference to the coordinates in Fig. 3.1, $\mathbf{E}$ will trace a clockwise circular rotation with increasing time when looking in the propagation direction. Conventionally, this is termed right circular polarisation. (Note that the same rotating vector observed from the opposite direction is still right circularly polarised, but appears rotating counter-clockwise.) The factor $1/\sqrt{2}$ results in a unit vector length so that Equation 13 actually defines a unit right circularly polarised vector. Using the polar form, this can be represented by the complex vector:

$$\mathbf{a}_R = \frac{1}{\sqrt{2}}(\mathbf{a}_X - j\mathbf{a}_Y) \tag{14}$$

To show the actual field variation, it is necessary to multiply by the scalar $\exp[j(\omega t - \beta z)]$ and take the real part. Since $\mathbf{a}_X$ and $\mathbf{a}_Y$ are unit orthogonal vectors, $\mathbf{a}_R$ is also a unit vector, as it fulfils the equation $(\mathbf{a}_R \cdot \mathbf{a}_R^*) = 1$.

Similarly, a unit left circularly polarised unit vector, $\mathbf{a}_L$ results when $\phi = \pi/2$ and $E_X = E_Y = 1/\sqrt{2}$:

$$\mathbf{a}_L = \frac{1}{\sqrt{2}} (\mathbf{a}_X + j\mathbf{a}_Y) \qquad (15)$$

As seen by an observer looking along the wave propagating direction, this unit vector will appear rotating counter-clockwise. $\mathbf{a}_R$ and $\mathbf{a}_L$ are also orthogonal, since the equation $(\mathbf{a}_R \cdot \mathbf{a}_L^*) = 0$ is fulfilled. As in the case of linearly polarised orthonormal vectors (i.e. orthogonal vectors of unit length), an arbitrarily polarised wave can also be expressed in terms of circularly polarised orthonormal vectors:

$$\mathbf{E} = \mathcal{R}\{[\mathbf{a}_R E_R' + \mathbf{a}_L E_L']e^{j(\omega t - \beta z)}\} \qquad (16)$$

where E_R' and E_L' represent complex scalars. Using the definitions established by Equations 14 and 15, and recognising that only the relative phase (θ) between E_R' and E_L' is important, Equation 16 can be rewritten as:

$$\mathbf{E} = \frac{1}{\sqrt{2}} \mathcal{R}\{[(\mathbf{a}_X - j\mathbf{a}_Y)E_R + (\mathbf{a}_X + j\mathbf{a}_Y)E_L e^{j\theta}]e^{j\omega t}\} \qquad (17)$$

where $z = 0$ has been assumed. This equation will also result in a pair of components, $X = f(\omega t)$ and $Y = g(\omega t)$, which can be solved parametrically to eliminate the terms in ωt. The result is again an ellipse, but expressed in terms of the circular components E_R, E_L and θ. In this case, however, the relationship is significantly simpler. With reference to Fig. 3.1, the axial ratio is given by:

$$a.r. = \left| \frac{E_R + E_L}{E_R - E_L} \right| \qquad (18)$$

and the tilt angle of the major axis, τ, is $-\theta/2$. (τ is measured from the X-axis and in a counter-clockwise right-circular assumption.) For example, $\theta = 20°$ results in an inclination of the major elliptical axis of $10°$ counter-clockwise from the X-axis as illustrated in Fig. 3.2. Alternatively, defining the ratio of the circularly polarised components by:

$$r = \frac{E_R}{E_L} e^{-j\theta} \qquad (19)$$

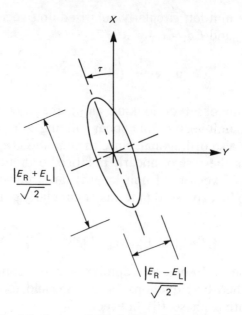

Fig. 3.2 Locus of elliptically polarised **E** vector.

then:

$$a.r. = \left| \frac{|r| + 1}{|r| - 1} \right|, \quad \tau = \tfrac{1}{2} \, arg(r) \tag{20}$$

The rotational direction of the resultant electric vector (right or left hand) simply takes the direction of the larger of the two components. Thus if $E_R > E_L$, the rotational direction, as viewed in the direction of propagation, is clockwise, whereas if $E_R < E_L$, the direction is counter-clockwise. These conditions are consistent with the definitions outlined in connection with Equation 13. The angular velocity of the vector (represented by ξ), however, is non-uniform and can be shown to be:

$$\frac{d\xi}{dt} = \frac{\omega(E_R^2 - E_L^2)}{E_R^2 + E_L^2 + 2E_R E_L \, \cos(2\omega t + \theta)} \tag{21}$$

3.1.2 MATRIX REPRESENTATION

The relationship between a wave described in terms of a linear $(X - Y)$ basis and the same wave described in terms of a circular basis $(R - L)$ can be established using Equations 6, 7, 14 and 15.

Thus, if $\mathbf{E} = E_X\mathbf{a}_X + E_Y\mathbf{a}_Y$, then the equivalent circular based components are:

$$E_R = \mathbf{E} \cdot \mathbf{a}_R^* = \frac{1}{\sqrt{2}}(E_X + jE_Y) \tag{22a}$$

$$E_L = \mathbf{E} \cdot \mathbf{a}_L^* = \frac{1}{\sqrt{2}}(E_X - jE_Y) \tag{22b}$$

since $(\mathbf{a}_X \cdot \mathbf{a}_X^* = 1$ and $(\mathbf{a}_X \cdot \mathbf{a}_Y^*) = 0$. The total electric field can then be written as:

$$E = \frac{1}{\sqrt{2}}(E_X + jE_Y)\mathbf{a}_R + \frac{1}{\sqrt{2}}(E_X - jE_Y)\mathbf{a}_L \tag{23}$$

Equivalently, written in matrix notation, this becomes:

$$\begin{bmatrix} E_R \\ E_L \end{bmatrix} = \frac{1}{\sqrt{2}}\begin{bmatrix} 1 & j \\ 1 & -j \end{bmatrix}\begin{bmatrix} E_X \\ E_Y \end{bmatrix} \tag{24}$$

This wave will be considered a transmitted wave and denoted by a superscript t, since it was assumed propagating away from an observer. The previous transform can then be written:

$$[E_{R,L}^t] = [T][E_{X,Y}^t] \tag{25a}$$

where

$$[T] = \frac{1}{\sqrt{2}}\begin{bmatrix} 1 & j \\ 1 & -j \end{bmatrix} \tag{25b}$$

For the backscattered wave, denoted by the superscript s, propagating to the receiver, the appropriate transform is:

$$[E_{R,L}^s] = [T^*][E_{X,Y}^s] \tag{26}$$

The effect of the conjugate is to account for the change in apparent rotational direction when the propagation direction of the wave is reversed. Given the circular based components, the corresponding linear based components can be derived with the following results:

$$[E_{X,Y}^t] = [T^{-1}][E_{R,L}^t] \tag{27a}$$

$$[E_{X,Y}^s] = [T^*]^{-1}[E_{R,L}] = [\tilde{T}][E_{R,L}] \tag{27b}$$

where -1 and $\sim$ denote the matrix inverse and transpose, respectively. Since $[T]$ is a unitary matrix, $[T^*]^{-1} = [\widetilde{T}]$, as indicated above.

3.1.3 RADAR TARGET SCATTERING MATRIX

The radar target acts to transform an incident (transmitted) polarisation state into a backscattered (received) polarisation state. Without being target specific, this transformation can be represented by a scalar matrix equation:

$$\begin{bmatrix} E_X^s \\ E_Y^s \end{bmatrix} = \begin{bmatrix} S_{11} & S_{12} \\ S_{12} & S_{22} \end{bmatrix} \begin{bmatrix} E_X^t \\ E_Y^t \end{bmatrix} = \begin{bmatrix} S_{11}E_X^t + S_{12}E_Y^t \\ S_{12}E_X^t + S_{22}E_Y^t \end{bmatrix} \qquad (28)$$

Generally, each element is complex and is expressed as an electric field component. These components, however, are related to the radar cross section, which is measurable as a power. From Equation 5 $\sqrt{\sigma_{ij}} = |S_{ij}|$. The addition of a phase factor, which is lost in a power measurement, completes the matrix formulation. Although the matrix is comprised of three complex elements, a constant phase factor can be ignored so that five independent quantities (three amplitudes and two phases) describe the matrix. The off-diagonal terms are equal, since reciprocity applies to the monostatic case being considered.

Equation 28 represented the scatter matrix in terms of the linear base vectors a_X, a_Y; however, any other orthonormal base vectors can be used. Of course, the elements of the matrix, given the same target, will be different. The change in the elements of the matrix when the base vectors are changed can be evaluated using a matrix transformation which is related to the transform between the field components expressed in the two different bases. For example, the relationships between the linear and circular base field components are described in Equations 24–27. Using these and the general expression, $[E^s] = [S][E^t]$, the following results are obtained after some matrix manipulation:

$$[S_{X,Y}] = [\widetilde{T}] [S_{R,L}] [T] \qquad (29a)$$

$$[S_{R,L}] = [T^*] [S_{X,Y}] [T^{-1}] \qquad (29b)$$

3.1.4 RECEIVED SIGNALS

The polarisation of the backscattered wave from the target is the result of the interaction of the transmitted wave polarisation with the polarisation characteristics of the target, as expressed by the scatter matrix. But a further interaction occurs when the back-scattered wave intercepts the radar receiving antenna. The result of this interaction is the generation of the signal voltage for processing by the radar. Representing the polarisation of the backscattered wave by the two components of the matrix $[E^s]$, the magnitude of the received voltage, considering only the wave polarisation interaction and ignoring the effect of target range, is given by $V = [E^r][E^s]$, where $[E^r]$ represents the polarisation characteristics of the receiving antenna when used for transmission. The signal voltage representing the complete radar–target interaction is then:

$$V = |[\widetilde{E}^r] [S] [E^t]| \qquad (30)$$

Obviously, an important case is that using a single duplexed radar antenna, for which $[E^r] = [E^t]$. Using Equations 28, 29 and 30, the received voltages for several combinations of antenna polarisations and three simple target scatter matrices are indicated in Tables 3.1 and 3.2. Note that the targets are identical in the two tables, but their representations differ in accordance with Equation 29, depending upon the polarisation bases. It should also be noted that the scatter matrices, while correctly representing the targets indicated, are an idealism. Actual targets consist of a large number of structures with differing polarisation characteristics. To the extent that the assembly of these structures is fixed during an observation period, a simple scatter matrix representation is possible; however, this representation generally varies as the target aspect changes. Nonetheless, the theory outlined still applies.

Clearly, the signal voltages depicted in Tables 3.1 and 3.2 vary, depending on the target and the polarisation of the transmitting and receiving antennas. To derive the optimum conditions, it is necessary to examine the scatter matrix in more detail.

3.1.5 OPTIMUM POLARISATIONS

Choosing the best transmitted and received polarisation depends upon the target and desired signal response. For most targets of

Table 3.1　Linear (*X-Y*) basis

		Constraints			
Target	$[S]$	$E^t=\begin{bmatrix}1\\0\end{bmatrix}$ $E^r=\begin{bmatrix}1\\0\end{bmatrix}$ E^s	$E^r=\begin{bmatrix}1\\0\end{bmatrix}$ V	$E^r=\begin{bmatrix}0\\1\end{bmatrix}$ V	$E^r=\frac{1}{\sqrt2}\begin{bmatrix}1\\1\end{bmatrix}$ V
Flat plate or sphere	$\begin{bmatrix}1&0\\0&1\end{bmatrix}$	$\begin{bmatrix}1\\0\end{bmatrix}$	1	0	$\frac{1}{\sqrt2}$
Dihedral corner (*X*-axis fold)	$\begin{bmatrix}1&0\\0&-1\end{bmatrix}$	$\begin{bmatrix}1\\0\end{bmatrix}$	1	0	$\frac{1}{\sqrt2}$
Long wire (45° orientation)	$\frac12\begin{bmatrix}1&1\\1&1\end{bmatrix}$	$\frac12\begin{bmatrix}1\\1\end{bmatrix}$	$\frac12$	$\frac12$	$\frac{1}{\sqrt2}$

Table 3.2　Circular (*R-L*) Basis

		Constraints			
Target	$[S]$	$E^t=\begin{bmatrix}1\\0\end{bmatrix}$ $E^r=\begin{bmatrix}1\\0\end{bmatrix}$ E^s	$E^r=\begin{bmatrix}1\\0\end{bmatrix}$ V	$E^r=\begin{bmatrix}0\\1\end{bmatrix}$ V	$E^r=\frac{1}{\sqrt2}\begin{bmatrix}1\\1\end{bmatrix}$ V
Flat plate or sphere	$\begin{bmatrix}0&1\\1&0\end{bmatrix}$	$\begin{bmatrix}0\\1\end{bmatrix}$	0	1	$\frac{1}{\sqrt2}$
Dihedral corner (*X*-axis fold)	$\begin{bmatrix}1&0\\0&1\end{bmatrix}$	$\begin{bmatrix}1\\0\end{bmatrix}$	1	0	$\frac{1}{\sqrt2}$
Long wire (45° orientation)	$\frac12\begin{bmatrix}-j&1\\1&j\end{bmatrix}$	$\frac12\begin{bmatrix}-j\\1\end{bmatrix}$	$\frac12$	$\frac12$	$\frac12$

interest a simple criterion is maximum received signal voltage. However, it is sometimes necessary to consider not only desired targets, but also those which should be rejected. For example, by simultaneously transmitting and receiving a single-sense circular polarisation it is possible to achieve some rejection of rain backscatter, while retaining detection of an aircraft.

For an undesired target, a zero signal voltage would be optimum. To the extent that the scatter matrix properly represents the target, appropriate radar polarisations can be found which will fulfil this condition. Assume an arbitrary pair of orthonormal vector components to represent the polarisation of a duplexed radar transmitting and receiving antenna:

$$[E] = \frac{1}{\sqrt{(|u_1|^2 + |u_2|^2)}} \begin{bmatrix} u_1 \\ u_2 \end{bmatrix} \tag{31}$$

where $[E][E^*] = 1$.

Using the general scatter matrix form of Equation 28 and substituting in Equation 30, the result is zero output for the following two conditions:

$$\left(\frac{u_1}{u_2}\right) = \frac{-1 \pm \sqrt{\left(1 - \dfrac{S_{11}}{S_{12}}\dfrac{S_{22}}{S_{12}}\right)}}{\dfrac{S_{11}}{S_{22}}} \tag{32}$$

This describes the polarisations as complex ratios in the coordinate basis used for defining the scatter matrix. Therefore, given the scatter matrix in a particular basis, there are two polarisations of the duplexed antenna which will result in rejecting the target described by the matrix. These are often referred to as the *copolarisation nulls*, since the matrix of a target which would produce this result using a single polarised component such as (1 0), or (0 1) would have zeros for the principal polarised terms, S_{11} and S_{22}. It should also be noted from Equation 32 that for some target matrices there will only be a single copolarisation null.

For maximum received signal voltage the components of the backscattered wave should be proportional to the complex conjugate of the receiving antenna parameters. Therefore:

$$[S][U] = \lambda[U^*] \tag{33}$$

in which $[U]$ represents the components of the duplexed transmitter-receiver antenna and λ is a scalar constant (not to be confused with its other representation for wavelength). Pre-multiplying both sides of this equation by $[U^*]^{-1}$, recognising that $[U]^{-1} = [\tilde{U}]^*$, and comparing the result with Equation 30, λ is the received signal voltage. Therefore, the problem is to find $[U]$. Equation 33 is similar to the well known eigenvector problem, with the exception that $[U^*]$ appears. An alternative to solving this special case is to consider the form of a scatter matrix when this optimum condition is fulfilled. From Tables 3.1 and 3.2, considering only a duplexed antenna (identical transmitting and receiving polarisations), maximum received signal voltage occurs when the scatter matrix is diagonal, i.e. $S_{12} = 0$. Then none of the target reflected signal is polarised orthogonal to the radar antenna. As shown by Boerner[3], the problem can be solved by finding a unitary matrix which will diagonalise the given scatter matrix using an appropriate transform. For example, it is known that if a unitary matrix, $[T]$, is used to transform the components of basis vectors $(\mathbf{a}_1, \mathbf{a}_2)$ to components of basis vectors $(\mathbf{a}_3, \mathbf{a}_4)$, then the congruent transform, $[\widetilde{T}]\,[S_{3,4}]\,[T] = [S_{1,2}]$, describes the relationship between the scatter matrices in the two bases. Determining an appropriate matrix, $[T]$, will also define the radar polarisation which should be used for maximum received signal voltage. The diagonalization of matrix $[S_{3,4}]$, written simply as $[S]$, is expressed by:

$$[\widetilde{T}]\,[S]\,[T] = [\lambda_i \delta_{ij}] \qquad (34)$$

where δ_{ij} is the Kronecker delta, and λ_i are the eigenvalues of $[S]$. Constraints on the relationships among the basis components in the two systems further define the form of $[T]$.

Consider the same wave expressed in two different bases:

$$\mathbf{E} = E_1 \mathbf{a}_1 + E_a \mathbf{a}_2 = E_3 \mathbf{a}_3 + E_4 \mathbf{a}_4 \qquad (35)$$

Referring to Equation 6, the projections of $\mathbf{E}$ along $\mathbf{a}_1$ and along $\mathbf{a}_2$ are:

$$\mathbf{E} \cdot \mathbf{a}_1^* \equiv E_1 = E_3(\mathbf{a}_3 \cdot \mathbf{a}_1^*) + E_4(\mathbf{a}_4 \cdot \mathbf{a}_1^*) \qquad (36a)$$

$$\mathbf{E} \cdot \mathbf{a}_2^* \equiv E_2 = E_3(\mathbf{a}_3 \cdot \mathbf{a}_2^*) + E_4(\mathbf{a}_4 \cdot \mathbf{a}_2^*) \qquad (36b)$$

Written in matrix form, this becomes:

$$[E_{1,2}] = \begin{bmatrix} E_1 \\ E_2 \end{bmatrix} = \begin{bmatrix} \mathbf{a}_3 \cdot \mathbf{a}_1^* & \mathbf{a}_4 \cdot \mathbf{a}_1^* \\ \mathbf{a}_3 \cdot \mathbf{a}_2^* & \mathbf{a}_4 \cdot \mathbf{a}_2^* \end{bmatrix} \begin{bmatrix} E_3 \\ E_4 \end{bmatrix} = [T]\,[E_{3,4}] \qquad (37)$$

In general, $\mathbf{a}_3$ and $\mathbf{a}_4$ can be expressed in terms of $\mathbf{a}_1$ and $\mathbf{a}_2$, as was the case for Equations 14 and 15:

$$\mathbf{a}_3 = \alpha_1 \mathbf{a}_1 + \alpha_2 \mathbf{a}_2 \qquad (38a)$$

$$\mathbf{a}_4 = \beta_1 \mathbf{a}_1 + \beta_2 \mathbf{a}_2 \qquad (38b)$$

Since $\mathbf{a}_3$, $\mathbf{a}_4$ and $\mathbf{a}_1$, $\mathbf{a}_2$ are orthogonal pairs of unit vectors,

$$|\alpha_1|^2 + |\alpha_2|^2 = 1 \tag{39a}$$

$$|\beta_1|^2 + |\beta_2|^2 = 1 \tag{39b}$$

Considering the relationships in Equations 37, 38 and 39, $[T]$ can be expressed as:

$$[T] = \begin{bmatrix} \alpha_1 & -\alpha_2^* \\ \alpha_2 & \alpha_1^* \end{bmatrix} \tag{40}$$

Adding the constraint that $[T]$ is unitary, letting $\alpha_1 = 1$ and writing $\varrho = \alpha_2/\alpha_1$, the form attributed to Kennaugh[4,5] is:

$$[T] = \frac{1}{\sqrt{(1 + \varrho\varrho^*)}} \begin{bmatrix} 1 & -\varrho^* \\ \varrho & 1 \end{bmatrix} \tag{41}$$

Applying the congruent transform to a general scatter matrix, Boerner[3] has shown that the optimised condition, for which $S_{12} = 0$, results in the following solution, for the monostatic case:

$$\varrho_{1,2} = \frac{-B \pm \sqrt{(B^2 + 4|A|^2)}}{2A} \tag{42}$$

where

$$A = S_{11}^* S_{12} + S_{22} S_{12}^*$$
$$B = |S_{11}|^2 - |S_{22}|^2.$$

Since this solution is based on zeros for the cross polarised component, S_{12}, ϱ_{12} are termed the *cross polarisation null pair*. The appropriate duplexed antenna polarisations, in the basis of $[S]$ which will result in zero cross polarisation backscatter, is given by the two columns of $[T]$. In terms of an eigenvalue problem, these represent the eigenvectors of $[S]$.

Further detail concerning the analytical aspects of radar target polarisation characteristics has been developed by Huynen[6]. Another formalism, in which the polarisation states are uniquely represented by points on a sphere, is useful in visualising the interrelationships among the transmitted and received polarisations, and the target characteristics, represented by its matched and null polarisations. Often termed the Poincaré sphere, after the French mathematician who proposed it for the study of optics in the nineteenth century, it is usually known as the *polarisation sphere*. Originally proposed by Kennaugh[4] for characterizing radar polarisation, Boerner[3] and Huynen[6] have developed detailed analyses of the techniques employed and of the associated geometric concepts.

3.2 Deterministic considerations

Although the scatter matrix formalism serves to characterise the radar target irrespective of the polarisation basis used, specific elements of the matrix are required. For typical targets such as aircraft or ships, direct measurement of actual targets or physical models has been the primary approach. Depending on the detail needed for radar design, a direct measurement is generally more accurate and easier to perform than an analysis of the scattering from the component structures, especially if only amplitude measurements are required. In fact a matrix formalism which depends on only power (radar cross section) measurements has been developed by Graves[7]. Alternatively, mathematical models of the target can, in principle, be developed using a variety of approaches derived from electromagnetic wave theory. For example, some first estimate the current distribution on the target and then calculate the scattered field. Such models can become very complex, but with the continued improvement in computer technology, theoretical work which began over forty years ago is becoming increasingly useful. In addition to the insight provided concerning the actual scattering mechanisms existing within a complex target, it also provides a valuable tool in diagnostics where particular features of target backscatter must be better understood.

3.2.1 SCATTERING REGIONS

Analytic modelling of radar targets is facilitated by recognising three regions, each of which is dominated by a particular scattering mechanism. This partition is not only convenient from the standpoint of target representation, it is also necessary, since to date the backscatter from only a few target types has been exactly calculated. The simplest of these is the sphere. Initially described by Mie[8], analyses have been published by numerous authors, including Adler and Johnson[9], Barrick[10] (Ruck's Vol. 1) and Blake[11]. A plot of the radar cross section of a conducting sphere is shown in Fig. 3.3. The curve is characterised by a monotonically increasing section, termed the Rayleigh region, followed by

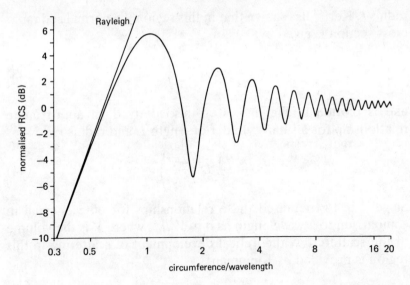

Fig. 3.3 Radar cross section of a sphere normalised to its projected areas, as a function of the circumference-to-wavelength ratio. Comparison indicated for a theoretical Rayleigh scatterer.

an oscillatory section, termed the 'resonance' or Mie region, which gradually decays until a constant cross section level is reached, termed the 'optics' or high frequency region. The boundaries of these three regions are not rigid. For example, the optics region, which theoretically contains no oscillations of cross section, has been considered to begin when the circumference of the sphere is greater than ten or even twenty wavelengths. Since the theoretical analysis for the resonant region involves terms with negative exponential factors, a point is eventually reached when the error in neglecting those terms is acceptable. Similarly, the Rayleigh region boundary has been considered to end when the circumference of the sphere is greater than one wavelength, or sometimes greater than 0.4 wavelengths. Again, it is the convergence of terms in a series which determines the factor which various investigators have used.

3.2.2 RAYLEIGH REGION

Backscatter in this region, which varies as λ^{-4}, applies to scatterers which are much smaller than the radar wavelength and is commonly known as Rayleigh, after Lord Rayleigh who studied light scatter in the nineteenth century. In the case of the sphere of radius r, Kerr[12] has shown that in this region the normalised radar cross section is given by:

$$\frac{\sigma}{\pi r^2} = 9\left(\frac{2\pi}{\lambda}r\right)^4 \tag{43}$$

and is plotted in Fig. 3.3. Kerr also derived an approximate relationship for a small cylinder of length L and radius r:

$$\sigma \approx \frac{9\pi}{4} L^2 \left(\frac{2\pi r}{\lambda}\right)^4 \tag{44}$$

Siegel[13] has generalised these relationships for objects small in comparison to a wavelength as $\sigma \propto V^2/\lambda^4$, where V is the volume of the scatterer. A theoretical development of scattering in this region is provided by Kleinman[14].

3.2.3 OPTICS REGION

As indicated in Fig. 3.3, the radar cross section of the sphere in this region is πr^2, the same as its projected area. This is essentially specular scatter, for which $\sigma = G \cdot A$, where A is the power intercept area and G is the gain in the receiver direction with respect to an isotropic radiator. As in the case for a uniformly illuminated aperture, $G = 4\pi A/\lambda^2$. Therefore, A is equivalent to the flat plate area. For a large smooth scatterer, this includes the area within $\lambda/4\pi$ of the front surface. For the sphere, this area is $r\lambda/2$.

This region is of great practical importance in radar applications, since nearly all targets of interest are large in the wavelength sense. But these targets are also complex, since they are rarely smooth and can be considered as composed of numerous 'simpler' shapes such as flat plates, cylinders, wedges, cones, etc. Fortunately, in most cases, sufficiently accurate results can be achieved by treating these composite shapes as independent scattering centres, thus making possible radar cross section estimation using contemporary computers.

3.2.4 RESONANCE REGION

This region can be considered to include a specular component together with an additional component due to 'creeping' waves which travel, in the case of the sphere, around the back surface. As the diameter of the sphere is increased, or the wavelength decreased, the path length for the creeping waves increases, accompanied by a corresponding decrease in their amplitude. The two creeping waves (travelling in opposite directions around the sphere) interfere with each other, producing the oscillations shown in Fig. 3.3. The resultant also adds vectorially to the specular component. With sufficiently large spheres or shorter wavelengths, the amplitude contribution from the creeping waves becomes negligible, resulting in the radar cross section value in the optics region.

3.2.5 ANALYTIC TECHNIQUES

Numerous techniques have been developed over the past forty years which provide the necessary simplifications to make possible calculation of the radar cross sections of simple shapes. As previously noted, solutions for composite shapes of a complex target can usually be used in combination to form a sufficiently accurate estimate of the total radar cross section. Details of these techniques and their application to calculations of specific shapes are beyond the scope of this text. Ruck[15], and Crispin and Siegel[16] contain considerable material on many of these subjects and include well over two hundred additional references. However, a summary of some of the techniques and their limitations is appropriate.

3.2.5.1 *Geometric optics*

Based on ray tracing, this technique applies to scatterers much larger than a wavelength and having finite radii of curvature. The results are only exact, theoretically, for zero wavelength. Moreover, since it is a corpuscular theory, wave interference effects are not considered. Backscatter is due to specular points on the target. It applies the familiar Snell's law for reflection and refraction (in the case of a dielectric) to the scatterer interface. The technique neglects polarisation and does not consider diffraction effects due to edges, corners or cone tips. For scatterers with radii of curvature r_1, r_2, geometric optics predicts a radar cross section of $\sigma = \pi r_1 r_2$, which leads to the familiar value for the sphere of $\sigma = \pi r^2$. Since finite radii are assumed, this technique fails to predict the cross section for flat plates.

3.2.5.2 *Physical optics*

This technique uses the field on the scatterer as determined by geometric optics to compute the scattered field by means of the

integral approximation to solution of the field equations. The
surface current at each elemental area of the surface is assumed
equal to that which would occur on an infinite plane tangent to
each point on the surface. Physical optics does result in a solution
for flat plates and cylinders, but is only valid within about 45° of
the specular direction. Thus near-in sidelobes are correctly
modelled, but at large angles from the specular direction, edge
diffraction effects, which are not accounted for, make this technique inaccurate. Results at shadow boundaries are inaccurate,
since application of the theory assumes zero current beyond the
shadow boundary. In addition, the results are independent of
polarisation.

3.2.5.3 *Geometrical theory of diffraction*

This theory, initially formalised by Keller[17] and usually referred
to as GTD, applies to targets several wavelengths in dimension
and extends the ray tracing approach used in geometric optics by
including diffraction effects from surface discontinuities. Moreover, it assumes that the scattered fields from adjacent smooth
parts of the target essentially cancel each other, so that scattering
only occurs from the points or edges of discontinuities. The
validity of this assumption has been confirmed from high resolution images of various targets. Therefore, these points or edges,
termed *scattering centres*, are the actual net sources of the backscatter; the proper combination of their scattered fields is then
used for calculating the radar cross section of a given target.
Figure 3.4 depicts a ray incident on an edge leading to a cone of
diffracted rays with a half-angle equal to the angle of incidence of
the ray. According to the theory, rays diffracted in the direction
of the radar lead to the observed radar cross section.

Application of this theory involves identifying the scattering
centres and determining their diffraction coefficients, which
specify the scattered fields around each of the centres. Then the
net effect at the radar is determined by vectorially adding all of
the contributions in the appropriate direction and with the appropriate path length phase. Since the diffraction coefficients depend
on the incident polarisation, GTD results include polarisation
effects. Although major scattering centres are usually considered
to act independently if they are several wavelengths apart, the
possibility of one diffracted ray illuminating one or more other
discontinuities leads to 'multiple' diffraction effects which can be
accommodated, but with increased complexity.

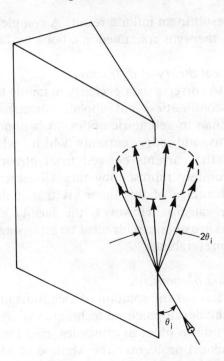

Fig. 3.4 Rays diffracted at an edge from incident ray at angle θ_i.

Since the diffraction from scattering centres is essentially local-ised, a powerful approach in applying this theory is the utilisation of idealised (canonical) solutions to diffraction problems which are geometrically similar to that on the target under study. These are typically solutions for diffraction from wedges, half planes, loops and convex surfaces. Combining these previously available solutions makes possible consideration of complicated geometries which may not be exactly solved.

For many geometries, GTD produces results which compare favourably with experimental results. For a flat plate, for example, results are accurate to within 10° of grazing incidence (Ross[18]). At grazing incidence, however, GTD predicts an infi-nite radar cross section, necessitating modifications to the theory. The same result occurs at caustics. These are regions where the density of rays becomes infinite, as is the case at the focus of a parabola or an axial view of a cylinder. A modification to GTD, the Uniform Theory of Diffraction (UTD), described by Kouyoumjian and Pathak[19], provides corrections to the diffrac-tion coefficients near shadow or reflection boundaries, where

GTD would result in an infinite result. A complete treatment of this important theory is contained in a book by James[20].

3.2.5.4 *Physical theory of diffraction*
This theory also corrects the deficiency in failing to represent the effects of discontinuities, but applies corrections to physical optics rather than to geometric optics, as is done in GTD. The approach is to add edge currents which, when considered together with the currents derived from physical optics, also results in accurately representing target backscatter (Knott *et al.*[21]). The advantage of this theory is that it does yield finite solutions near caustics. However, the facility and speed with which solutions are obtained for most targets using GTD make its use generally preferable.

3.2.5.5 *Method of moments*
Use of computers for the solution of electromagnetic field problems spurred the development of techniques which, although still based on well known physical principles, could not be otherwise applied to practical problems. The Method of Moments, sometimes abbreviated by MOM or MM, is detailed by Harrington[22] and is further described by Poggio and Miller[23]. Basically it is a technique for reducing field integral equations to a system of linear algebraic equations which can then be solved numerically for the surface currents on the target, given the characteristics of the incident fields. As in the techniques provided by the theories previously described, the scattered fields can then be evaluated and the radar cross section determined. The approach followed, however, is such that sampling of the target surface as close as one hundred or more samples per square wavelength, together with appropriate numerical integrations, are required for accurate results. Recall that most problems in the optics region can be simplified owing to the localised nature of the scattering from composite bodies of complex targets, so that MM tends to be applied to small targets or to problems involving longer wavelengths. But, since other techniques have produced generally satisfactory results in the Rayleigh region, MM is very useful for scattering problems in the resonance region. Polarisation effects are properly accounted for, since the scattered fields are calculated for any given incident field component.

The equations expressing the target surface electric and magnetic current densities as functions of the incident electric and magnetic fields are derivable from Maxwell's equations. Known as the *electric and magnetic field integral equations*, they are usually abbreviated by EFIE and MFIE in the literature. Both of these equations can be expressed in operator notation by $L[S(z)] = T(z)$. $T(z)$ is the incident field on the target, $S(z)$ is the source or surface current which, when operated on by L representing the integrations prescribed by MFIE or EFIE, will result in $T(z)$. Since $T(z)$ is known from the radar geometry, the problem is to find $S(z)$, subject to the operator L.

A solution to the problem amounts to determining an inverse operator L^{-1} so that $S(z)$ can be determined from the known values of $T(z)$. For this purpose, a series expansion for $S(z)$, known as a basis or trial function, is assumed. Then the unknowns become the coefficients of the trial function, so that the operator relationship becomes:

$$\sum_{i=1}^{n} a_1 L[f_1(z)] = T(z) \tag{45}$$

where

$$S(z) = \sum_{i=1}^{n} a_1 f_1(z)$$

and f_1 are the terms of the assumed basis function. The procedure then requires selecting a set of m weighting or testing functions, W_1, which are used to take an inner product (Shields[24]) with $L[f_1]$ and with $T(z)$. Geometrically, this is equivalent to finding the projection of $L[f_1]$ on W_1 and $T(z)$ on W_1. The result of this operation on the terms of Equation 45 can be written in matrix form as follows:

$$\begin{bmatrix} <W_1, L[f_1]> & <W_1, L[f_2]> & <W_1, L[f_n]> \\ <W_2, L[f_1]> & <W_2, L[f_2]> & <W_2, L[f_n]> \\ \vdots & \vdots & \vdots \\ <W_m, L[f_1]> & <W_m, L[f_2]> & <W_m, L[f_n]> \end{bmatrix} \begin{bmatrix} a_1 \\ a_2 \\ \vdots \\ a_n \end{bmatrix} = \begin{bmatrix} <W_1, T> \\ <W_2, T> \\ \vdots \\ <W_m, T> \end{bmatrix} \tag{46}$$

The solution for (a_1) can then be obtained by computing the inverse of the matrix and multiplying it by the matrix on the right. Knowing the coefficients, a_1, makes possible specification of the surface current on the target in terms of the series expansion of the trial function, f_1.

Clearly, MM is computationally intensive, since in addition to inverting a very large matrix, the terms of the matrix must be computed. Each of these terms, as noted, is an inner product and requires calculating the integral of the product of two functions. Moreover, the choice of basis function will affect the number of terms in the expansion which are necessary to achieve an accurate representation of the surface currents. Inevitably tradeoffs are necessary. For example, although it may be computationally efficient to select a basis function which can match the anticipated form of the surface currents (e.g. cylindrical, spherical or exponential) such a selection may introduce too much specialisation in the problem formulation. Another choice which affects computational efficiency is the selection of the weighting function. There are limitless possibilities, however; one which is particularly efficient involves using the Dirac delta function. Known as *point matching*, the resultant inner product is reduced to evaluation at a single selected point, rather than over a surface. By this means, the target surface currents are only matched at the points on the surface specified by the function. Therefore, the density of match points must be high if the solution is to be accurate. This in turn means a larger matrix.

The description given above is intended merely to sketch the concepts and procedures involved in MM. More details appear in the published literature and in the basic references by Harrington[22] and Mittra[25].

3.2.5.6 *Hybrid techniques*

The trend in recent years has been to combine analysis techniques so that weaknesses in one can be overcome by the capabilities of another. Foremost of these is the combination of MM and GTD. MM makes possible accurate solution of electromagnetic field problems, but accomplishes this at the expense of large amounts of computer storage and running time. This is especially true when a target dimension is over ten wavelengths in dimension. On the other hand, GTD is usable for larger targets and is more conservative of computer resources. However, its use depends on including diffraction coefficients derived from the solution of similar geometrical problems. Therefore, only problems for which the diffraction coefficients are known can use the theory. But in the hybrid MM-GTD method, unknown diffraction coefficients can be treated using MM. This enables larger complex targets to be analysed efficiently. Ekelman and Thiele[26] used this method to analyse the interaction between an antenna and a cylinder. Burnside *et al.*[27] described its efficiency and accuracy in handling two-dimensional problems, and Shalos and Thiele[28] extended its application to three-dimensional problems. MM has also been combined with other theories concerning target body surface currents. These are described by Kim and Thiele[29], and by Taflove and Umashankar[30].

3.2.6 COMBINED TARGET RADAR CROSS SECTION

Most radar targets of interest can be considered as comprising a collection of scatterers whose radar cross section characteristics can be estimated using one or more of the approaches outlined above. Even a very complex target can be approximated using comparatively few basic shapes such as cylinders, cones, flat and curved surfaces, etc. Each of these basic scatterers may or may not be significantly larger than the radar operating wavelength so that the appropriate theory for calculating the radar cross section of any particular feature will differ, depending on the radar. However, given the radar cross section of all of the significant features of the target, an estimate of the total radar cross section can be made. The quality of this estimate depends on the assumptions made in combining the separate results. Each scatterer, when acting independently, is characterised by a particular radar cross section profile as a function of aspect angle, with its centre located at a distinct range from the radar. Therefore, one approach is to add all of the cross section values, taking into account the appropriate distances:

$$\sigma \approx \left| \sum_{i=1}^{N} \sqrt{(\sigma_i)}\, e^{\frac{j4\pi d_i}{\lambda}} \right|^2 \qquad (47)$$

where i represents a given scatterer specified in terms of its radar cross section and distance (range) at the particular aspect angle for which σ is being calculated. Since a large number of these scatterers is likely, the calculation of radar cross section as a function of aspect angle is extensive. In addition, for many aspects the backscatter from one scatterer will be occluded by another, further complicating the calculation. But even taking these factors into account, the result is still an approximation, since multiple scattering among scatterers was neglected, as were travelling wave effects. These primarily occur when waves are incident on an extended smooth surface near grazing incidence.

Nonetheless, careful calculations when averaged over modest aspect angles have achieved accuracies which are within the experimental error in measuring actual radar targets.

A further approximation which greatly simplifies the calculations may be warranted. This results in merely adding the radar cross section values of the constituent scatterers, without regard for their differing ranges. This approximation assumes that the phase factor in Equation 47, $\exp(j(4\pi/\lambda)d_i)$, is unlikely to remain static in view of even small changes in target aspect and/or flexures of the target itself. This approximation leads to a uniform distribution of the phase factor, so that Equation 47 becomes:

$$\sigma \approx \sum_{i=1}^{N} \sigma_i \qquad (48)$$

3.2.7 RADAR CROSS SECTION FORMULAE

Accurate representation of actual radar targets requires application of a combination of several approaches, many of which have been outlined here. Their descriptions, however, are intended more as an overview of most of the important techniques. Details abound in the technical literature and new approaches continue to improve the accuracy and speed with which radar cross section estimates can be made.

Nonetheless, it is useful to consider some simple expressions for several well known shapes, since complex targets can often be synthesised from comparatively few basic elements. These formulae were derived from physical optics, so that the angular region over which they are valid is restricted.

The radar cross section for a square flat plate with edge a at angles θ from the surface normal is:

$$\sigma(\theta) = \frac{4\pi a^4}{\lambda^2} \left[\frac{\sin\left(\frac{2\pi}{\lambda} a \sin\theta\right)}{\frac{2\pi}{\lambda} a \sin\theta} \right]^2 \cos^2\theta \qquad (49a)$$

When $\theta = 0$, this becomes:

$$\sigma(0) = \frac{4\pi a^4}{\lambda^2} \qquad (49b)$$

For a circular flat plate with a radius a, the corresponding radar cross sections are:

$$\sigma(\theta) = \frac{4\pi^3 a^4}{\lambda^2} \left[2 \frac{J_1\left(\frac{4\pi}{\lambda} a \sin \theta\right)}{\frac{4\pi}{\lambda} a \sin \theta} \right]^2 \cos^2 \theta \qquad (50a)$$

$$\sigma(0) = \frac{4\pi^3 a^4}{\lambda^2} \qquad (50b)$$

For a circular cylinder of radius a and length L, with θ measured from broadside, the radar cross sections are:

$$\sigma(\theta) = \frac{2\pi}{\lambda} aL^2 \left[\frac{\sin\left(\frac{2\pi}{\lambda} L \sin \theta\right)}{\frac{2\pi}{\lambda} L \sin \theta} \right]^2 \cos^2 \theta \qquad (51a)$$

$$\sigma(0) = \frac{2\pi}{\lambda} aL^2 \qquad (51b)$$

For most purposes, Equations 49–51 yield accurate results within the range $+45° \leqslant \theta \leqslant +45°$. The radar cross section of a circular cone with an apex angle 2ϕ from a nose-on aspect is:

$$\sigma = \frac{\lambda^2}{16\pi} \tan^4(2\phi) \qquad (52)$$

The wavelength dependence of these shapes varies widely. In addition, if the wavelength independence of a large sphere and the λ^{-4} dependence of small scatterers is also considered, it is clear that combinations can result in differing and often non-integer wavelength exponents.

3.3 Statistical characterisations

In principle, the radar reflectivity pattern of a rigid target can be calculated. As previously outlined, solutions for comparatively elemental geometric shapes have been derived and methods have been established to deal with more complex geometries by combining composites of these shapes. Alternatively, patterns can be measured, either statically on properly configured pattern ranges or dynamically using the actual targets under controlled conditions. For targets many wavelengths in dimensions, reflectivity patterns contain significant fine structure. For example, based on a simple cylinder model, a target 15 m in length observed by a 3 cm radar could contain reflectivity lobes only 0.1° wide, when the line of sight is approximately normal to its length. Therefore, accurate representation of the detailed reflectivity pattern would require a very large number of carefully controlled measurements. Of course, as the radar wavelength is increased the widths of the lobes increase, thereby decreasing the complexity in the pattern. This change is illustrated in Fig. 3.5, which shows a sample of pulse-to-pulse backscatter data from a large aircraft recorded at three frequencies simultaneously during a test run close to the radar site, as described by Olin and Queen[31]. Aircraft aspect angle was in the vicinity of broadside so that the reflectivity pattern was dominated by the fuselage. The null-to-null spacings are approximately in the ratio of the frequencies used: 9225 MHz, 2800 MHz, 1300 MHz. However, such 'clean' patterns are an exception, since radar backscatter usually results from a composite of many shapes of differing dimensions.

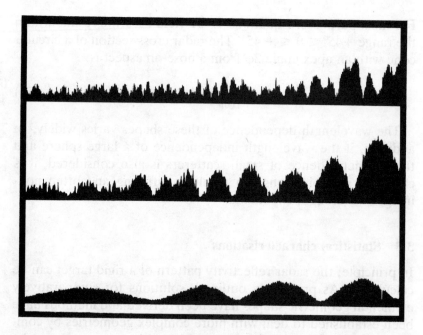

Fig. 3.5 Pulse-to-pulse recording of a large aircraft crossing near broadside. Radar bands (*top to bottom*) are X, S and L.

Although the radar cross section of static targets can be described in a deterministic sense, moving targets generally contain sufficient random motions that their characteristics must be described statistically. It is this statistical description of target reflectivity which is important to the radar engineer, since it can be used in parameter tradeoffs to optimise the radar design and to predict detection performance. Unfortunately, a precise statistical description of a given target depends on many factors. In addition to the target configuration and its own motion, radar sampling period, resolution, polarisation, wavelength, and radar movement all influence the observed statistics. Moreover, utilisation of the statistics for performance prediction is facilitated by employing mathematically tractable distributions; in radar, as in other technical fields, it is useful to employ a menu of standard distributions. With regard to radar cross section, which is proportional to received power, distributions which have often been used to represent the target characteristics include at least the *Chi-Square*, *Rice* and the *Log-Normal*. These distributions are generic in the sense that they can represent aircraft as well as ships and, in the case of Log-Normal, have been used for clutter.

3.3.1 CHI-SQUARE DISTRIBUTION

The density function of degree 2k for a Chi-Square random variable is given by:

$$p(\sigma) = \frac{k}{(k-1)!\,\bar{\sigma}} \left(k\frac{\sigma}{\bar{\sigma}} \right)^{k-1} \exp\left(-k\frac{\sigma}{\bar{\sigma}} \right) \qquad (53)$$

where σ is the radar cross section, and $\bar{\sigma}$ is the average radar cross section of the sample. Thus for $k = 1$ and $k = 2$, the respective density functions are given by:

$$p(\sigma) = \frac{1}{\bar{\sigma}} \exp\left(-\frac{\sigma}{\bar{\sigma}} \right) \qquad (54)$$

$$p(\sigma) = \frac{4\sigma}{(\bar{\sigma})^2} \exp\left(-\frac{2\sigma}{\bar{\sigma}} \right) \qquad (55)$$

The cumulative distribution function, expressed as the probability that the radar cross section is greater than a given value, is then determined by evaluating the following integral:

$$P[\sigma > \sigma_c] = \int_{\sigma_c}^{\infty} p(\sigma)\,d\sigma \qquad (56)$$

The cumulative distributions, corresponding to Equations 54 and 55, then become:

$$P[\sigma > \sigma_c] = \exp\left(-\frac{\sigma_c}{\bar{\sigma}}\right) \qquad (57)$$

$$P[\sigma > \sigma_c] = \left(2\frac{\sigma_c}{\bar{\sigma}} + 1\right) \exp\left(-2\frac{\sigma_c}{\bar{\sigma}}\right) \qquad (58)$$

Figure 3.6 shows several of the Chi-Square distributions, each of which has been plotted using a median (50% probability) value of 1 m² (0 dBsm). (As a practical matter in dealing with actual radar data, the median radar cross section is a more meaningful

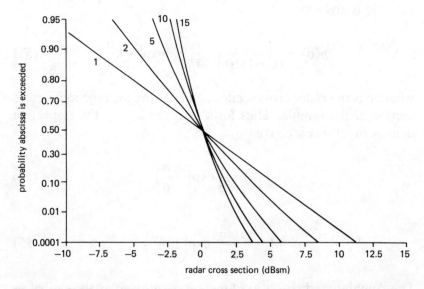

Fig. 3.6 Chi-Square cumulative distributions for a median value of 0 dBsm. Numbers refer to the value of k, where 2k is the degree of the distribution.

reference point, since its specification avoids the need to measure extreme values precisely.) The Chi-Square distribution is particularly significant, since the well known target fluctuation cases described by Swerling[32] included the curves for which k = 1 and k = 2. Swerling Cases I and II, described by k = 1, are intended to represent targets comprised of a large number of equal independent randomly fluctuating scatterers. The two cases are distinguished by differences in their temporal characteristics. Slowly fluctuating signals which are correlated during an antenna scan, but are decorrelated from scan to scan, are termed Case I. Signals which vary from pulse to pulse are described as Case II. These cases are usually referred to as Rayleigh, since the detected signal voltages from the radar are Rayleigh distributed. This, in turn, means that corresponding power (radar cross section) fluctuations are exponentially distributed, as indicated by Equation 57. Cases III and IV, for which k = 2, were intended to represent targets which include an additional large dominating random scatterer. These cases are similarly distinguished by their temporal characteristics. Thus, Case III is for slowly fluctuating signals, whereas Case IV is for signals which fluctuate from pulse to pulse.

Although curves for which k = 1 and k = 2 have been used to represent a wide variety of targets, it must be emphasised that these values are by no means all inclusive. Other values of k, both fractional and integer, have been derived from measured data. Reilly[33], in measuring in-flight aircraft, has found values of k ≤ 20, depending on aspect angle and observation time. The common practice of representing radar targets by the Swerling cases should, therefore, be understood to be an approximation. It is usually dictated by the facility with which subsequent detection calculations can be made, or in the absence of knowledge of the precise nature of the target distribution.

An additional factor in using these distributions concerns the required range of cross section over which it is necessary to represent the statistics. For example, it may be acceptable to represent a given target with a Swerling I or II if only the probability range of $[0.01 < P < 0.99]$ is important for detection calculations. However, if the target has some points of high reflectivity, albeit infrequently observed, which will be important in setting detection thresholds, then a different statistical model which conforms to the target characteristics over a greater range may be required, e.g. $[0.001 < P < 0.99]$.

3.3.2 RICE DISTRIBUTION

Subsequent to Swerling's work, Scholefield[34] related the Rice Distribution to the cases which included a randomly phased, constant amplitude dominant scatterer, together with the Rayleigh scatterers. It was pointed out that this distribution more accurately represents a target for which the Swerling Cases III and IV were intended. However, the form of the distribution is not as easily handled mathematically. The density function for this distribution is given by:

$$P(\sigma) = \frac{1+s}{\overline{\sigma}} \exp\left[-s - \frac{\sigma}{\overline{\sigma}}(1+s) \right] I_0\left(2\sqrt{\left[\frac{\sigma}{\overline{\sigma}}s(1+s)\right]}\right) \quad (59)$$

where $s = \dfrac{\text{RCS the steady reflector}}{\text{Combined avg. of the Rayleigh scatterers}}$

$\overline{\sigma}$ = the combined average RCS of the Ricean distributed target.

I_0 is the modified Bessel function of the first kind of order zero.

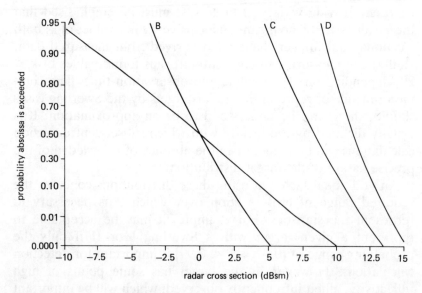

Fig. 3.7 Rice cumulative distributions. Curves A and B plotted for median values of 0 dBsm, but with values for *s* of 1 and 10, respectively. Curves C and D plotted for the same Rayleigh background as A, but with values for *s* of 10 and 20, respectively.

The cumulative distribution can be determined by evaluating the integral in Equation 56. This can be done numerically, since a simple closed form cannot be determined. Figure 3.7 shows several members of the Ricean family for different parameter values. The ordinate in this figure, as well as that for Fig. 3.6, is proportional to $\log(-\ln P)$ so that an exponential function will plot as a straight line when the independent variable is expressed in decibels. For curves A and B the values were selected so that the median radar cross section is 0 dBsm, when $s = 1$ for A and $s = 10$ for B. In the case of B the median value constraint together with the larger value of s required a much smaller background of Rayleigh scatterers, resulting in less variability for the distribution. Curves C and D depict cases in which the Rayleigh background is unchanged from that of A. Again the increase in the value of s results in a steeper appearing distribution. When $s = 0$, there is no dominant scatterer, and as expected Equation 59 reduces to the Chi-Square with k = 1.

3.3.3   LOG-NORMAL DISTRIBUTION

The Log-Normal distribution results from scattering formed by the product of independent scatterers. The distribution is important because the long 'tails' characteristic of this distribution are frequently found in measured data. The density function is given by:

$$p(\sigma) = \frac{1}{\sqrt{(2\pi)}\varrho\sigma} \exp\left[-\frac{1}{2\varrho^2} \ln\left(\frac{\sigma}{\sigma_m}\right)^2 \right] \tag{60}$$

where σ_m is the median radar cross section, and ϱ is the standard deviation of $\ln \sigma$ in natural units (Fenton[35]). If K is the standard deviation in decibels, then

$$\varrho = (K/10)\ln 10$$

Several plots of the cumulative distribution for this function are shown in Fig. 3.8. In this case the ordinate is proportional to the normal probability scale, so that the distribution will plot as straight lines when the abscissa is scaled logarithmically. This is facilitated using the approach described by Urkowitz[36] in which, given the probability, P, the ordinate is proportional to $n[F - Y]$, where

$$F = \sqrt{[-2 \ln(P')]}; \text{ if } P \leqslant 0.5, \ P' = P \text{ and } n = +1$$
$$\text{if } P > 0.5, \ P' = 1 - P \text{ and } n = -1$$

$$Y = (C_1 + C_2F + C_3F^2)/(1 + C_4F + C_5F^2 + C_6F^3),$$
$$C_1 = 2.515517, \ C_2 = 0.802853, \ C_3 = 0.010328$$
$$C_4 = 1.432788, \ C_5 = 0.189269, \ C_6 = 0.001308$$

As expected, increasing values of K result in longer distribution 'tails', while an increase in the median value results in a translation of the curve.

The Log-Normal distribution does not have a simple target analogue, as is the case for the Chi-Square and Rice distributions. However, Pollon[37] has shown that the reflectivity distributions from randomly oriented directive scatterers, such as rods, cylinders and plates, are fitted over moderate ranges by this distribution. For a circular cylinder with a large length-to-wavelength ratio, Pollon derives a value for K of 12.6 dB, as the fitted Log-Normal curve. Figure 3.9 illustrates the cumulative distributions for a circular cylinder, expressed as the probability that the radar cross section is less than the abscissa value. For comparison a Log-Normal distribution with K = 12.6 dB is included. Both curves for the cylinder used the cross section formulation given in Equation 51a, with an equal number of angular values selected randomly within the range of 0° to 30°, 0° corresponding to an aspect normal to the cylinder axis. For one curve the distribution of selected angles was uniform over the 0° to 30° range. This is the curve for which the Log-Normal estimate applies. For the other curve the angular distribution was selected so as to simulate a sinusoidal oscillation of the cylinder. Therefore, in the latter case proportionally more angular samples were observed near the 0° and 30° end points than in the mid-range region. This serves to illustrate the effect differing target motions can have on the resulting observed distribution.

Although the distributions described above are intended to fulfil different assumptions concerning the nature of the target scattering, it is nonetheless instructive to compare several of them using a common basis. Figure 3.10 shows the Chi-Square for k = 1 (Swerling I and II), k = 2 (Swerling III and IV), the Rice and Log-Normal distributions plotted against a common probability scale and with median value of 0 dBsm. Note that the Log-Normal distribution no longer plots as a straight line, as in Fig. 3.8. With $s = 1$, the Ricean Distribution falls between the Chi-Square for k = 1 and k = 2. However, with reference to Fig. 3.6, if the value of s were increased, while maintaining the same median value, then the resulting curve would be steeper and

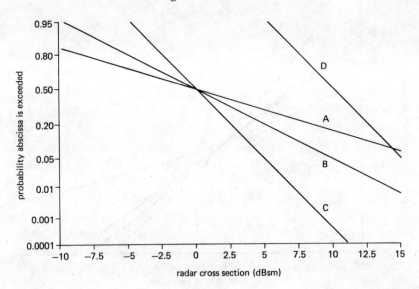

Fig. 3.8 Log-Normal cumulative distributions. Curves A, B and C plotted for median values of 0 dBsm, but with values for K of 10 dB, 6 dB and 3 dB, respectively. Curve D is plotted for a median value of 10 dBsm and K of 3 dB.

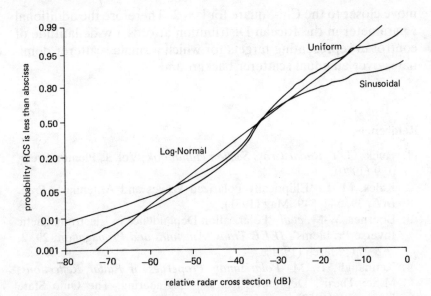

Fig. 3.9 Cumulative distributions for a circular cylinder 20 wavelengths long. 'Uniform' curve is for a uniform angular sampling over 0°–30° is normal to the cylinder axis. 'Sinusoidal' curve is for a sampling over the same angular interval, but simulating a sinusoidal motion of the cylinder. Log-Normal curve fit with K = 12.6 dB, shown for comparison.

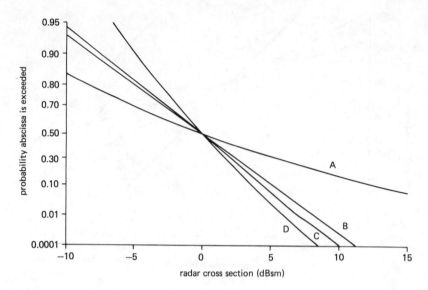

Fig. 3.10 Comparison of statistical distributions. Curve A: Log-Normal, K = 10 dB; Curve B: Chi-Square, k = 1; Curve C: Rice, s = 1; Curve D: Chi-Square, k = 2.

move closer to the Chi-Square for k = 2. Therefore the additional s parameter in the Ricean Distribution affords a wide latitude of control in representing targets for which a single scatterer dominates over an equal scatterer background.

References

1. Ruck, G. T. *Radar Cross Section Handbook*, Vol. 1, Plenum Press, p. 9 (1970).
2. Kales, M. L. 'Elliptically Polarized Waves and Antennas', *Proc. IRE*, 39, 544–549, May (1951).
3. Boerner, W-M. *et al.* 'Polarisation Dependence in Electromagnetic Inverse Problems', *IEEE Trans. Antennas and Propagation*, **29**, 2, 262–271, March (1981).
4. Kennaugh, E. M. *Polarization Properties of Radar Reflections*, M.Sc. Thesis, Dept. of Electrical Engineering, The Ohio State University (1952).
5. Kennaugh, E. M. *Contributions to the Polarization Properties of Radar Targets*, Commemorative Collection of Unpublished Notes and Reports, Electroscience Lab., Dept. of Electrical Engineering, The Ohio State University, June (1984).

6. Huynen, J. R. 'Phenomenological Theory of Radar Targets', in *Electromagnetic Scattering*, P. L. E. Uslenghi (ed.), Academic Press, 653–712 (1978).
7. Graves, C. D. 'Radar Polarization Power Scattering Matrix', *Proc. IRE*, **44**, 2, 248–252, Feb. (1956).
8. Mie, G. 'A Contribution to the Optics of Turbid Media, Especially Colloidal Metallic Suspensions', *Ann. Physik*, 25, 377–445, March (1908).
9. Adler, S. B. and Johnson, R. S. 'New Backscattering Computation and Tables for Dielectric and Metal Spheres', *Applied Optics*, **1**, 5, 655–660, Sept. (1962).
10. Barrick, D. E. *Radar Cross Section Handbook*, Ruck, G. T. (Ed.) Vol. 1, chap. 3, Plenum Press (1970).
11. Blake, L. V. *Calculation of the Radar Cross Section of a Perfectly Conducting Sphere*, NRL Memorandum Report 2419, Apr. (1972).
12. Kerr, D. E. *Propagation of Short Radio Waves*, p. 452, McGraw-Hill Book Company (1951).
13. Siegel, K. M. 'Far Field Scattering from Bodies of Revolution', *App. Sc. Res.*, **B**, 7, 293–328 (1959).
14. Kleinman, R. E. 'The Rayleigh Region', *Proc. IEEE*, **53**, 8, 848–856, Aug. (1965).
15. Ruck, G. T. (Ed.) *Cross Section Handbook*, Vols. 1, 2, Plenum Press (1970).
16. Crispen, J. W. Jr. and Siegel, K. M. *Methods of Radar Cross-Section Analysis*, Academic Press (1968).
17. Keller, J. B. 'Geometrical Theory of Diffraction', *J. Opt. Soc. Amer.*, 52, 116–130, Feb. (1962).
18. Ross, R. A. 'Radar Cross Section of Rectangular Flat Plates as a Function of Aspect Angle', *IEEE Trans. Antennas and Propagation*, **14**, 3, 329–335, May (1966).
19. Kouyoumjian, R. G. and Pathak, P. H. 'A Uniform Theory of Diffraction for an Edge in a Perfectly Conducting Surface', *Proc. IEEE*, **62**, 11, 1448–1461, Nov. (1974).
20. James, G. L. *Geometrical Theory of Diffraction for Electromagnetic Waves*, Peter Peregrinus Ltd., UK (1980).
21. Knott, E. F. *et al. Radar Cross Section*, Artech House, Inc. (1985).
22. Harrington, R. F. *Field Computation by Moment Methods*, The Macmillan Co. (1968).
23. Poggio, A. J. and Miller, E. K. 'Integral Equation Solutions of Three-Dimensional Scattering Problems', in *Computer Techniques for Electromagnetics*, Mittra, R. (Ed.), Pergamon Press (1973).
24. Shields, P. C. *Elementary Linear Algebra*, 2nd Ed., Worth Publishers, Inc. (1973).
25. Mittra, R. (Ed.) *Computer Techniques for Electromagnetics*, Pergamon Press (1973).

26. Ekelman, E. P. and Thiele, G. A. 'A Hybrid Technique for Combining the Moment Method Treatment of Wire Antennas with the GTD for Curved Surfaces', *IEEE Trans. Antennas and Propagation*, **28**, 6, 831–839, Nov. (1980).
27. Burnside, W. D. *et al*. 'A Technique to Combine the Geometrical Theory of Diffraction and the Moment Method', *IEEE Trans. Antennas and Propagation*, **23**, 4, 551–558, July (1975).
28. Shalos, J. N. and Thiele, G. A. 'On the Application of the GTD-MM Technique and its Limitations', *IEEE Trans. Antennas and Propagation*, **29**, 5, 780–786, Sept. (1981).
29. Kim, T. J. and Thiele, G. A. 'A Hybrid Diffraction Technique – General Theory and Applications', *IEEE Trans. Antennas and Propagation*, **30**, 5, 888–897 (1982).
30. Taflove, A. and Umashankar, K. 'A Hybrid Moment Method/Finite-Difference Time-Domain Approach to Electromagnetic Coupling and Aperture Penetration into Complex Geometries', *IEEE Trans. Antennas and Propagation*, **30**, 4, 617–627, July (1982).
31. Olin, I. D. and Queen, F. D. 'Dynamic Measurement of Radar Cross Sections', *Proc. IEEE*, **53**, 8, 954–961, Aug. (1965).
32. Swerling, P. 'Probability of Detection for Fluctuating Targets', *IRE Trans. Information Theory*, **6**, 2, 269–308, Apr. (1960).
33. Reilly, J. P. 'On the Statistical Representation of Targets for Detection Studies', *IEEE Trans. Aerospace and Electronic Systems*, **5**, 3, 560–561, May (1969).
34. Scholefield, P. H. R. 'Statistical Aspects of Ideal Radar Targets', *Proc. IEEE*, **55**, 4, 587–589, Apr. (1967).
35. Fenton, L. F. 'The Sum of Log-Normal Probability Distributions in Scatter Transmission Systems', *IEEE Trans. Comm. Sys.*, **8**, 1, 57–67, March (1960).
36. Urkowitz, H. 'Hansen's Method Applied to the Inversion of the Incomplete Gamma Function, with Applications', *IEEE Trans. Aerospace and Electronic Systems*, **21**, 5, 728–730, Sept. (1985).
37. Pollon, G. E. 'Statistical Parameters for Scattering from Randomly Oriented Arrays, Cylinders, and Plates', *IEEE Trans. Antennas and Propagation*, **18**, 1, 68–75, Jan. (1970).

CHAPTER 4
Radar ECM and ECCM

STEPHEN L. JOHNSTON

4.1 Introduction

Radar was developed into a very useful military weapon during World War II. It was only natural that means to reduce the effectiveness of radar soon followed. Since radar is an electronic device, it was obvious that the principal counter to radar should also be electronic. Electronic warfare came of age in World War II. The widespread development and employment of radar by both sides quickly resulted in the introduction of electronic warfare, primarily by the USA and UK. EW has subsequently played a prominent role in the wars in Vietnam and the Middle East. The history of US Electronic Warfare in World War II has recently been described by Price[1]. Radar engineers then developed means to counter this threat to radar. Efforts to improve radar performance in the face of enemy interference involved both improvements in radar technology and in the creation of special methods and devices to reduce the effects of enemy interference. This history was presented in 1980[2]. Radar developers in the UK recognised the possibility of enemy interference, almost from the start of their radar development programme resulting in the first recorded programme to combat the effects of enemy interference[3,4]. As expected, activities in this field continued after World War II, so that today all military radars must include means to combat enemy interference from their initial design onwards. Indications of Soviet activities in this field have been reported recently[5]. It is essential that military engineers be intimately familiar both with ways to create interference to radar and with ways to combat that interference. This chapter will treat both matters.

119

4.2   Definitions and EW organisation

Activities to combat radar and to improve radar effectiveness in their presence have had various names. During World War II, the umbrella term RCM (radar countermeasures) usually, but not always, included both aspects. The terms *jamming* and *anti-jamming* (AJ) came into being. Currently, the umbrella term electronic warfare (EW) is used by both NATO and the US Department of Defense. Russia uses the umbrella term Radio-Electronic Warfare[5] (REC) or *Maskirovka*. REC has divisions similar to the US/NATO EW divisions, with the major addition of physical destruction of NATO emitters such as radar and ECM apparatus. This author once referred to this as physical counter-measures (PCM)[6]. In the West, jamming is now called *electronic countermeasures* (ECM), while anti-jamming has become *electronic counter-countermeasures* (ECCM). A third division of EW, called *electronic warfare support measures* (ESM) has also been created. DOD definitions of EW and related terms are as follows[7]:

Electronic warfare (EW) is military action involving the use of electromagnetic energy to determine, exploit, reduce, or prevent hostile use of the electromagnetic spectrum, and actions which retain friendly use of the electromagnetic spectrum.

Electronic countermeasures (ECM) is that division of electronic warfare involving actions taken to prevent or reduce an enemy's effective use of the electromagnetic spectrum.

Electronic counter-countermeasures (ECCM) is that division of electronic warfare involving actions taken to insure friendly effective use of the electromagnetic spectrum despite the enemy's use of electronic warfare.

Counter ESM (CESM)[8] is that subdivision of ECCM involving actions taken to reduce the effectiveness of enemy ESM systems. Two classes of CESM are *low probability of intercept* (LPIn) and *low probability of identification* (LPId). The intention of CESM is to delay interception of the radar signal, prevent/confuse identification of the radar signal to result in delay of initiation of ECM, or employment of an improper ECM, and thus permit the radar to accomplish its intended mission. A CESM technique may also have other ECCM benefits in addition to CESM. It should be noted that this term has not yet been adopted by the Department of Defense.

Electronic warfare support measures (ESM) is that division of electronic warfare involving actions taken to search for, intercept, locate, record, and analyse radiated electromagnetic energy for the purpose of exploiting such radiation in the support of military operations. Thus, electronic warfare support measures provide a source of electronic warfare information required to conduct electronic countermeasures, electronic counter-countermeasures, threat detection, warning, avoidance, target acquisition, and homing.

Electromagnetic compatibility (EMC) is the ability of electronic equipments, subsystems and systems to operate in their intended operational environments without suffering or causing unacceptable degradation because of unintentional electromagnetic radiation or response. EMC is *not* a division of electronic warfare, although it is closely related to ECCM in the techniques used.

Electronic intelligence (ELINT) is the intelligence information product of activities engaged in the collection and processing, for subsequent intelligence purposes, of foreign, non-communications electromagnetic radiations emanating from sources other than nuclear detonations and radioactive sources. Although not a division of electronic warfare, ELINT is closely related to ESM in the techniques used. The principal difference is how and by whom the information is used.

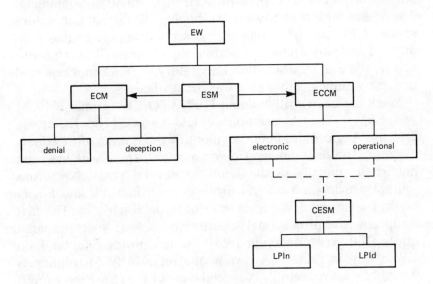

Fig. 4.1 The EW tree.

The study of any large subject is facilitated by organising it into divisions, subdivisions, and sub-subdivisions, etc. Each of the divisions of electronic warfare embraces a large number of techniques. Each division can be organised in a number of ways. Various authors use different methods of organising each of the divisions of EW. There is no best or unique method of organisation of any of the divisions of EW. As will be seen later, many ways have been proposed for organisation of both ECM and ECCM. Various ways of organising each will be presented. The 'organisation chart' or 'tree' for EW can take many forms, depending on how the various EW elements are organised. The official DOD EW organisation includes only the three divisions; organisation of the three divisions themselves is done differently by various writers[9]. Figure 4.1 depicts the EW organisation which reflects the definitions previously presented. A principal utility in an EW tree of any form is to show newcomers that there is much more to EW than just ECM or ESM.

4.3 Prior publications

The jamming and anti-jamming techniques developed during World War II were declassified after the war. Historical works on EW and ECCM have been cited above[1–4]. The *Summary Technical Report* of the US NDRC Division 15[10] extensively described American jamming work, with less attention to anti-jamming. The Massachusetts Institute of Technology Radiation Laboratory series of twenty-eight volumes[11] described important anti-jamming techniques without indicating their applicability. Unfortunately, some of the Radiation Laboratory work was not reported in these volumes, although it was declassified.

Much has been written about US/NATO EW (primarily ECM and ESM). The Association of Old Crows (The Electronic Defense Association) publishes monthly the *Journal of Electronic Defense*. The *International Countermeasures Handbook* has been published annually in the USA for several years. Numerous journal articles and several professional American and Soviet books on various EW topics have been published[12–16]. The first comprehensive professional American book on EW was prepared under DOD sponsorship in 1961[12]. A new professional book on EW is now in press[14]. A review of American ECM techniques was published recently[17]. A special issue of the *IEE Proceedings*, Part F, was devoted exclusively to EW[18]. Maksimov[16] devoted an entire chapter to a review of ECM, which has been published separately[19].

Several ECCM techniques have applicability to radars which operate in both benign and hostile environments and are usually treated in the well known radar texts. Most ECCM techniques are intended for hostile environments, however. Brick and Galejs published the first open comprehensive paper on ECCM techniques in 1958[20]. A more recent comprehensive radar ECCM survey paper listed over 200 ECCM techniques[21]. Two professional books on radar ECCM have been published, one in the USA[15], and one in Russia[16]. The latter has been translated into English. There are over 100 American patents on radar ECCM which are readily accessible for anyone to read[22]. An American short course on Radar ECCM has been given at many locations[22]. Several survey papers on ESM have been published in the USA[29–32]. One Soviet and two American professional books on ESM/ELINT have been published[27–29]. These several books and many journal articles represent a very substantial open information base on EW.

4.4 Effects of elements of electronic warfare

The definitions of Section 4.2 are straightforward; however, it is helpful to describe the effects of each element. These effects make possible a better appreciation of the functions of each element. As will be seen, these functions form the basis for possible means of organisation of the elements. The effects of ECM are shown in Table 4.1[22]. While the usual connotation of ECM is to deny/delay detection/tracking or to deny measurement of target position or range rate, an increase of errors in the measured values of target position or range rate may sufficiently increase the associated weapon miss distance, causing the weapon

Table 4.1[22]   ECM effects

Denial of detection
Operator confusion/deception
Delay in detection/tracking initiation
Tracking of an invalid target
Overloading of computer (excessive number of targets)
Denial of measurement of target position, range rate
Target tracking loss
Errors in values of target position, range rate

kill probability to be greatly reduced. This reduction of weapon kill probability may result in survival of the attacking aircraft. An ECM may not sufficiently delay detection/tracking to prevent destruction of an aircraft. The ECM specialist must therefore consider the effect of his ECM on overall weapon system performance. This is addressed more fully in Section 4.8.3.

Principal radar ECCM effects are shown in Table 4.2[22]. The basic purpose of ECCM is to enable the radar to perform its intended purpose in spite of the presence of hostile ECM. The items of Table 4.2 are specific effects of various ECCM techniques towards amelioration of ECM effects. As with ECM effects, the effectiveness of ECCM techniques must be considered in the overall weapon system effectiveness. It would be insufficient to double the detection range of a radar in an ECM environment if the new detection range were still insufficient for the weapon system to engage the attacker at a range sufficient to protect the specified target. This point will be further discussed in Section 4.8.3.

Table 4.2[22]   ECCM effects

Prevention of receiver saturation
Constant false alarm rate (CFAR)
Enhancement of S/J ratio
Directional interference discrimination
Rejection of invalid targets
Maintenance of track

Table 4.2 above does not consider counting the steps in implementing ECM employment. It is inappropriate to turn on a jammer too early in an engagement. Early initiation of jamming may alert the radar, since a jammer is essentially a beacon and the beacon detection range of a radar is much greater than its skin detection range. Similarly, it is inadvisable to initiate jamming until the proper radar frequency and radar radiating characteristics are determined. The latter are necessary in order to select the proper type of ECM, e.g. whether swept frequency jamming or false target generators should be used. The steps necessary for employment of ECM are shown in Table 4.3[8]. It is clear that an ESM receiver is essential for ECM employment. Any ECCM which delays detection by the ESM receiver or delays/confuses proper identification of the radar signal by the hostile ESM receiver may cause a delay in initiation of jamming or use of an

Table 4.3[8] Steps in ECM employment

1. Search in frequency, azimuth, and elevation angles as appropriate
2. Detect radar signal
3. Identify radar signal by its emission characteristics
4. Assess importance of radar signal (priority)
5. Select proper ECM(s)
6. Commence ECM operation

ineffective type of ECM. These may permit the radar to perform its intended mission in a timely manner. CESM techniques include two basic categories, low probability of interception and low probability of identification. CESM techniques may also provide other ECCM benefits at the same time.

Electronic warfare support systems (ESM) as defined by the US DOD provide support of both ECM *and* ECCM systems. The latter role is rarely mentioned in articles on ESM. ESM functions in support of ECM are listed in Table 4.4[22]. Most of these are well known and are represented by radar homing and warning (RHAW) equipments, intercept receivers, etc. Most modern jammers include an intercept receiver function to place the jammer onto the frequency of the victim receiver. ESM also includes the function of signal identification and threat assessment. This is a vital function, in that it enables the allocation of priorities and decision making on which signal(s) are to be jammed and which ECM types are to be employed.

Table 4.4[22] ESM effects in support of ECM

Provision of data on:
    Radiation characteristics of radars:
        Frequency, modulation characteristics, antenna pattern, etc.
    Angular position location of radars
    Identity, type and purpose of radars
    Information for ECM/ARM (anti-radiation missile) employment
    Weapon targetting information

Effects of ESM in support of ECCM are shown in Table 4.5[22]. While all the effects of this table are important, perhaps the use of an ESM receiver as part of a frequency agile radar is the most important application. A frequency agile radar can randomly change frequency, but it is more beneficial to monitor the next intended transmission frequency before transmission, since transmission on a frequency which is already jammed is generally

Table 4.5[22]   ESM effects in support of ECCM

Provision of data on:
   Warning of possible hostile activity (alerting)
   Angular locations of hostile jammers
   Information on radiation characteristics of jammers
   Information for ECCM selection
   Data for 'home on jam'/'track on jam' (HOJ/TOJ) employment
   Jammer targetting information
   Information for jammer avoidance

imprudent. The above effects strongly influence the inclusion of ESM receivers in modern military radars. The ESM receiver functions may be accomplished by the regular radar receiver (perhaps with some complications) or by an additional receiver. The 'ESM receiver' is often not called by that name and may not provide all the effects of the table. It should be noted that ESM receivers in a radar are subject to confusion from spoofers and standoff jammers.

The initial conception of EW by a newcomer to EW might be that friendly ECM is the response to hostile use of radar (as the definition of ECM indicates) or that radar ECCM is a response to

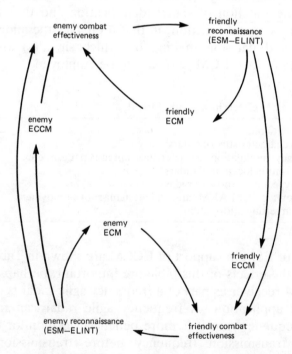

Fig. 4.2 The interactions of electronic warfare.

hostile ECM employment. Actually, in a modern military situation all elements of EW may be used by both sides in an engagement, as depicted in Fig. 4.2[30]. This figure clearly shows that hostile forces may employ ECCM in their radar in an attempt to dilute the effectiveness of our ECM/ESM[31]. A thorough knowledge of ECCM techniques is thus essential for both military radar *and* ECM/ESM engineers.

Further, one should not consider the situation as being merely the application of an ECCM (or ECCM combination) to improve the radar performance against one ECM, nor the use of one ECM against a radar, but rather a continuing action of many 'rounds'. Figure 4.3[32] clearly shows the cyclical nature of EW in World War II as reflected in the change of RAF bomber loss rate. It should be appreciated that this figure reflects the involvement of many different ECMs against many different hostile electromagnetic systems, i.e. not radars only. Although not labelled in the figure, the valleys are also of great significance. These valleys with subsequent increase of loss rate indicate German introduction of various ECCMs, better operator training, electronic tech-niques[33], change of defensive tactics, etc.

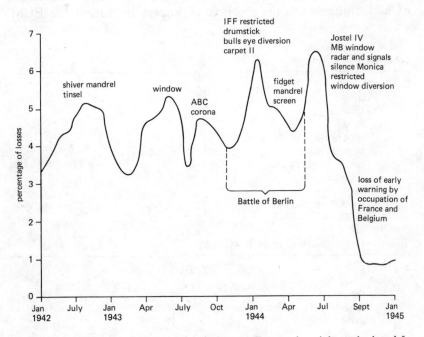

Fig. 4.3 Percentage of losses of aircraft over Europe by night, calculated for each 3000 sorties, from Jan. 1942 to Jan. 1945.

4.5   Electronic countermeasures

Although the main thrust of this chapter is on ECCM techniques, knowledge of ECM is necessary in order to understand fully the various ECCM techniques and to appreciate the necessity for ECCM. The field of ECM is a very detailed one; accordingly the treatment of ECM here will of necessity be brief. The serious ECM reader is referred to other works previously cited on ECM[10,12–14,16–19] for more exhaustive discussion of the many ECM techniques.

ECM techniques may be organised or classified in a number of ways, e.g. by 'basic' purpose, energy involvement, emission characteristics, employment/deployment, etc., or by a combination of ways. Lake[34] proposed a classification of ECMs regarding the target signature. There are two 'basic' ECM purposes, denial and deception. In denial ECM, the ability of the opponent's receiver to receive a message or to detect a target is attacked and hopefully degraded/defeated. The usual connotation of denial ECM is that of active jamming at or near the operating frequency of the victim radio/radar receiver.

Organisation by energy involvement is based upon whether the ECM technique utilises a source of energy or not. If the ECM

Table 4.6[22]   ECM types

---

1. Denial
   (a) Active:
       CW
       long pulse
       spot noise
       barrage noise
       medium/fast sweep
       impulse
       short pulse
       sidelobe repeaters
   (b) Passive:
       chaff
       radar absorbing materials (RAM)

---

2. Deception
   (a) Active:
       repeaters
       false target generators
   (b) Passive:
       chaff
       Radar absorbing materials (RAM)

---

involves an energy source, it is said to be active. Conversely, if the ECM does not contain a source of radiating energy, it is said to be passive. Examples of the latter include chaff, decoys, and radar cross section alteration. Certainly all ECMs, whether active or passive, involve energy. The distinction here is whether an ECM contains an energy source. Passive ECMs are very important. The elimination of weight and space for a primary energy source makes them attractive.

Organisation by emission characteristics considers the jammer emission characteristics. Various jamming waveforms may be used. During World War II, noise jamming was conceived and developed in many forms. A list of ECM waveform types is shown in Table 4.6[22]. The first UK jammer concepts involved pulsed waveforms, probably based on the concept that a hostile radar receiver was designed to handle pulsed signals; hence it would generally be susceptible to pulsed jammers if the jammer characteristics approximated to those of the victim radar. It soon became obvious to UK jammer designers that noise jammers would be more universal and more effective[1].

Another means of ECM organisation considers ECM employment/deployment. The jammer may be based on the ground, on a ship or in an aircraft. Airborne deployment/employment methods include self-screening jamming (SSJ) (carried on the attacking aircraft), escort jamming (ESJ) (carried on an aircraft which accompanies the attacking aircraft, which is then sometimes called a 'quiet' aircraft), standoff jamming (SOJ) (the jammer is carried in a dedicated jammer aircraft which flies in an orbit out of lethal range of the defending forces), and expendable jamming (the jammer is dropped/ejected near a victim radar). Tsipouras *et al.*[17] recently discussed both passive and active current US offboard expendables. He pointed out that the goal of expendables is to provide a brief time window for the aircraft to evade a defensive threat. Additionally, expendables could be deployed near intended victim ground radars in attempt temporarily to jam them at close range in support of air attacks.

Several other means of organisation have been proposed. One of these is by use against various types of victim radars, e.g. ECMs useful against CW Doppler radars or against search radars. This is not a unique classification method since some ECM types are useful against several types of radar. Another possible ECM classification method is the alphabetical method. This method does not facilitate general understanding of ECM and also suffers from the fact that many ECM techniques are known by several names, often slang or non-descriptive. Unfortunately no organisation, government or professional has yet attempted to standardise names for ECM techniques. Parkhomenko[35] presented a very complex Soviet scheme for classifying ECMs. It includes over 40 classification criteria. This shows that the Soviets have a wide knowledge of ECM types. Since no ECM organisation is unique, the frequent practice is to use a combination of organising methods for ECM, e.g. purpose and employment/deployment.

4.5.1   DENIAL ELECTRONIC COUNTERMEASURES

Denial ECM techniques are generally brute force ECM schemes, intended to prevent a radar from detecting/tracking a target. They may be active or passive. They generally employ some form of noise waveform. Deployment may be by any means; however, standoff jamming is a very popular form of denial ECM. It should be appreciated that due to the characteristics of the signal-to-jam ratio with range (see Section 4.8.5), it is impossible to prevent detection/tracking. The important idea is so to limit the detection/tracking range that it is too late to permit target engagement by the associated weapon system. As will be indicated in Section 4.8.3, some weapon systems do not require detection for engagement. Denial ECM is thus not a foolproof ECM, even though it can be very useful. The simplest denial ECM is a free running oscillator operating at the victim radar frequency. Modern denial ECM systems will include an ESM receiver which controls operation of the ECM transmitter.

Emission characteristics for denial jammers can be any of several, e.g. simple CW, pulse, or noise. The CW denial jammer is very simple, but difficult to employ, and easy to counter if used without an ESM system. The early UK radar ECCMs included simple tuneable filters to reject CW jamming[3,4]. The jammer must be tuned to exactly the proper radar frequency (which may well not be steady), at least within the victim receiver passband. An ESM receiver or some form of automatic search and lock equipment is required. Additionally, look through or periodic verification of the victim radar frequency is necessary in order to assure that the jammer is still on the radar frequency. Presence of several victim radars at different frequencies requires use of several CW jammers. CW jamming will often be employed in conjunction with other jamming waveforms, especially noise, to reduce the effectiveness of certain ECCMs.

Because of these factors, simple CW is seldom used alone in denial jammers. Instead, the jammer is usually operated either as a swept frequency jammer periodically covering a wide region of frequencies, or as a wide band barrage noise jammer. Sometimes CW jamming will be used in conjunction with rapid sweep frequency jamming in an attempt to capture the limiter in the Dicke Fix ECCM (see Section 4.7.4.1) and thus reduce its effectiveness.

Pulsed jamming is seldom employed for denial jamming, since it must be tailored to the victim receiver and there are a number of ECCM techniques which can readily reduce its effectiveness. Many EMC (electromagnetic compatibility) techniques can serve this purpose.

Some form of noise is generally preferable for denial jammers since noise is more nearly universal in its effectiveness against most types of radar emission. Airborne ECMs will generally face a variety of radar functions, e.g. both search/acquisition and track. Additionally, there generally will be several different types of radar for a given function. Often these radars will operate at different frequencies, usually in several different frequency bands. These factors require that the denial ECM is not tailored to a single victim radar.

Denial noise jammers are conceptually very simple. They are of two basic types: DINA (direct noise amplification[12]) and noise modulation. In the first type a broadband noise is generated by say the current passing through a resistor or by a special noise photoelectric cell and then directly amplifying the resulting noise signal through broadband amplifiers. This proved very satisfactory at VHF frequencies in World War II. This same noise source may be used to amplitude modulate a microwave RF source. As Steer pointed out[36], amplitude modulation is a very inefficient process, since it requires both an increase of RF output (on the positive modulation crest) in addition to the output decrease on the negative modulation trough. Since microwave RF sources are usually already operating at maximum power output, amplitude modulation is undesirable for jammers. It is better to frequency modulate the jammer with a video noise source. It can be shown that radar receivers, being inherently amplitude sensitive receivers, convert FM noise into AM noise[12]. This FM noise can be swept at rapid rates electronically over a radar passband. The backward wave oscillator (BWO), e.g. the Thomson-CSF

Carcinotron[TM] is a very efficient rapid sweep FM noise jammer.

Chaff has long been a very effective passive ECM, both for denial and for deception/confusion. It is popular because it is passive. Frequently, chaff serves in both the functions of denial and of deception/confusion at the same time. Since the predominant role of chaff is usually that of deception/confusion, chaff characteristics will be discussed under deception ECMs in Section 4.5.2.

Radar cross section alteration (either reduction or change of target signature characteristics) is another very important passive denial/deception ECM. RCS reduction not only decreases radar detection range in both benign and hostile environments even without accompanying active jamming, but also reduces the amount of chaff or the amount of active jamming power required to protect a given target. This has long been appreciated by Russia[5]. Lake recently proposed a new category of ECM– low observable countermeasures (LOCM)[34]. He specifically suggested new designs of warships to reduce vulnerability to radar guided anti-ship missiles and gave several examples.

4.5.2 DECEPTION ELECTRONIC COUNTERMEASURES

In deception ECM, false signals ('spoofers') are used to mislead/ confuse the victim radio or radar receiver operator. This includes false communication messages, dummy reflector targets, e.g. decoys such as flares in the IR region, false electronic targets, erroneous radar beacon replies, erroneous target angle modulations, etc. DECM emission characteristics will generally be very similar to those of the intended victim radar, whether it be a pulse or CW radar. This must be so since radars can easily distinguish between their own returned signals and those of DECM systems unless the DECM closely approximates that of the victim radar. Frequently, the DECM will use the victim radar signal by delaying and amplifying it, or by applying deceptive modulation to it. In main beam DECM, large amounts of power are not necessary and are undesirable. Most false target generator DECM systems work into the victim radar antenna sidelobes and thus require copious power. DECM may be either active or passive.

Active DECM are of two general types: repeaters and transponders (responsive). In a repeater jammer the received radar signal is amplified, delayed and possibly modulated, then retransmitted. In a transponder, the received radar signal is used to trigger a responder oscillator. Pett[37] gave an excellent treatment· of the two types of DECM. His basic block diagrams of the two are shown in Figs 4.4 and 4.5. The delayed response of the repeater is usually some form of frequency memory loop. Pett showed several forms. Digital frequency memories are currently widely used for this. Ideally, both repeaters and responders should be used under the control of an associated ESM receiver as described below. Figure 4.6 from Steer[36] shows the block diagram of a responsive jammer with appropriate ESM elements (although not so named) included. In the general case, the ESM elements could also select the modulation to be used, although not so shown here.

False target generators are an important form of deception ECM. Search/acquisition radars are susceptible to electronic deception by various schemes which create the apparent presence of multiple aircraft when there may be only one real target, or many targets at ranges/angles where none are present. The intent is to cause the defensive radar network to commit defensive resources improperly, especially fighter aircraft, or divert attention away from some other attack, be it aircraft or surface vessels as in the Normandy invasion fleet in World War II. The UK 'Moonshine'[38] false target generator of World War II which

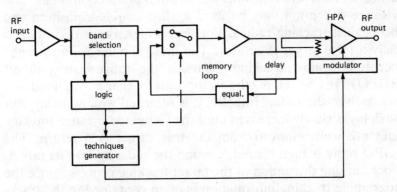

Fig. 4.4 Simplified repeater jammer.

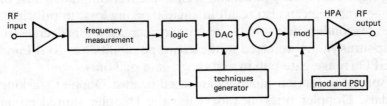

Fig. 4.5 Simplified responsive jammer.

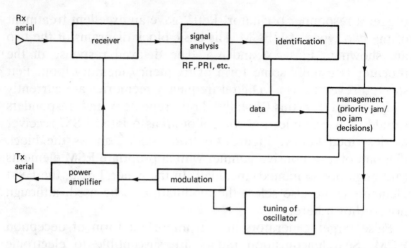

Fig. 4.6 Simplified block diagram of responsive noise jammer.

produced the apparent effect of many targets deceived the German Freya radar for a while. Currently, false target generators use the poor antenna sidelobe levels of some surveillance/acquisition radars. Search radar active DECM also includes the 'inverse gain' repeater mentioned by Steer[36]. An inverse gain DECM was developed for the US Radio Research Laboratory[10] during World War II but was not put into production then.

Range deception may be used against search/acquisition and also against tracking radars. For the former, range deception is really a false target generator. The most popular form of range deception against tracking radars is the range gate pull off (RGPO) DECM. Here, the victim radar signal is amplified and sent back to the radar. Initially, it is returned with no delay, but the delay is slowly increased until the victim radar range tracking gates are well removed from the true target skin return. The RGPO reply is then ceased, causing the radar to lose its target, hence causing disruption of the target tracking process. Since the radar angle tracking information is often contained in the tracking signal, especially in conical scan angle tracking radar, loss of range tracking can also result in angle tracking loss. In principle, the responder delay may be either increased or decreased. Tispouras *et al.*[17] referred to these two possibilities as RGPI and RGPO (range gate pull in and range gate pull out).

Special deception jammers are used against Doppler tracking radars. Doppler tracking radars use the Doppler shifted target return for tracking in a manner analogous to the range tracking gates in a pulsed tracking radar. Here, a velocity gate pull off (VGPO) DECM performs the same effect as the RGPO DECM in a pulsed tracking radar, being pulled either in or out, i.e. decreasing or increasing the false Doppler frequency. Again, Tispouras *et al.* applied the designations VGPI and VGPO to velocity gate pull in and pull out. One can also create false Doppler signals using various means, e.g. pseudo-noise[39], to confuse Doppler tracking radars.

Deception jammers may also be used against angle tracking radars. The two principal methods of angle tracking in target tracking radars are *conical scan* and *monopulse*. The former was widely used in World War II. Early in its development in the USA, a scheme of creating false target conical scan amplitude modulations by passively alternatingly varying the target radar cross section was conceived[3]. Subsequently, electronic means for doing this by receiving the victim radar signal and recovering and inverting its conical scan modulation were devised and tested as Projects Peter and also Saltpeter at the US Radio Research Laboratory[10], but not produced in World War II. This is sometimes improperly called 'inverse gain jamming'. Grant *et al.*[40] referred to this as AGPO, angle pull off angle deception. Effectiveness of this technique has been vividly shown[41]. Several variants of inverse gain jamming have been conceived[42], the principal variant being sometimes called 'swept audio frequency modulated jamming'.

This vulnerability of simple conical scan greatly contributed to the widespread switch to monopulse angle tracking. Although monopulse has been developed into an excellent tracking method, it is more complex, heavier, and more expensive than conical scan. Accordingly, conical scan is still attractive for special applications, e.g. missile-borne tracking systems. The continued presence of older conical scan radars preserves interest in inverse gain angle DECM and variants thereof.

All angle tracking systems sense the phase front of the target return signal and attempt to align themselves perpendicularly to that phase front. Accordingly, any means artificially to distort this phase front could conceptually deceive the angle tracking radar, even if monopulse. Several schemes for disturbing the phase front have been conceived and are known by various names. They generally use some sort of electronic manipulation of the received victim radar signal and retransmission from multiple spatial locations, either on the same aircraft or from nearby aircraft.

Chaff has been a very important passive deception ECM since its first use on a massive scale in the British air raid on Hamburg in July 1943[1]. Chaff was used extensively in the Russian invasion of Czechoslovakia. It may be utilised in short bursts to deceive/confuse radars. US chaff development has been described in detail[10], and a recent UK chaff survey paper[43,44] described current chaff types and characteristics. US discussions of chaff have been given[45,46], and Maksimov[16] devoted over ten pages to discussion of the properties of chaff under the heading 'passive jamming'. Chaff usually consists of electrically conducting material which is made in half-wavelengths at the radar frequencies of interest. Currently, chaff is available for the principal radar frequencies, L-, S-, X-, and Ku-bands (1–20 GHz). The three principal types of chaff in current use are the perennial aluminum foil strips, aluminum coated glass filaments, and the silver-coated nylon monofilament[43]. Other chaff materials are zinc-coated glass filaments and copper-coated polyester filaments.

The most important chaff characteristic is the radar cross section which it presents to the radar, for it is the return signal from this cross section which must compete with the return from the target radar cross section when chaff is used to conceal a target. The chaff employment planner must consider both the radar illumination volume and the radar cross section of the target to be screened. Current trends to smaller radar cross section of aircraft reduces the amount of chaff required to screen a target while exacerbating radar detection problems. Since the target is moving, a single chaff cloud the size of the radar illumination volume will not suffice for screening, but may be adequate for deception. Screening thus requires massive amounts of chaff. Steer indicated that chaff corridor densities with echoing area of 10^{-6} m^2/m^3 should be expected[36].

The significant physical properties of chaff include bulk density, fall rate, number of dipoles per unit of payload volume, and dipole width/diameter. Fall rate is both material and shape dependent, e.g. use of bent dipoles can affect fall rate. Current fall rates at sea level are in the range of 0.3–0.6 m/s[43]. Fall rate is an approximately linear function of altitude; typically its fall rate at an altitude of 10 km is double its sea level value[46].

The width/diameter ratio of the chaff affects its bandwidth, which is extremely important, since radars are generally widely dispersed in frequency within a single radar band, as well as over several frequency bands. Bandwidth can be increased by including in one package dipoles cut to different lengths and made of different materials. Advantage can also be made of harmonic resonances of chaff dipoles (the long wire antenna effect); however, the radar cross section decreases as the harmonic number increases.

Chaff polarisation is important since different radars may use different polarisations, or a given radar may employ polarisation agility/variation as an ECCM against chaff[22]. Chaff polarisation is affected by the descent motion characteristics of the chaff material or shape. Chaff cloud polarisation may be somewhat tailored by weighting one end of the dipole to influence descent pattern. Cost is of course also important since chaff will usually be consumed in large quantities. It will be appreciated that a large number of factors are involved, but it can be seen that chaff radar cross section within the illumination volume of a radar of the order of 20 dB or more than a fighter aircraft at nose-on aspect are achievable. Because of gravity and winds, chaff will usually have a low non-zero velocity, different from ground clutter or from aircraft. A list of most of the standard US chaff packages with their manufacturers has been published[47,48]. Technical characteristics of many of these are contained in US military specifications. Chaff cutters/dispensers are also important. Brief information on US chaff cutters/dispensers has also been published[48].

Radar cross section alteration may be accomplished by shaping of the target, by application of radar absorbing materials (RAM), by addition of reflectors, or by electronic augmentation. The use of additional reflectors may cause change of the apparent target RCS at the victim conical scan frequency if the reflector(s) are rotated, or induce erroneous target glint (and thus increase target tracking errors), or make a physically small decoy appear to be a larger valid target.

4.6   Electronic warfare support measures

Electronic warfare support measures can be used in support of both ECM and ECCM, as indicated previously, with common functions in both applications. ESM includes signal interception and detection, measurement of signal parameters, signal identification, and threat signal evaluation. Signal parameters include frequency, emission type, PRF, pulsewidth, antenna scan characteristics, antenna polarisation, etc., not all of which are utilised in every ESM application. There are of course differences in the type of signal sought and use made of the detected signal. In many applications, the ESM function is integrated into an overall system and the ESM portions are often not identified as such, because of lack of standardisation of EW terminology. Figure 4.6 is an example of this.

4.6.1   ESM IN SUPPORT OF ECM

There are two principal forms of ESM in support of ECM: radar warning (RWR), and radar homing and warning (RHAW), with which it is sometimes combined. RHAW is extensively used in US aircraft to warn of the presence of specific radar types. Both RWR and RHAW include an intercept receiver and means to establish identity of certain radar signals based on their emission characteristics, such as operating frequency, PRF, pulse duration, antenna scan characteristics, etc. This identification is often done automatically without operator action. Sometimes approximate directional information to the radar is also provided, along with approximate signal strength. Frequently a RHAW receiver is used in conjunction with various defence suppression actions such as the US Wild Weasels. This is a form of physical countermeasures and is in consonance with the Russian practice of the physical destruction of hostile emitters[5].

Radar warning receivers are often different in configuration from other ESM receivers. Rhodes[49] recently presented a review of low cost radar warning receivers which use pulse information. His systems all utilise digital instantaneous frequency measurement (DIFM) with delay line discriminators. Wiseman[50] proposed the use of raw video for radar warning receivers. His premise is that new radars using a combination of pseudo-noise and frequency agility could not be handled by a current RWR which uses computer-oriented signal processing. Certainly, the human ear is a very sensitive detector of raw video.

The other application of ESM to ECM is that of providing information for ECM employment. Successful ECM employment, especially denial ECM, requires timely initiation of the proper ECM on the correct frequency. Initiation of ECM too late, on the wrong frequency, or of the wrong type may not protect the aircraft. Initiation of ECM too early may give the victim radar adequate warning to take action such as radar shut down. The ESM receiver must search in azimuth and/or elevation angles, in frequency and in time. Once detected, the signal must be identified using radar emission characteristics. A decision must then be made on whether and when to initiate jamming and which jamming type(s) should be employed. This identification is frequently based on computer stored radar characteristics.

Since an ESM receiver must simultaneously search a very wide band of frequencies while also searching in azimuth and/or elevation in an extremely dense signal environment, there are very severe demands on its performance. This is further exacerbated by the need to minimise the time required for signal detection. New forms of radar waveforms beyond the simple pulse, such as pulse compression and pseudo-noise together with frequency agility, further complicate ESM receiver design. A number of ESM receiver types have been developed[23-26]. These include the simple but low sensitivity crystal-video receiver (CVR), the ubiquitous superheterodyne, the instantaneous frequency measurement receiver (IFM), compressive receiver (microscan), channelised receiver, Bragg Cell receiver (acoustic-optic), radiometric receiver, and multiplicative receiver. According to Harper[24] the last two are currently being studied for special applications. He also indicated that hybrid ESM receivers are very attractive. A comparison of the principal ESM receiver types together with performance requirements is contained in Table 4.7[57]. Grant *et al.*[40] discussed recent advances in ESM receivers with extensive treatment of application of SAW (surface acoustic wave) devices to both channelised and compressive ESM receivers. Potential capabilities of three types of ESM receivers as enumerated by Grant *et al.* are given in Table 4.8. Several papers in the IEE EW special issue[18] address the CVR, channelised ESM receivers, digital IFM, and SAW compressive ESM receivers.

The advent of new radar technologies is having an impact on the design of future ESM receivers. Several authors have addressed the impact of receivers[52-56], usually as a ratio of the ESM receiver signal detection range to the detection range of the radar. The ESM receiver designer wishes to maximise this ratio while the radar designer wishes to minimise it. Although not so stated, both groups are concerned with the previously discussed CESM concept. Low probability of intercept (LPI) radars are of great concern to ESM receiver designers. The above multiplicative and radiometric receivers discussed by Harper reflect this concern.

Table 4.7[57]   Receiver technology tradeoff analysis

Performance characteristic	Requirement	CVR[1]	Superhet[2]	IFM[3]	Compressive receiver[4]	SAW filter channeliser[5]	Bragg cell receiver[4]
Probability of intercept	High/low	High	Low	High	High	High	High
Sensitivity	−60 dBm min.	No	Yes	Yes	Yes	Yes	Yes
Dynamic range	50 dB, min.	Yes	Yes	Close	Close	Close	Yes
Bandwidth, instantaneous	2 GHz, min.	Yes	Yes	Yes	Yes[6]	Yes[6]	Yes
Simultaneous signals	Yes/no	No	Yes	No	Yes	Yes	Yes
Resolution frequency	10 MHz	Yes	Yes	Yes	Yes	Yes	Yes
Dense environment	Yes/no	No	Poor	No	Poor	Yes	Yes
Hardware complexity	High/low	Low	Mod.	Mod.	High	High	Mod.
Size-weight	—	Med.	Med.	Small	Med.	Large	Low
Production cost	High/low	Low	High	Med.	Mod.	High	Low
Risk	High/low	Low	Low	Low	High	Mod.	Mod.
Maintainability/reliability	Good/poor	Good	Good	Good	Fair	Fair	Good

1. Basically for reference; no frequency information
2. Slow; long 'look-through' times
3. No simultaneous signal capabilities
4. Poor pulse performance
5. Large in size, due primarily to peripheral components required.
6. Multiple devices required.

Table 4.8[40] Summary of potential capabilities for radar ESM receivers based on new techniques

	Acousto-optic	*SAW compressive*	*SAW channelised*
Type	integrated	IDT filters	IDT filters plus IFMs
Design	custom	custom	custom
Bandwidth (MHz)	1 000	250	250
Weighted resolution (MHz)	1.4	1	1
Effective time-bandwidth product	700	250	250
Sidelobe limited dynamic range (dB)	25–30	20–25	50
Power dissipation (W)	5	20	50
Estimated component cost (£)	10 000	10 000	10 000

4.6.2 ESM IN SUPPORT OF ECCM

Modern radars incorporate ESM receivers to assist in the employment and selection of available ECCMs. Sometimes the regular radar receiver is used in two modes, including ESM, although ideally a separate additional receiver should be provided for ESM functions. ESM receivers in radars do not usually provide for specific ECM identification since noise is noise, whatever the specific jammer used. ESM receivers are generally not used to detect the presence of DECM. This is normally done by special circuits in the receiver. At present the principal ESM receiver application in radars is that of frequency monitoring to provide information in frequency agile radars as to whether a particular frequency is being jammed. This application is quite like the employment of the panoramic adapter by radio amateurs who monitor the adjacent frequency spectrum in an attempt to find a vacant frequency nearby for transmission. Applications have been proposed for providing information on ECCM selection. Some radar ECCM techniques greatly reduce the resulting ECM presence in radar displays, causing the radar operator to have little if any indication of the ECM presence although the ECM may severely affect the radar performance. For this reason, a separate ECM display driven by the ESM receiver is sometimes used with a special ECCM operator.

A very special and most important application of ESM in radar is the monitoring of hostile ECM characteristics to facilitate improved radar design for amelioration of ECM effects. During World War II, the UK conceived and implemented its 'J-Watch' for this purpose[3]. Interestingly, the USA apparently learned of the British 'J Watch' but chose not to use the very extensive US intercept receiver capability to monitor hostile jamming during the many US ferret operations in World War II. (A ferret operation uses aircraft equipped with intercept receivers to search for enemy radar signals.)

4.7 Electronic counter-countermeasures

Over 200 radar 'electronic' ECCM techniques have been identified[20,21]. These include a number of variants of basic techniques and special combinations of techniques. Over half occur in the receiver. The most 'important' ECCMs are shown in Table 4.9[22]. Those techniques marked with (T) are used in tracking radars while those marked with (S) are used in search radars. Frequency

Table 4.9[22]   Most important ECCMs

1. Electronic types	
Transmitter	
Frequency agility/PRF agility	
Pulse compression	
Higher frequency (MM/EO)	(T)
Higher average power	
Coherent transmitter	
Antenna	
Lower sidelobes	
Sidelobe canceller/blanker	(S)
Monopulse	(T)
Higher gain (narrower beam)	
Receiver	
CFAR	(S)
Dicke-fix	(S)
MTI/Doppler filtering	
Leading edge tracking	(T)
Clean design	
Large dynamic range	
System	
Passive strobe	(S)
Passive track (TOJ/HOJ)	(T)
2. 'Operational'	
The operator	

S = Search
T = Track

agility and PRF agility are sometimes used separately but usually together. The coherent transmitter is used together with MTI/ Doppler filtering. Some of the search ECCM techniques may also be employed in a tracking radar to facilitate its necessary initial target search and detection prior to target lock-on and tracking initiation. Current ECCM emphases are listed in Table 4.10[22].

Table 4.10[22] Current ECCM emphases

---
1. Complex, wideband, flexible transmitted waveforms
2. LPI radar
3. Very low sidelobe antennas
4. Sidelobe cancellers/blankers
5. Coherent processing/MTD
6. Millimetre wave radar
7. Radar netting

Numerous programmes are underway in these areas in the USA. Additionally, bistatic radar is receiving extensive attention in the UK at present. Many of the radar ECCM techniques can be applied to EO/IR systems and to communication systems. Russia has stressed physical destruction of opposing jammers by Soviet field artillery as a viable ECCM. Many writers on both US/ NATO and Soviet EW have either not considered ECCM or only mentioned it in passing. This is most unfortunate, since ECCM is important both in US radar programs and in Russia. The Russian radar ECCM book[16] indicates a clear and strong Soviet knowledge of radar ECCM. Certainly, the possible effects of Soviet use of ECCMs on US/NATO radar ECM/ESM systems must be considered. As indicated elsewhere[31], the Soviets are well aware of many US radar ECCM techniques and could readily retrofit or suddenly activate a number of radar ECCM techniques in an attempt to negate the effects of US/NATO ECM/ESM systems and thus present problems for them. No open studies of the effect of specific Soviet ECCMs on US ECM/ESM systems have been identified. ECCM techniques, whether used by US/NATO or by Russia, can constitute a powerful means for ameliorating the effects of ECM/ESM by the opposing forces.

4.7.1 ORGANISATION OF ELECTRONIC COUNTER-COUNTERMEASURES

The large number of radar 'electronic' ECCM techniques which have been identified makes it imperative that the techniques are organised by some means in order to facilitate understanding of the individual techniques. There are many ways of classifying ECCM techniques, including their location in a radar system, 'basic function', ECCM effect, etc. As was seen in the organisation of ECM techniques, there is no unique or best way to organise ECCM techniques.

One method of organisation of ECCM techniques is by the location of the ECCM technique in the radar/system. The principal shortcoming of this method is that it assumes that an ECCM

Table 4.11[20]   R-F interference reduction

Method	Techniques
Spatial selectivity (Utilises direction or entrance path to select desired from undesired signal)	Shielding. Sidelobe reduction. *Sidelobe blanking*
Frequency Selectivity (Discriminates against wideband off-frequency and impulsive signals; also uses velocity discrimination)	Proper tuning. Tunability. Filtering. Balanced Mixing. Frequency. Discrimination. *Guard band techniques. Lamb suppressor.* Moving target indicator. Doppler radars
Amplitude selectivity (Uses amplitude characteristics to discriminate against e.g. high energy or impulsive interference)	Limiting. *Guard band techniques. Lamb suppressor. Sidelobe blanking.* Log amplifier. *Instantaneous automatic gain control. Detector balanced bias*
Time selectivity (Uses time of arrival of signal or time separation between successive returns to distinguish between interference and target return)	Pulse interference separator and blanker. *Delay-line integration. Lamb suppressor.* Sensitivity time control
Signal selectivity (employs signal statistics, shape, spectrum, or polarisation)	*Instantaneous automatic gain control.* Fast time constant. *Detector balanced bias.* Circular polarisation, Optimum filtering. *Guard band techniques.* Pulse shape discrimination. Detection enhancement (Coherent detection. 'Mouse under the rug'). Unconventional modes of operation. *Delay-line integration*

(The last two methods, Time selectivity and Signal selectivity, are marked "Closely related".)

technique appears in only one place in a radar; monopulse, for instance, involves both the antenna and the receiver. While the method of classifying ECCMs by their principal place of application in a radar is also not unique, it has been used by several writers[21,57] and is very logical, since the engineering staffs of many radar manufacturing firms are organised into receiver, transmitter, antenna, etc., groups. This method of ECCM classification thus lends itself well to the industrial radar world, and will be used in this chapter; the various ECCM techniques will be treated according to their 'principal' place in a radar.

Regardless of their system location(s), ECCMs have certain basic functions, recognition of which facilitates understanding of the ECCM. Brick and Galejs[20] proposed the classification of ECCMs by their basic function, as shown in Table 4.11[20]. Maksimov[16] used this same method. It will be noted from Table 4.11 that this method is not a unique system.

Table 4.2, which lists ECCM effects, is an interesting but not a unique method of ECCM organisation. Some ECCM techniques have more than one primary benefit, others both primary and secondary benefits. Certainly the benefit(s) of an ECCM are important, but they do not provide a unique method of ECCM organisation.

Other possible methods of ECCM organisation include use of the type of radar, e.g. search or track, the ECM against which an ECCM is useful, and the ubiquitous alphabetic system. Some ECCM techniques are applicable to more than one type of radar. Some are effective against several ECM types. Others have several names; a few bear the name of their inventor. None of these are unique methods of organisation and have less merit than the other methods above.

4.7.2 ECCMS IN THE TRANSMITTER

ECCMs in the transmitter may be subdivided for convenience into four sub-groups – those involving the radar frequency, power, PRF, waveform; and 'others'. Admittedly, PRF is usually included in waveform, but it is broken out separately here for emphasis. In the first sub-group we seek to choose radar frequencies to avoid or minimise the effects of hostile jamming. One may employ multiple frequencies simultaneously, varying frequency, etc. Power type transmitter ECCMs involve changing the radar power to avoid or minimise the effects of hostile jamming. PRF transmitter ECCMs also are generally intended to work against deception ECMs. In the employment of PRF transmitter ECCMs, allowance must be made for their effects on radar performance. A change of PRF alone will cause a corresponding change of radar average power output, and hence detection range; it will also cause a corresponding change in the number of hits per scan and hence the number of pulses available for non-coherent integration. An increase of PRF will cause a corresponding reduction in the radar unambiguous detection range, which may be of little consequence, since in the presence of jamming the detection range will generally be considerably less than the radar unambiguous detection range.

Various radar waveforms have been conceived, from CW through complex pulse chains, pulse compression, and currently pseudo-noise. Pulse compression was conceived in Germany in World War II as an ECCM against chaff[2,33], in that it would put more energy on the target and less on the surrounding chaff. As will be shown in Section 4.8.4, the detection of a target in chaff is determined by the effective signal-to-chaff (s/c) ratio, which is in turn affected by the radar illumination volume.

Radar transmitters are of two general types: the single oscillator (which may consist of several tubes (valves)) and the MOPA (master oscillator power amplifier). Early US radars used the single oscillator configuration, since it provided adequate output power, was more compact, and made the resulting radar more mobile. The advent of the cavity magnetron during World War II made possible the use of microwaves (an ECCM in itself). The magnetron is a simple, cheap, and very reliable device. Development of microwave ECMs (especially rapidly tuneable jammers and chaff) has now caused transmitters to return to the coherent MOPA configuration of the first British radar, the CH[4].

Some improvements have been made in magnetrons, such as the coaxial magnetron, frequency agility[58], injection locking to provide coherent operation for low powers[59], and the use of magnetrons as amplifiers[60]. MOPA transmitters are also used at millimetre wave frequencies[61], along with injection locking. Current output tubes (valves) are the TWT, CFA (crossed field amplifier, e.g. the Twystron), klystron at UHF, and solid state up to L-band. Phase coherent operation is desirable to permit cancellation of second time around clutter and to permit use of Doppler processing of MTI (moving target indicator) techniques[62].

Transmitter requirements include clean output (freedom from spurious emissions), linearity, frequency stability, uniformity of output over the pulse spectrum, wide bandwidth for some operations, phase and frequency stability/coherence, and capability of operation over a wide band and ease of rapid frequency change. Some of these requirements are incompatible.

Some radar system engineers may tend to treat a tuneable wide instantaneous bandwidth MOPA transmitter as a perfect transmitter. Gardner[63] has addressed performance of MOPA transmitters with regard to power supply ripple, phase change with change of drive power, amplitude and phase distortion as a function of frequency, amplitude and phase distortions as a function of time, and non-linear considerations. As he indicated, ECCM transmitter waveforms such as fast binary codes, polyphase codes, and short pulse burst codes could be seriously modified with consequences not predictable from linear analysis. Development of non-linear analytical techniques backed by experimental corroboration is needed to predict the effects of tube (valve) non-linearities on these waveforms. Transmitter tube performance can greatly affect the performance of MTI radars, especially in Doppler MTI types. Weill[60] presented an excellent discussion of this and presented a more complete table of transmitter tube modulation sensitivities and relationships to modulator ripple than that of Gardner cited above.

Representative transmitter ECCMs are listed by the above subgroups in Table 4.12[22]. It should be recognised that the ECCMs in this list do not apply to all types of radars and are not useful against all ECMs; each ECCM must be considered individually. Several transmitter ECCMs may have to be used in combination, e.g. when the PRF is changed it may be necessary to make a corresponding opposite change in pulse duration to retain the same value of average transmitter power output. Other resulting effects on the radar performance must also be considered, of course.

4.7.2.1 *Transmitter frequency ECCMs*

Frequency agility is perhaps the most important transmitter frequency ECCM. It has importance also in the benign environment for its well known improvement of radar performance, both in detection and in tracking. In the hostile environment, it is best accompanied by an ESM receiver for control of the transmitted signal frequency. If there is already interference, either hostile or

Table 4.12[22]   ECCM in the transmitter

Frequency:
    Fast manual frequency shift
    Fine frequency
    Frequency agility
    Frequency diversity
    Frequency shift (variable frequency)
    Higher frequency
    Multi-frequency radar (multi-band radar)
    New frequency bands
    Pulse-to-pulse frequency shift

Power:
    Increased power output
    Power management (power output control)

PRF:
    Interpulse coding, pulse position modulation
    Jitter PRF (PRF change)
    Linear intrapulse FM (CHIRP)
    Modulated PRF
    Modulation on pulse
    Non-linear intrapulse FM
    Pulse burst mode
    Pulse compression and stretching (CHIRP)
    Pulse frequency modulation
    PRF agility
    Short pulse radar
    Staggered PRF
    Variable PRF

Waveform:
    Coded waveform
    CW
    FM
    Noise/spread spectrum (pseudo-noise)
    Pulse doppler

Other:
    Diplexing

---

friendly, there is no benefit from transmitting on that frequency. Similarly, it is unnecessary to change frequency until jamming appears on that frequency, although initial use of frequency agility could complicate the operation of some hostile ESM receivers. Frequency should be changed by a minimum of $1/T$, where T is the transmitted pulse duration, to avoid spot jamming at the first frequency from interfering with the new transmission frequency. For target echo decorrelation, Maksimov[16] stated that the transmission frequency must be changed by greater than c/L_T where c is the velocity of propagation and L_T is the target length.

Some two dozen methods of frequency agility have been patented[22], starting from the 1952 patent of Larson[64]. His scheme used a rotating loop which pulled the frequency of a fixed frequency magnetron as governed by the well known Rieke diagram. There are better means for accomplishing frequency agility, however, including the voltage controlled oscillator (VCO) (e.g. the voltage tuned magnetron (VTM)), switching a bank of fixed frequency crystal oscillators, surface acoustic wave (SAW) devices[65], and the frequency agile magnetron[58]. When frequency agility is employed, it should be pulse-to-pulse, unless Doppler MTI processing is used. Similarly, if switched frequencies are used, the number should be as large as possible. It is preferable to change the specific switched frequencies from time to time if possible in order to make it more difficult to predict the next radar transmission frequency. The frequency agile magnetron may be utilised in several ways[66,67], e.g. by continuously rotating the tuning device by a motor, by randomly rotating the tuning device, or by tuning the device to a pretuned frequency such as that of one of a bank of microwave cavities. This last method can provide MTI operation.

Doppler MTI processing is incompatible with random pulse-to-pulse frequency agility. Taylor and Sinclair[68] and Petrocchi *et al.*[68] have also conceived schemes to improve the compatibility of frequency agility and coherent MTI operation. The Taylor and Sinclair method employs transmission of a pair of pulses for each transmission period. The frequencies of the pulses in the pair are controlled for each transmission period so that in successive transmission periods there are pulses at the same frequency. A dual channel receiver uses appropriate local oscillator signals from a frequency synthesiser to permit a two-pulse MTI reception.

Petrocchi *et al.*[69] transmitted in a random sequence on a number of fixed frequencies. Received echoes are stored in a computer memory bank and labelled according to the transmission frequency used. Ultimately, target echoes are received from several different transmissions on the same frequency, enabling MTI processing. While both of these schemes have drawbacks, they are attempts to address the incompatibility of frequency agility and Doppler MTI processing.

Bergkvist[70] indicated that the use of frequency agility in combination with PRF agility can greatly improve the effectiveness of frequency agility. This combination forces the jammer to spread its jamming over a wider frequency than if frequency agility were to be used alone. This is of course based on certain assumptions regarding the nature and characteristics of the ESM receiver used with the ECM jamming transmitter.

Frequency diversity is the (simultaneous) operation of radar equipments in widely separated frequency bands. Two techniques of frequency diversity are used. One, which uses a common antenna aperture but with separate antenna feeds, is exemplified by the HSA Flycatcher radar[71]. It is a dual-band aircraft fire control radar operating at X- and K_A-bands. The US Army World War II SCR-545 fire control radar, designed and built by Western Electric Company[72], was a dual-band radar with a common antenna 'face' where a 200 MHz mattress array surrounded an S-band parabolic antenna. At the Anzio beachhead, the Germans dropped P-band chaff which greatly affected the P-band portion of the SCR-545, but only slightly affected the S-band portion. The harmonic response of the P-band chaff was negligible at S-band and the Germans did not have microwave chaff then.

The other frequency diversity technique uses separate antenna apertures, usually back-to-back as in the Marconi types S631 and S690 radars. The US Army Signal Corps in 1940 built an experimental version of the SCR-270 long range search radar with back-to-back antennas operated at different frequencies[73]. The other antenna operated at 'three halves' of the frequency of the main antenna. Its purpose was to serve as a gap filler to fill in the vertical coverage of the main antenna. Although not recognised then as having ECCM capabilities, it certainly could have provided ECCM. Both frequency diversity techniques require the enemy to carry jammers operating at both radar frequencies. They also provide increased system reliability, but at the expense of increased complexity.

Use of higher frequencies as a transmitter frequency ECCM is well represented in the use of millimetre wave frequencies for radars[61]. A number of advantages obtain from their use[74,75]. Several of these are of ECCM benefit, especially the reduction of chaff illumination volume which results from the narrower beamwidths, assuming a constant antenna aperture.

A multi-frequency radar transmits on several frequencies simultaneously in the same radar band through the same antenna. This technique was considered by the UK as an ECCM in 1938, based on a 1931 multi-frequency generation scheme[3,76,77]. This is another means to force the jammer to spread its power over a wider frequency region and hence dilute its power density. Use of multi-frequencies can also improve target detection in the benign environment.

4.7.2.2 *Transmitter power ECCMs*

For many years the British radar rule was said to be 'It is more blessed to transmit than to receive'. With the advent of modern ESM receivers and the ARM (anti-radiation missile), the current trend is use of LPI (low probability of intercept) radars. Use of pseudo-noise, discussed in Section 4.7.2.4, will spread the radar average power output over a wide frequency spectrum and hence make the radar signal more difficult to detect by conventional ESM receivers. Under certain conditions, the radar transmitter power output may be reduced to hinder hostile ESM receiver detection of the radar signal. One such possibility would be in a tracking radar when the associated search/acquisition radar has indicated that the desired target is at much less than maximum tracking range. Certainly, the power output of a search/acquisition radar should not be reduced unless it is certain that detection at maximum detection range is not required. The transmitted power may be varied in order to deceive deception type ECMs, or to deceive hostile ESM systems. During World War II, Alvarez conceived the VIXEN scheme whereby the power output of an airborne air-to-surface radar was caused to vary as a function of range after it detected a surfaced submarine and the aircraft flew towards it[3,8]. If the radar power varied as R^N where $2<N<4$, the ESM receiver operator could be misled into believing that the aircraft was not approaching and hence was no threat to the submarine.

4.7.2.3 *Transmitter PRF ECCMs*

Jittered PRF is perhaps the oldest transmitter PRF ECCM. It was used in the British CH radar[4] and was patented in the USA in 1954, having been filed in 1942[78]. It is effective against a number of deception ECMs and is also useful in combination with frequency agility, as previously indicated. Change of PRF may be used to increase the radar average power output on a temporary overload basis, as proposed by Gardner[63]. This will also increase the number of hits per scan, increasing the number of pulses available for non-coherent integration. It may also be a CESM, especially if the PRF is a new value, never used before by that radar. Use of a different radar PRF may confuse ESM radar identification functions and thus delay or prevent the application of appropriate ECMs[8,31].

4.7.2.4 *Transmitter waveform ECCMs*

Pseudo-noise (PN) is the most important waveform transmitter ECCM. PN techniques spread the transmitted energy out over the spectrum (hence the alternative name of 'spread spectrum techniques') and thus impede its detection by ESM receivers. The most popular technique for generating a PN waveform is the shift register with feedback, as described by Reid[79]. Some PN variants such as Gold codes were recently described by Moser and Stover[80]. Albanase[81] and Forest[82] both presented PN surveillance radars at RADAR-77. Winnberg[83] described a new PN radar at RADAR-82. It was intended to reduce the radar signal detectability by an ARM receiver (and hence could be classified as a CESM). US PN radar work has been reported[84,85].

As discussed in Section 4.6.1, radar transmitter waveforms, especially the new waveforms such as pulse compression and pseudo-noise, are of great importance to ESM receiver designers. Gager[84] compared the performance of radars with various waveforms at RADAR-82. Forrest[52] discussed the influence of several aspects of low probability of intercept radar. Albanase[81] analysed the effect of using a pseudo-noise waveform on the ECCM performance of a radar. This will be discussed further in Section 4.8.4. Clearly, radar transmitter waveform can have a strong effect on the ECM performance of a radar, especially as a CESM. The radar system engineer must certainly give careful attention to this matter.

4.7.2.5 *Other transmitter ECCMs*

Other transmitter ECCMs include various ECCM techniques in the transmitter which do not fit under the above transmitter ECCM categories. Diplexing, the operation of two radar transmitters through a common antenna, is one such transmitter ECCM. They may be pulsed simultaneously or separately while operating in the same or different frequency bands. In one method, the two transmitters are on the same frequency and are pulsed alternately, providing a 3 dB increase of radar power output. Operation in two different frequency bands, as in the HSA Flycatcher[71], the NRL TRAKX[86], or the experimental PEAB shipboard search radar[88], requires the enemy to employ jammers in the two frequency bands. The first two of these radars operate at X- and K_A-bands, while the last one operates at C- and X-bands. Other transmitter ECCMs may be envisioned such as radiating dummy signals through a separate antenna to mask the sidelobe signals of the main antenna. This concept, patented by Powell[89], is tantamount to the use of a dummy decoy transmitter.

4.7.3 ECCMS IN THE ANTENNA

The radar antenna provides opportunity to reduce the effectiveness of hostile ECMs through the use of various properties of antennas such as polarisation, antenna pattern, antenna directivity (angle measurement), and antenna sidelobes. These apply for both denial and deception ECMs. Some of the antenna ECCMs also involve other portions of the radar, such as the transmitter or the receiver. Antenna ECCMs may be subdivided into angular measurement techniques, main lobe pattern characteristics, sidelobe characteristics, and the ubiquitous 'others'. They reflect various properties of antennas. Representative ECCMs in the antenna are listed in Table 4.13[22].

Antenna types for microwave search radars include fan beams in shaped parabolas, stacked beams when target height information is required, frequency scanning in elevation (also used to provide target height data), and the phased array. The latter is often used in multi-function radars, e.g. search and track in air defence weapons systems, but it may be used in elevation only in conjunction with antenna mechanical rotation in azimuth. Tracking radar antenna types include the parabola, several types of the Cassegrain, and the metallic lens. Most newer tracking radars employ the Cassegrain[90] because of its improved performance over the prime focus parabola.

Radar antenna requirements in an ECM environment include:

Operation over a very broad frequency band for frequency agile radars.

Very low sidelobes over these wide frequencies.

Low cross polarisation over the wide frequencies.

Narrow beamwidth for tracking antennas to reduce the chaff illumination volume.

Polarisation agility to reduce effectiveness of certain ECMs.

'Lobe on receive only' for conical scan tracking radars.

Boresight stability for tracking radars.

Table 4.13[22]   ECCM in the antenna

Angular measurement techniques:
  Adaptive angle scan modulation
  Compensated conical scan
  Hybrid monopulse
  Lobe on receiver only (LORO)
  Monopulse
  Monopulse MLC
  Multisimul antenna
  Phased array radar
  Scan rate amplitude modulation
  Variable scan rate

Main-lobe pattern characteristics:
  Bistatic radar
  Circular polarisation
  Increased angular resolution
  Mainlobe cancellation (MLC)
  Polarisation diversity/selector
  Polarisation main lobe cancellation

Sidelobe characteristics
  Sidelobe blanker (SLB)
  Sidelobe canceller (SLC)
  Sidelobe reduction/suppression
  Sidelobe suppression by absorbing materials

Others:
  Dummy antenna/dummy load
  Single lobe blanking (SLB)

4.7.3.1 *Antenna angular measurement ECCMs*

Target angular measurement is important in search radars, but much more so in tracking radars. Some missile guidance systems depend exclusively on target angular measurements. In search radars, target angle is of moderate importance, although degradation of target angle in a search radar can impede ultimate initiation of tracking by the associated target tracking radar. Conical scanning was developed in World War II and was widely used first in the US Army SCR-584 tracking radar[91]. Development of the so called 'inverse gain' jammer[42] hastened the demise of conical scanning after World War II. In this concept, a receiver intercepts the transmitted signal and extracts the lobing modulation (generally in the frequency range of 10–100 Hz), inverts it in polarity, and retransmits it to the victim radar. Cikalo and Greenbaum[41] vividly show the effectiveness of such a jammer. Alvarez[92] conceived this scheme (but with different implementation) during World War II. Several versions were implemented at the Radio Research Laboratory in World War II[42] and were tested experimentally, but never placed into production.

A number of ECCM techniques to reduce the effectiveness of the 'inverse gain' jammer have been devised[42]. These include monopulse, 'lobe on receive only' (also known as 'conical scan on receive only' (COSRO)), scan rate amplitude modulation, variable scan rate, scan modulation cancellation, and hybrid conical scan-monopulse. There are a number of patents on these schemes[42]. Monopulse, widely used now, is insensitive to target amplitude fluctuations since it makes angular measurements on one pulse. While monopulse has been highly developed, it is more complex (generally requiring extensive RF plumbing and more than one mixer and IF receiver channel), weighs more, and is more complex than conical scan. These factors are extremely important in missile borne radar applications. While the classical monopulse is used for tracking radars, a form of monopulse is used on a single axis (usually azimuth) on some search radars to improve angular accuracy and to provide ECCM benefits[22]. It is known by various names such as 'electrical correction system', 'monopinch'[93], etc.

Natural 'conical scan on receive only' capabilities may result from other system considerations such as in a CW tracking radar, in passive homing seekers, in semiactive missile seekers (actually a bistatic radar), and bistatic radars themselves. In CW tracking radars, separate antennas (*not* bistatic!) are required to isolate the transmitted signal from the receiver; hence COSRO results, since it is not necessary to use conical scan on both transmit and receive. In semiactive seekers, scan on transmit in the illuminating radar could contaminate or confuse the required conical scan in the missile receiver. COSRO may also be implemented by a number of methods[42], but subsequent ECM advances resulted in a technique known as 'swept audio frequency jamming', where a jammer is modulated by an audio frequency which is slowly swept through the anticipated conical scan frequency region of a radar while the radar signal is monitored. When the audio frequency reaches the radar conical scan frequency pass band, the radar antenna generally takes a sudden jump in angle. The audio frequency is clamped at this frequency to continue tracking disruption. Several forms of this jammer have been devised[42].

This jamming technique is effective against most 'simple' COSRO systems. More effective ECCMs against this jammer include scan rate frequency variation, the scan modulation cancellation scheme of Schmidt[42,94], and the hybrid conical scan-monopulse schemes. Interestingly, a scan modulation cancellation scheme was conceived and demonstrated at the MIT Radiation Laboratory in 1941 while conical scan was being developed[95]. It was not used on the SCR-584 then since it was believed that the Germans did not possess the ability to employ conical scan jamming. This concept was not described in any radiation laboratory report although it was documented in laboratory notebooks. Several versions of scan rate frequency variation have been reported, including use of pseudo-noise[42] and scan reference phase reversal[42].

The last group of ECCMs useful against amplitude modulated jamming include CONOPULSE[96], the Russian Scan With Compensation[97], and several hybrid conical scan-monopulse tracking schemes[42]. These hybrid schemes generally start with a conventional monopulse four-horn antenna feed followed by the usual four hybrid junctions to form the sum (or reference) azimuth error, and elevation error signals plus an unused combination of the four horn signals which is normally terminated in a load. In the hybrid conical scan-monopulse schemes, these three signals are usually combined in a microwave resolver which is rotated at a 'conical scan' frequency. Further processing produces the required azimuth and elevation angle error signals which drive the antenna servos. These hybrid conical scan-monopulse systems are usually a little simpler than the conventional monopulse in that they frequently use less than the three conventional receiver channels, but they are more complex than conventional conical scan. In principle, variable scan rate and scan modulation cancellation schemes seem to offer a more viable approach to ECCMs against improved conical scan angle deception jamming.

4.7.3.2 *Antenna main lobe pattern ECCMs*
Antenna main lobe pattern ECCMs include jammer signal discrimination using antenna polarisation, bistatic radar, and main lobe cancellation. Certainly, the antenna main beam lobe should be kept as small as possible to minimise the chaff illumination volume. However, in search radars this reduces the hits per scan and also increases the time required to scan a given volume and hence reduces the radar data rate. Several ECCM schemes involving antenna polarisation have been devised, starting from the Radio Research Laboratory in 1945[98]. Others include polaris-

ation selection, polarisation cancellation, adaptive polarisation, polarisation diversity, etc. Polarisation ECCM schemes are generally suited to only one-on-one situations, i.e. one jammer against one radar, and then only when the jammer employs one fixed linear polarisation. Even in World War II, the US employed rotating polarisation to reduce the effectiveness of certain German ECCMs. Today, a jammer may confront several different radar types using various polarisations. Accordingly, the jammer must not radiate only a single linear polarisation. Polarisation ECCM schemes are generally not too difficult to implement, requiring both horizontal and vertical antenna feeds for example[99]. Their effectiveness should not be depended upon, however.

Bistatic radar is an interesting ECCM in that since the location of the radar receiver is not disclosed, it is difficult to direct ECM or take counter action against the receiver. Although the radar transmitter power output required for a bistatic radar is greater than that for a monostatic radar, it will generally be located in a more distant and safer area. Currently there is extensive British interest in bistatic radar, but only limited activity in the US.

Several main lobe jammer cancellation (MLC) schemes have been devised[22,100,101], both analogue and digital. MLC, which is also known variously as 'mainbeam notcher' and 'null steering', is useful against standoff jammers when the radar main beam illuminates the standoff jammer as well as when an escort jammer is in the main beam, but slightly off the axis of its accompanying target aircraft. If the jammer is on exactly the same azimuth angle as the target, the jammer cannot be cancelled. If the jammer is an escort jammer and is a fraction of the beamwidth off the target, reasonable jammer cancellation may be achieved. Dicken[100] described two potential methods of null steering, both using monopulse. He described application of AGC techniques and correlation receiver techniques, and predicted an improvement of 35 dB for target and jammer separation of 0.1 beamwidth. Chapman *et al.*[101] claimed an angular measurement accuracy of 1/20 beamwidth for target and jammer separation of 0.1 beamwidth.

The phased array radar is now well known for its ECCM capabilities, such as the ability to move the beam rapidly and to increase dwell at selected angles. It uses only one beam even though it can be moved without inertia. Formation of many simultaneous beams would permit simultaneous detection and tracking of many targets in many directions at the same time.

'Digital radar' is such a concept, in which outputs from a number of separate antenna feeds are processed separately simultaneously in the digital computer. Thus a number of beams may be formed simultaneously, including nulls. A simplified block diagram of the digital beam forming radar (DBFR) is shown in Fig. 4.7[102]. This is of course an alternative approach to the now well known sidelobe cancellers. Usually DBF is discussed for bistatic/multistatic operation, whereas the phased array is generally used for monostatic operation. DBFR is not a new concept[103–107], but recent advances in digital techniques, especially the US VHSIC programme now make digital beam forming more

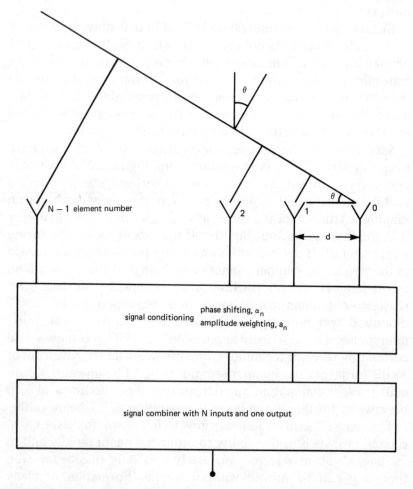

Fig. 4.7 Block diagram of antenna array system for digital beam forming radar.

attractive. Requirements for computations in a DBFR are very large[108]. Recent US work on DBFR has been reported[102,109]: Spaulding examined the anticipated performance of a DBFR in an ECM environment; Loomis and Rose described a prototype eight-element radar and gave experimental results; Valentino[110] recently described the DBFR, and Wardrop[95] recently presented a survey of digital beam forming radar technology and reported European experimental DBFR work.

4.7.3.3 *Antenna sidelobe ECCMs*

The low sidelobe requirement applies primarily to search radars, although tracking radars of relatively small aperture, e.g. some airborne radars, may also be affected. Sidelobe levels of many tracking radars coupled with the large main beam gain are usually such as to make sidelobe jamming of tracking radars impractical. Low sidelobe requirements apply to both the transmitting and the receiving antenna patterns. Reduction of receiving antenna sidelobes is useful against standoff jammers and false target deception ECM. Reduction of transmitting antenna sidelobes is useful against ARMs and hostile ESM receivers. It thus constitutes a very powerful CESM[8]. Accordingly, attention should be devoted to reduction of sidelobe levels of both the receiving and the transmitting antenna patterns in a search radar.

Dax[112] studied the effect of various search radar receiving antenna sidelobe levels and showed that sidelobe levels of −20 dB are inadequate. While antenna sidelobe levels have been of concern since the earliest days of radar, it was not until the time of the US Air Force AWACS program that concerted effort was devoted to reduction of antenna sidelobes. There are two basic methods of reducing the effectiveness of jamming in radar receiving antenna sidelobes: sidelobe reduction, and sidelobe cancellation.

Antenna receiving sidelobe levels are affected by several factors, including aperture blockage by the antenna feed, by the illumination taper, by the presence of reflecting objects in or near the antenna beam, antenna tolerances, etc.[113]. Evans and Schrank recently described achievements in ultra low sidelobe antennas[114]. Typical present RMS sidelobe levels of 50 dB have been achieved, but not without penalties. Rudge presented results by Hansen[115] which showed that an illumination edge taper of −44 dB results in a −50 dB sidelobe level, but with the main beam one way gain reduced by 6 dB and the main beam

3 dB one way beamwidth increased by a factor of about 1.5[113]. This means that the radar maximum detection range in a benign environment will be reduced by a factor of about 2 unless the antenna is made larger. The detection range in both jamming and in chaff will be reduced. The resulting beamwidth increase will result in more hits per scan and thus more pulses available for non-coherent integration in both jamming and chaff environments. It will increase the chaff illumination volume and hence degrade the signal-to-chaff ratio. The manufacturing tolerances required can cause increase of antenna manufacturing costs for ultra-low sidelobe antennas. Tolerance errors for ultra-low side-lobe antennas was addressed by Fante[116]. Care must be taken in both the field handling and the site selection of low sidelobe antenna radars in the field, especially on shipboard[117–120].

Extensive work has been done on the use of cancellation techniques for receiving antenna sidelobe level control, starting from the simple cancellation schemes using two separate antennas with appropriate amplitude and phase variation. The principal advances on antenna sidelobe cancellers resulted from the work of Howells[121]. Here an effective artificial null is generated in the direction of the jammer by use of an auxiliary receiving omnidirectional antenna located in proximity to the main receiving antenna. Since it requires one auxiliary antenna and canceller loop per jammer and since there may be several standoff jammers at different azimuths, several antennas and cancellers will generally be employed in a search radar. Canceller design has been developed along several lines.

Two approaches are possible for reduction of the effects of sidelobes of the transmitting antenna. The first is of course reduction of the sidelobes themselves as used in reduction of the receiving antenna discussed previously. If a common antenna is used for both receiving and transmitting, reduction of the receiving sidelobes must also reduce the sidelobes on transmission. Some stacked beam radars use separate feeds for transmission and for reception. Accordingly, separate treatment of the transmitting antenna may be required. In any event, the matter of sidelobes in the transmitter antenna must certainly be addressed.

Another approach for the reduction of the effects of sidelobes in the transmitting antenna is to use an additional transmitter (generally of low power) and an additional antenna rotated with the regular antenna to radiate signals which mask the radiations from the sidelobes of the main antenna. This technique was mentioned briefly in Section 4.7.2.5. Such a scheme was conceived by Powell[89]. Auxiliary transmitter power output requirements may be minimised if the main radar antenna already possesses low sidelobes.

Sidelobe blanking (SLB) is another technique useful for reduction of the effects of radar antenna sidelobes[122,123]. It originated in World War II both at the MIT Radiation Laboratory and also in the UK[3], and is useful in both benign and hostile environments. In the benign environment, the SLB is useful as an EMC in reduction of the effects of interference from nearby radars which operate at adjacent frequencies. Since the SLB employs a blanking gate rather than a canceller, it is useful only against low duty cycle interference such as from false target generators or other pulsed deception jammers. As indicated previously, noise jamming is generally used for denial jamming, especially in stand-off jamming.

4.7.3.4 *Other antenna ECCMs*

These include such schemes as fences, single beam blanking, dummy loads, and modified frequency scanning antennas. The use of fences to control low angle clutter is well known. They can also be used to reduce interference from ground based jammers near the radar, unfortunately at some cost to the ability of the radar to detect low elevation angle targets. Single beam blanking is an ECCM technique which is useful in stacked beam radars. If a jamming signal is received in a single beam of a stacked beam radar, that beam may be blanked easily; however, all targets in that beam would be undetectable.

The dummy load is very useful for EMCOM (emission control) situations where it is desired to have radar silence, but without the possible ill effects of turning the transmitter off and then on. It is useful against ARMs and hostile receivers and is thus a CESM. Of course the radar cannot detect targets in an active mode while the transmitter power output is dumped into a dummy load. Great attention must be given to prevent signal leakage when using dummy loads, which must be designed to dissipate the radar power output (it may be possible to reduce transmitter output, but not turn if off) and must be capable of rapid switching.

The usual design of a frequency scanned radar is to drive the serpentine feed at one end in order to provide elevation scanning in some search radars. In that case, a hostile ESM receiver can determine its elevation angle with respect to the radar by measuring the received frequency, and a jammer can screen all targets at that elevation angle by jamming at that one frequency. Boothe[124] conceived an ECCM for frequency scanning radars. In his concept, three circulators are added with an additional antenna drive port at the other end of the antenna serpentine feed. This permits the serpentine feed to be driven from either the top or the bottom, which can complicate the jamming task.

4.7.4 ECCMS IN THE RECEIVER

The radar receiver plays a very important role in an ECM environment in that it is almost a 'court of last resort'. The radar transmitter and antenna have made their contribution to successful operation in an ECM environment. Now it is up to the receiver to combat ECM effects. Historically, the radar receiver is a descendant of communication receivers. Many years have been devoted to the development of ECCM techniques in communications receivers as pointed out by Maksimov *et al.*[16]. A number of communications ECCM techniques were developed by radio amateurs who have had to live in a very crowded portion of the frequency spectrum. Here, too, a number of communications ECCM operating techniques were developed primarily as EMCs rather than ECCMs.

Receiver ECCM techniques will be organised in accordance with the signal flow as it progresses from antenna output through the receiver to the radar indicator. Receiver ECCM sub-organisations include pre-detection, detection, post-detection, and displays. Pre-detection ECCMs are sometimes referred to as *coherent ECCMs* since they contain target phase information. They include ECCMs in the RF amplifier if used, the mixer, and the IF amplifier. Post-detection ECCMs are sometimes called *non-coherent ECCMs* since the target signal after detection contains no phase information. Representative receiver ECCMs are shown in Table 4.14[22].

For a number of reasons there are more ECCM techniques for the receiver than in all other parts of the radar combined. Certainly there is a large number of variants of basic types of receiver ECCMs. Receiver ECCMs are generally easier and cheaper to implement than those in the transmitter or the antenna. A very important, but sometimes not recognised reason is that receiver ECCMs are generally of a non-disclosure type, i.e. their presence cannot normally be determined from signal interception, so that the employment of effective ECMs can be greatly hindered. A radar receiver should have several characteristics – a wide dynamic range, excellent stability, good linearity (for fire control radars), freedom from spurious responses, capable of handling rapid rate of change of input signals including jamming, passage of conical scanning modulation without distortion, phase delay/gain stability over a wide range of input signal levels for monopulse radars, and freedom from desensitisation. To many radar engineers, these points will seem obvious, but they were not recognised by some early radar design groups.

Galenian[125] presented an excellent review of basic considerations in radar receiver design. Desensitisation is the apparent loss of sensitivity of a receiver in the presence of large unwanted out of pass band signals. It is well known to communications engineers but not to many radar engineers. The usual manifestation is that the received signal seems to have dropped greatly for no obvious reason. Usually there is no cross modulation of the desired signal by the modulation of the interfering signal.

Hansen[126] showed that the mechanism is an apparent increase in receiver noise factor. This increase is a square law function of the form $F = F_0(1 + (V_1/V_0)^2)$ where F_0 is the small signal noise factor, V_1 is the interfering signal voltage, and V_0 is the value of V_1 which doubles the noise factor. Desensitisation may occur in either the receiver RF amplifier or the mixer or both. Hansen described procedures for measurement of desensitisation in communication receivers and presented illustrative experimental results. No similar information on radar receivers has been located. Quite possibly desensitisation may well be more of an EMC matter than ECM in radar receivers. Even so, it is recommended that desensitisation measurements be made on new radar receivers using several different values of interfering signal frequency at 'large' power levels. Appropriate steps should be taken then to reduce the observed desensitisation. One obvious method would be the incorporation of appropriate filters to reduce the level of the interfering signal sufficiently at the RF amplifier/mixer input.

4.7.4.1 *Receiver pre-detection ECCMs*

A balanced mixer is useful in reducing the effects of local oscillator noise in the benign environment, in addition to benefits in the hostile situation. It will reduce the effectiveness of jamming at

Table 4.14[22]   ECCM in the receiver-signal processor

1. General considerations
   Desensitisation
   Dynamic range
   Linearity
2. Predetection
   Balanced mixer/image suppressor
   Broad band receiver
   Coherent long pulse discrimination
   Compressive IF amplifier
   CW jamming canceller
   Dicke fix:
      Clark Dicke-fix (cascaded
         Dicke-fix)
      Coherent MTI Dicke-fix
      Craft receiver
      Dicke log fix
      IF canceller MTI Dicke-fix
      IF Dicke-fix (CFAR) (zero
         crossings, Dicke-fix (CFAR)
      Instantaneous frequency
         Dicke-fix
      Non-coherent MTI Dicke-fix
      Video Dicke-fix (CFAR)
   Frequency preselection (narrow
      band widths)

   Gain control techniques:
      Anticlutter gain control
      Automatic back bias
      Automatic gain control (AGC)
      Automatic noise levelling
      Dual gated AGC
      Fast AGC
      Gated AGC
      Instantaneous AGC (IAGC)
      Jam attenuator control
      Manual gain control
      Pulse gain control
      Sensitivity-time control (STC)
   Guard band blanker
   IF diversity, IF limiter
   Integration (coherent):
      Coherent IF integration
      Coherent IF integration
         (moving target)
      Coherent IF integration
         (stationary target)
      FM delay line integration
   Jamming cancellation receiver
   Kirbar fix
   Lamb suppressor
   Lin-log IF (log receiver)

   Local oscillator off
   Matched filtering
   Moving target indicators (MTI):
      Area MTI (velocity filter)
      Cascaded feedback canceller
         MTI
      Clutter gated MTI
      Coherent MTI
      MTI-CFAR
      Non-coherent MTI
      Pseudo coherent MTI
      Pulse Doppler
      Re-entrant data processor
      Single-delay line canceller MTI
      Three-pulse canceller
      Two-pulse canceller
   Narrowband limiter
   Passive receiver for DF strobe
   Shielding
   Swept local oscillator receiver
      (SLOR)

3. Detection
   Aural detection
   Correlation detection
   Detector back bias
   Detector balanced bias
   Double threshold
   Jammer tracked by azimuth
      crossing
   Least voltage coincidence
   Video correlator
   Zero crossing counter

4. Post detection
   Audio limiter
   Autocorrelation signal processing
   Automatic cancellation of
      extended targets (ACET)
   Automatic video noise levelling
   Conical scan guard band
   Constant false alarm rate (CFAR):
      Automatic threshold variation
      Cross-gated CFAR
      Dispersion fix CFAR
      IF Dicke-fix CFAR
      Instantaneous frequency CFAR
      MTI CFAR
      Unipolar video CFAR
      Video Dicke-fix CFAR
      Wideband CFAR
      Zero crossings CFAR

Table 4.14[22] ECCM in the receiver-signal processor – *continued*

Cross correlation signal processing	Pulse length discrimination
Fast time constant	Pulse shape discrimination
High video pass	Pulse width discrimination
Integration (non-coherent):	(PWD)
AM video delay line integration	Random pulse discrimination
Delay integration	Range gating of video
Non-coherent (video)	Video correlator
integration	Video discrimination
Pulse integration	Wide band limit
Video delay-line integration	Widepulse blanking (WPB)
Log FTC	
Log video	5. Displays
Logical ECCM processing	Azimuth *vs.* amplitude
Post canceller log FTC	Baseline break
PRF considerations:	Electronic implementation of
High PRF tracking	baseline break
PRF discrimination	Elevation *vs.* integrated log (EVIL)
Pulse edge tracking	Jam strobe (jamming amplitude *vs.*
Pulse interference eliminator	azimuth) (JAVA)
(PIE)	
Pulse interference suppression	
and blanking (PISAB)	

image frequencies while reducing local oscillator radiation[127]. Local oscillator radiation can be another source of locating a radar through the use of ESM receivers even in periods of EMCOM.

The Dicke fix[22] was conceived by Professor Dicke as an ECCM against fast sweep jammers of the backward wave oscillator (BWO) type, such as the CARCINOTRON. It closely resembles the Lamb noise silencer which is well known in amateur radio communications[20,128]. The Lamb noise silencer concept was also described subsequently in the UK by Wald[129], although the Lamb paper was not cited. Maksimov[16] described the Dicke fix concept, which he called the WLN (wideband-limiter-narrowband), and a number of interesting variants. Apparently the Lamb noise silencer/Dicke fix concept was known in Russia about forty years ago[130]. The basic configuration is shown in Fig. 4.8[22]. The wideband amplifier is made as wide as possible and the narrow band amplifier is set to the optimum bandwidth $(2/T)$. The performance of the Dicke fix is determined by the ratio B_w/B_n. Improvement factors of 20–40 dB have been indicated[22]. The Dicke fix is one form of constant false alarm (CFAR) techniques. One problem of the Dicke fix is the susceptibility of the limiter to capture

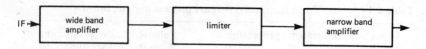

Fig. 4.8 The Dicke fix receiver.

by a strong CW signal. Thus the 'standard' Dicke fix performance may be degraded by the use of CW jamming in conjunction with the backward wave oscillator fast sweep. A method for ameliorating this problem will be shown later in conjunction with MTI. The WLN variants shown by Maksimov include one with tandem wideband amplifiers, addition of an auxiliary oscillator, and one with a gate selector system.

Gain control techniques include a number of types and are well known in radar. They are forms of CFAR. As such, they will not increase detection of targets in a hostile environment, but can reduce false alarms and scope clutter. Accordingly, they can be very useful in an ECM environment. The various automatic gain controls are well known. Manual gain control permits the radar operator to adjust receiver gain for optimum performance. Manual gain control is useful principally when raw video is employed. Most modern radars use synthetic video, making manual gain control less useful. When manual gain control is employed, it may be beneficial to make provisions to control the gain separately in more than one receiver portion, e.g. at IF and at video.

Guard band techniques are very important ECCMs. They may be implemented in a number of domains–frequency (RF, IF, Doppler video, etc.), time, angle, etc. The basic block diagram of the guard band family is shown in Fig. 4.9[22]. Although two auxiliary 'guard' channels are shown here, the number may be as small as one and as large as desired, though generally no more than four. Various arrangements of logic may be used to accept outputs of the guard channels in gating the main channel.

Moving target indicators (MTI) are extremely important in modern radar in both benign and hostile environments. In the benign environment, returns from trees, buildings, mountains, water, slow moving ground vehicles, birds, or clouds may interfere with detection of wanted targets. In the hostile environment chaff (originally called 'window' and 'rope' by the Allies and 'Doppel' by Germany in World War II) may present a severe problem to search radars. It can be shown that current chaff

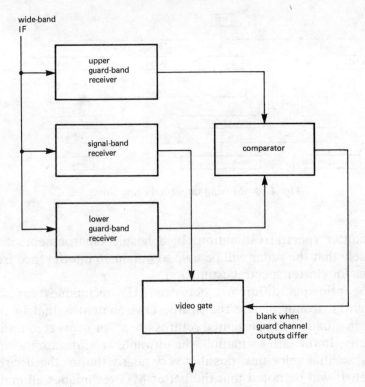

Fig. 4.9 Guard band blanker.

dispersal techniques may introduce excessive chaff returns in the narrow beamwidths and range gates of modern tracking radars, making the use of MTI desirable in tracking radars. This problem was addressed in a RADAR-80 paper[131].

MTI techniques as ECCMs against chaff were reviewed[62]. The MTI 'family' is shown in Fig. 4.10[22]. Current interest is centred on digital MTI, the MTD (moving target detector)[132] and various adaptive MTI techniques[133]. Adaptive cancellation techniques are currently being pursued. Farina and Studer[133] gave an excellent review of five current adaptive processing techniques, including the parametric estimator (PE), the Gram-Schmidt (GS) ortho-normalisation algorithm, the direct matrix inversion (DMI) technique, the maximum entropy method (MEM), and the Kalman filter (KF). The maximum entropy method is of great current interest in the US. While adaptive techniques are very powerful, they require many pulses, typically 16, to obtain sufficient estimates of the clutter spectra. Adaptive MTI performance is degraded by a reduction in the number of pulses available

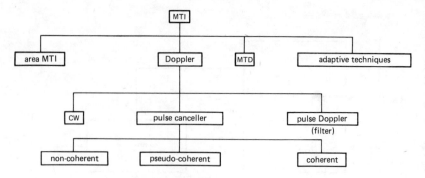

Fig. 4.10 Moving target indicator family.

for clutter spectral estimation. In a hostile environment, it is unlikely that the radar will be able to obtain 16 interference free pulses for clutter spectral estimation.

The principal difference between MTI techniques for the benign environment and the hostile environment is that in the former situation the unwanted returns are at, or near, zero radial velocity. In the latter situation, the unwanted returns are moving at substantial velocities, possibly very nearly that of the desired target. It will be noted that the better MTI techniques all make use of the Doppler shift of moving targets.

On occasion, various individual ECCM techniques may be used in specific combination to provide a synergistic effect against combinations of ECMs. Such a case is that of the MTI-CFAR patented by Evans[134]. It will be recalled that capture of the limiter in the Dicke fix by CW jammers can degrade Dicke fix performance. Evans described a combination of pulse compression, the Dicke fix, digital MTI, and special associated digital processing. This digital processing, with a threshold device, prevented limiter capture by CW jammers in addition to accomplishing digitally the well known log fast time constant circuit.

As indicated earlier, the use of combined jamming and chaff can be very effective against conventional Doppler MTI systems since Doppler systems require use of a fixed radar frequency for several pulses. Full random pulse-to-pulse frequency agility, which is an effective ECCM against jamming, is thus not desirable when Doppler MTI is used. Two palliatives for this situation have been reported, as mentioned in Section 4.7.2.1. The Taylor and Sinclair scheme[68] as originally described has an insufficient number of pulses on the target for integration. The scheme of

Petrocchi *et al.*[69] may be degraded by the elapsed time between pulses on the same frequency. In both systems it would be desirable not to change frequency unless there is interference on that frequency. Similarly, it should be considered that MTI should not be used unless clutter and chaff are present. When MTI is not used, full frequency agility should be employed.

4.7.4.2 *Receiver detection ECCMs*

Detection ECCMs include detection types such as coherent detection and aural detection. Aural detection was used in World War II in the venerable British CH radar[4], by Germany as their Nurnberg ECCM[2,33], in the US FD radar[2] and is still useful. Its principal current application is in CW Doppler radars and in anti-personnel radars. In the latter application its advantages are that headphones consume no power, are very light weight, and give off no light as does a CRT. In the hostile environment, an aural display is useful against various ECMs such as the VGPO and facilitate threat assessment. In any environment, the human ear is a very sensitive detector and an excellent integrator of tones.

4.7.4.3 *Receiver post-detection ECCMs*

Post-detection ECCMs include the well known CFAR family, non-coherent integration, pulse edge tracking (leading edge tracking), and various pulse discrimination techniques. CFAR techniques are not true ECCM techniques, although they can reduce operator and computer load. Skolnik[135] stated that CFAR is not in the same category as other ECCMs. Its reduction of false alarms to the computer and radar scope cleanup is at a penalty. This will be further discussed in Section 4.8.4. Noise spectral distribution can have a severe effect on the performance of certain CFAR circuits. Tong and Steichen[136] analysed the performance of cell averaging, log CFAR, and distribution-free (non-parametric) detection and showed that the false alarm rate of the first two CFAR devices is greatly affected by change of jammer noise distribution. This was based on the authors' assumed Weibull noise distribution. Turner *et al.*[137] introduced the term 'noise quality' and showed that a change of jammer noise quality could result in a 17 dB change in jammer power required.

Pulse discrimination techniques are useful against pulse jamming such as false target generators, and are more generally EMCs. They include pulse length/width discrimination, pulse

frequency discrimination, pulse clipping, etc. Maksimov
described many in this group.

4.7.4.4 *Receiver display ECCMs*

Numerous special display ECCMs have been conceived. Target
strobing displays can be very useful in locating a jammer, but are
not useful if a quiet target is present and standoff jamming is
used. A special separate jamming display can be very beneficial
since some ECCMs remove the jamming so effectively that the
radar may be unaware that jamming is present. Such a separate
display and a special ECCM operator may improve selection of
ECCMs to be employed against specific ECMs.

4.7.5 ECCMS IN THE SYSTEM, OPERATIONAL, AND OTHER ECCMS

We now move outside the radar proper and into both the 'system'
and operational matters. In the system we consider manipulating
radar data in various ways, which is as important as treating the
radar itself since certain benefits may obtain from various
ECCMs in the 'system'. It is important to remember that a
weapon system includes more than just a radar. Accordingly, it is
essential that the radar data be used in such a manner as to
provide maximum benefit to the system, even in the presence of
ECM.

ECCMs in the system, operational and other ECCMs have
been subdivided into radar data manipulation/analysis, target
data from other sources, operational techniques, radar employment, and others. In radar data manipulation, we use *a priori*
knowledge of the characteristics of true targets, such as their
permissible acceleration to determine whether a target is bona
fide. In another situation, we compare indicated target measurements to see whether they are consistent. We may also use target
data from other sources to augment data from a radar. This
combined data may thus permit at least a modicum of weapon
system operation in a hostile environment. Representative
ECCMs in the system and operational and other ECCMs are
shown in Table 4.15[22]. This list is brief and intended to indicate
possibilities for ECCMs in this category.

4.7.5.1 *Radar data manipulation/analysis*

In acceleration limiting, we use knowledge of the behaviour of
true targets and apply limits to the value of measured target

Table 4.15[22] ECCMs in the system and operational and other ECCMs

---

Radar data manipulation/analysis:
  Acceleration limit
  Azimuth blanking
  Azimuth gain reduction
  Beam-to-beam correlation
  Doppler-range rate comparison
  Jammer finder
  (Manually) aided tracking
  Manual rate aided tracking
  Passive angle tracking (PAT)
  Passive detection and tracking
  Prediction computer
  Pulse-to-pulse correlation
  Range/angle rate memory
  Range rate memory
  Velocity tracker

Target data from other sources:
  Acoustic listening
  D/F on VHF communications
  Dual radars
  Laser radar
  Passive tracking/HOJ/TOJ
  Use of data from remote battery
  Use of range from acquisition radar with optical tracker
    instead of tracking radar
  Visual/IR tracking

Operator:
  Training

Operation methods:
  Appropriate assignment of normal operating frequencies to
    various radars
  Intermittent operation of radars
  Minimisation of operating time
  Reservation of certain frequencies for emergencies
  Use of combined ECCMs to meet two combined ECMs
  Use of dummy transmitters to draw ECM to other frequencies

Radar deployment:
  Optimum siting
  Overlapping deployment
  Radar mobility
  Remote location of antenna to protect operators

ESM:
  Monitor A/C communications

Other:
  Attack chaff drop A/C
  Close liaison between development engineers and the field
  Multiple weapon types
  Rapid exploitation of capture of hostile EW and radars
  Strong QRC ECCM research programme
  Tight security on our radar development

---

acceleration. In Doppler-range rate comparison, we differentiate measured range and compare it with Doppler derived range rate as a check on their consistency. This is useful against both range gate stealers (RGPO) and velocity gate stealers (VGPO). It requires that the radar be of the pulse Doppler type. Passive angle tracking (home on jam/track on jam) (HOJ/TOJ) is a very important ECCM against active ECMs where the jammer is aboard the target (SSJ). HOJ/TOJ systems as in missile homing guidance are important ECCMs in that they do not require measurement of range. They depend on measurement of rate of change of line of sight to the target, which is readily extracted from target angular measurements.

4.7.5.2 *Target data from other sources*
Data from other sources can be a very important adjunct to a weapon system. Radar netting with target prediction can be valuable for both low flying aircraft and for ECM. In the latter situation radar strobing from several radars can make possible target location for SSJ targets. Hiner[138] described one method of radar netting. Trunk[139] described the US Navy NTDS radar netting system. Correlation direction finding may also be used to locate jamming targets passively. Norsworthy[140] described such a system. Correlation may also be used to estimate the number of targets in a raid, as described by Hammerlie at RADAR-85.[141] Laser radar is a powerful adjunct to microwave radar, as described by Jelalian[142,143] for short ranges in good weather. Although not mentioned by Jelalian, laser radars can also provide excellent angle tracking. Some European laser range finders also incorporate goniometers for angle measurement.

4.7.5.3 *Operator and operation methods*
In the matter of operational and other ECCMs, the operator has probably been the single most important radar ECCM. A good radar operator can do a very good job of detecting targets amidst jamming. This requires extensive training in real jamming. The past tense of the first sentence in this paragraph should be well noted. Modern radars use synthetic video which takes away from the radar operator the opportunity to serve as a target detector. The addition to early radars of intensity modulated displays such as the PPI and B-scopes did somewhat the same thing to replacement of A-scopes. Some modern radars provide 'raw video' as an optional alternative to synthetic video. Even without raw video,

radar operators should be trained in operation in a severe jamming environment.

There are a number of radar operation methods which should be considered. Some of these are intermittent radar operation, variation of radar operating procedures, minimising of radar operation, and use of dummy transmitters. Radar operation in chaff also requires attention. During World War II, the UK thoroughly tested all their radars and several US radars against chaff[144]. A subsequent UK report[145] contained extensive recommendations for operation of all UK radars in chaff. Although US radars were tested against chaff in the US and some training manuals for radar operation were prepared, they were much less extensive than the UK work. A recent paper[62] presented several ECCM operating techniques in a chaff environment. These include observation of the chaff cloud on the PPI, then looking outside the cloud for stray aircraft, reduction of radar pulse width, and variation of radar operating frequency.

4.7.5.4 *Radar deployment*

Consideration of radar deployment can also be of benefit in an ECM environment. Optimum siting may permit use of terrain features to screen out ECMs. Overlapping radar deployment may permit acceptable target detection from another viewing aspect angle. It is well known that it is very difficult to mask a target at broadside aspect with either chaff or jamming. In any event the radar operators should be remotely located from the operating position to protect them from bomb damage. ESM can be of assistance to radar operations by monitoring of aircraft communications as a means of alerting the radar operators. During World War II Allied aircraft communications over England were shielded from German interception by flying communications jammers on US/UK frequencies over Germany. Allied communications over England were not affected by this jamming, but German intercept receivers were prevented from detecting Allied communications.

4.7.5.5 *Other ECCMs*

In other operational ECCMs, there should be close liaison between development engineers and the military field forces. Sometimes a radar is not properly operated. In other cases, new environments arise, making changes in the radar design necessary. It is often extremely useful to describe to others various anomalous radar operation conditions. Several times during World War II jamming was misinterpreted by untrained radar operators as radar failure.

4.8 ECCM efficacy

4.8.1 GENERAL CONSIDERATIONS

In previous sections we have discussed various ECCM techniques. While the individual ECCM techniques are indeed important, it is essential that their performance in a weapon system be addressed. It will be appreciated that the performance of these ECCM techniques is not equal; some ECCM techniques are better than others against the same ECM. Note that ECCM performance should be considered in terms of some associated weapon system, not merely the radar set alone. A radar set is not an end item; it is almost always today part of a weapon system. Several recent writers on ECCM performance assessment have missed this vital point. Consider for example an air defence system. Suppose ECM reduces the associated search radar detection range to R_1, but the weapon system requires a target detection range of R_D and $R_1 \ll R_D$. Now suppose we add an ECCM to the search radar where its new detection range against the ECM is now doubled from R_1 to $2R_1$, but even so $2R_1 < R_D$. Clearly, this ECCM is inadequate, even though it did double the radar detection range against this ECM. Admittedly, introduction of the associated weapon system performance does complicate this ECCM performance assessment, but it is not an impossible task.

4.8.2 ECM/ECCM MATRICES

The first step in selection of ECCMs to be used in a radar is the establishment of the ECM(s) to be considered. Generally there will be more than one type of ECM specified. These may often be used in combination, e.g. chaff and noise jamming. One may then consult a matrix of ECMs and ECCMs to identify candidate ECCMs for consideration. Many authors have prepared such ECM/ECCM matrices[20,21,57], even prior to US entry into World War II[146] and during the war[147]. Such matrices can serve as starting points to identify candidate ECCMs. It should be recognised that some ECCMs are useful only in certain radar types, e.g. search radars only or pulsed radars only. Most matrices are not so arranged although one was arranged by search and tracking radars[148]. Additionally, most matrices do not indicate compatibility problems of certain ECCMs when used in combinations, e.g. Doppler MTI and frequency agility incompatibility, discussed previously.

4.8.3 MEASURES OF EFFECTIVENESS

ECCM performance assessment requires a measure of effectiveness, or MOE in the terms of operations researchers. Although burnthrough range is frequently used as a MOE for ECMs, it has a number of drawbacks even for ECM performance assessment[149]. Some of these are:

- Its usual form is incomplete.
- Its usual form does not recognise variability of several factors in the burnthrough equation.
- It does not apply to all ECMs.
- In some weapon systems burnthrough may mean nothing.

Modern radars are not an end item alone, but are part of a weapon system.

The usual form of burnthrough range does not include ECCMs in the radar under consideration, although provisions could be made for doing this. If this were done the specific ECCM types included should be stated. The usual form of the burnthrough range does not take into account detection probability, radar antenna elevation beam pattern, variation of target radar cross section with aspect angle, target radar cross section fluctuation, etc. Burnthrough range applies to only 'power type' ECMs, and does not apply to deception ECMs such as false target generators, RGPO, VGPO, chaff, etc. It applies only to search radars or to tracking radars in their lock-on phases, nor does it consider the detection range required by the associated weapon system.

Some weapon systems do not require range measurement, e.g. homing missile systems require only angle measurements (other than a crude one-time range measurement to tell when or whether to fire) in order to determine the rate of change of line of sight to the target from the missile. Initiation of jamming in such systems permits homing on the jammer for an SSJ and usually actually decreases the missile miss distance and increases its kill probability. This obtains since a jammer is normally a point target with practically no glint.

From the above, it will be seen that burnthrough range is not a single valued number and is a very poor MOE even for ECM, to be used with great caution. A proper MOE for ECCM should reflect the performance of an ECCM as part of a weapon system in the presence of ECMs as compared to performance without it. This implies that the ECCM will change the weapon system performance by, for example, a change in first engagement range, in the number of targets killed in an attack, in the weapon system kill probability, or in probability of survival of the attacking aircraft. Mitchell[150] proposed 'Delta P_K' as a MOE for ECCMs. This requires that the weapon system performance be determined for *two* conditions, first with ECM alone, then with ECM and ECCM(s). The resulting change of P_K is then an indicator of the merit of the ECCM(s) involved.

4.8.4 REPRESENTATION OF ECCM PERFORMANCE

Incorporation of the effects of ECCMs in radar performance analysis is very important. Johnston[151] devised the term ECCM improvement factor (EIF) as a means of representing the performance of 'power type' ECCMs. It has been defined by the IEEE[152] as the ratio of the jammer power required to produce a given J/S ratio at the radar receiver with the ECCM switched on to the jammer power required to produce the same J/S ratio without the ECCM. The term EIF was patterned after Steinberg's MTI improvement factor[152]. Several papers have been written recently about the ECCM improvement factor[153–156] and radar performance assessment in an ECM environment[157–158]. Unfortunately, several of these papers indicated a lack of full understanding of the EIF. Consequently, Johnston recently wrote a new paper on properties of the EIF with illustrative applications for its use[159]. This paper also gave equations for the EIF of a number of 'power type' ECCMs. These are shown in Table 4.16.

Analysis of the EIF of frequency agility is critically dependent upon both the radar transmitter characteristics and the characteristics of the jammer and its associated ESM receiver. Bergkvist[70] analysed the performance of combinations of four radar transmitters and two modulators (fixed PRF and jittered PRF) against four types of jammers. Results were presented in terms of required jammer RF bandwidth in MHz. In some cases, use of frequency agility greatly increased required jammer RF bandwidth. Resulting equivalent EIF values ranged from 0 to 24 dB in the cases examined by Bergkvist. In one interesting case, use of

Table 4.16[22]   Illustrative EIF and chaff equations

$\text{EIF}_{FA} = 10 \log N - 10 \log TB_2/2$

$N = \dfrac{BT}{2}$, B = band extent

$\text{EIF}_{Pavg} = \text{EIF}_{Ppk} + \text{EIF}_{PRF} + \text{EIF}_T$

$\text{EIF}_{Ppk} = 10 \log P_2/P_1$

$\text{EIF}_{PRF} = 10 \log f_2/f_1 + 5 \log N_2/N_1$

$\text{EIF}_T = 10 \log T_2/T_1 - 10 \log T_2 B_2$

$\text{EIF}_{PN} = 20 \log L$

$L = (2^n - 1)$

$\text{EIF}_{ANT} = 10 \log CR$

$\text{EIF}_{SL} = -2\,(G_1 - G_2) + SL_1 - SL_2 + 5 \log \dfrac{N_2}{N_1}$

$\text{EIF}_{mti} = I$

$\text{EIF}_T = 10 \log \dfrac{T_1}{T_2} - 10 \log \dfrac{T_2 B_2}{2}$

$\text{EIF}_R = 20 \log \dfrac{R_1}{R_2}$

$\text{EIF}_A = 10 \log \dfrac{A_1}{A_2} = 5 \log \dfrac{N_2}{N_1}$

$\text{EIF}_E = 10 \log \dfrac{E_1}{E_2}$

PRF jitter with frequency agility produced an EIF of 17 dB over use of frequency agility alone.

In the employment of frequency agility, there are potentially available $N = BT/2$ operating channels in a radar frequency band, where B is the radar band extent, and T is the radar pulse duration. The value of B varies from 185 MHz at L-band to 2180 MHz at X-band in accordance with the ITU frequency allocations for radiolocation (*cf.* table 1 in ref. 160). For $T = 0.5$ µs and assuming an achievable RF bandwidth of 10% for a TWT transmitter[63], there would be approximately 225 potential operating channels at X-band. If the jammer is assumed to concentrate its power in the radar passband (i.e. $B_j = B_r$), $\text{EIF}_{FA} = 10 \log N - 10 \log TB_2/2$ where B_2 is the RF bandwidth of the radar receiver with frequency agility. The second term accounts for *instantaneous* RF bandwidth of the radar receiver with frequency agility. If a tunable pre-selector is used, the receiver RF bandwidth can be made $= 2/T$, causing this last term in the above EIF expression to be zero.

The EIF for radar transmitter average power output increase can be determined for the several possible changes in peak power, increase of pulsewidth, or PRF. Gardner[63] examined possible transmitter ECCMs in a radar through use of all three of these factors:

$$EIF_{Pavg} = EIF_{Ppk} + EIF_{PRF} + EIF_T$$

$$EIF_{Ppk} = 10 \log P_2/P_1$$

$$EIF_{PRF} = 10 \log f_2/f_1 + 5 \log N_2/N_1$$

where f is the PRF and N is the number of pulses integrated non-coherently by the radar. The second term in the third equation (which was not given by Gardner) arises since the number of pulses available for integration (pulses per beamwidth) is a function of radar PRF. Accordingly, an increase of PRF increases both the average power output and the number of pulses available for integration:

$$EIF_T = 10 \log T_2/T_1 - 10 \log T_2 B_2$$

where T is the radar pulse duration and B_2 is the new radar receiver bandwidth. This second term (also not given by Gardner) shows the importance of changing receiver bandwidth when changing pulse duration. The EIF_T applies for only active ECM (jamming); for operation in a chaff environment, $EIF_T = 10 \log T_1/T_2$, since the radar illumination volume which affects radar S/C ratio is a function of T[161]. Thus in a chaff environment, a short pulse is advantageous[62].

Changes in PRF were addressed above. Doubling the radar PRF to double the average power output as discussed by Gardner will also halve the unambiguous radar range. Techniques for resolving range ambiguity are well known. It is possible that the radar detection range with ECCM may be less than the new unambiguous range, ameliorating the range ambiguity problem.

Comparison of different possible radar waveforms may also be made by the EIF. Gager[86] showed different radar designs for several radar waveforms without giving a numeric comparison of the ECCM aspects. For pulse compression radar the EIF is $10 \log C$, where C is the radar pulse compression ratio. For pseudo-noise radar, Albanese[81] showed that $EIF_{PN} = 20 \log L$, where $L = (2^n - 1)$ and n is the number of shift register stages. For $n = 6$, and $L = 63$, EIF = 36 dB. Reid[76] and Fahey and O'Reilly[84] gave the considerations for choosing the value of L and other design relations for a pseudo-noise radar.

In conical scan angle tracking radars, one could conceive of a 'threshold EIF'. Cikalo and Greenbaum[41] showed that their conical scan radar broke lock for a J/S ratio of 17.5 dB. Using break-lock as a criterion, one could examine various ECCMs for their effectiveness in reducing the ability of various jammers to achieve this threshold value. A number of such ECCMs were discussed in Section 4.7.3.1.

In antenna main lobe characteristics, $\text{EIF}_{\text{ANT}} = 10 \log CR$, where CR is the main beam notcher cancellation ratio or cross polarisation ratio, as appropriate. Change of antenna azimuth or elevation beamwidth is a possible ECCM against chaff since the radar illumination volume (and hence the S/C ratio) is a function of the product of the two beamwidths. The chaff illumination volume is normally computed using the 3 dB beamwidths. This is inappropriate for shaped elevation beam antennas, e.g. the popular cosecant^2 pattern when the target is not at maximum antenna gain, for instance near the horizon.

In antenna sidelobe characteristics, $\text{EIF}_{\text{SL}} = 10 \log CR$ where CR is the cancellation ratio achievable from the sidelobe canceller. For sidelobe reduction:

$$\text{EIF}_{\text{SL}} = SL_1 - SL_2 + G_2 - G_1 + 5 \log A_2/A_1$$

where SL is the antenna sidelobe level in dB below the main lobe antenna gain, G is the mainbeam gain in dB, and A is the antenna azimuth beamwidth. This expression results from the reduction in antenna sidelobes which is accompanied by a mainbeam gain loss and an increase in the beamwidth. The last factor causes an increase in the number of pulses available for integration. An antenna with Gaussian pattern and uniform illumination taper has its first sidelobe at 13 dB, hence a 50 dB SL antenna would have an EIF of 37 dB over a simple antenna if only sidelobe reduction were considered. In a benign environment the term $(G_2 - G_1)$ must be increased by a factor of 2 for identical transmitting and receiving antennas. In the chaff environment,

$$\text{EIF}_{\text{SL}} = \text{EIF}_{\text{A}} + \text{EIF}_{\text{E}}$$

where

$\text{EIF}_{\text{A}} = 10 \log A_1/A_2 + 5 \log N_2/N_1$ and
$\text{EIF}_{\text{E}} = 10 \log E_1/E_2$

where A is the antenna azimuth beamwidth and E is the antenna elevation beamwidth.

180 *Modern Radar Techniques*

The EIF of most of the receiver ECCM techniques has not been established. Some of these are not amenable to mathematical analysis, but must be obtained experimentally. Some are functions not only of receiver J/S ratio, but also of jammer noise spectral characteristics as was indicated in Section 4.7.4.3.

The many CFAR circuits require a separate analysis, as can be seen by the Tong and Steichen paper cited above. The Dicke fix (*cf* Section 4.7.4.1), which is sometimes called the Lamb suppressor, is a widely known CFAR. Maksimov et al.[16] presented a brief analysis of the Dicke fix which he referred to as the WLN. The analysis considered the WLN output S/J ratio as a function of several quantities, including the ratio of bandwidths B_w/B_n and the input J/S ratio in his equation 8.3.15 (p. 326 in Ref. 16). Since this equation involves both S/J output and J/S input, an EIF may be determined. The resulting expression indicates that the EIF for the Dicke fix is a function of the input J/S. This was anticipated earlier[151]. By conversion of the ordinate y of Fig. 8.7 of Maksimov to decibels, it is found that for the cases shown there, an output S/J of 13 dB approximately corresponding to $y = 4.5$ is achieved only if $B_w/B_n > 12$ or if the input J/S is very small. The 13 dB S/J output corresponds to a P_d of 0.5 and a P_{fa} of 10^{-9} from the figure of Toomay[162] to be discussed below. Also from Fig. 8.7 it can be ascertained that the EIF decreases with an increase of S/J output.

Generally, CFAR circuits actually introduce a loss in radar detection performance as a penalty for maintenance of a constant false alarm rate. This may be seen from the radar detection probability curves when plotted with S/N as a parameter, as was done by Toomay[162]. For a detection probability P_d of 0.9, P_{fa} of 10^{-10} requires an increase of 3 dB S/N over a P_{fa} of 10^{-4}. This difference is slightly greater at say P_d of 0.5. The CFAR penalty, a negative EIF, may be obtained from curves such as Toomay's.

Moving target indicator (MTI) techniques are frequently used as an ECCM against chaff[62]. Here $EIF_{mti} = I$, where I is the MTI improvement factor as analysed by Shrader[163]. The MTI used against chaff must be clutter locked/referenced, since chaff is generally moving rather than fixed as in land clutter. If the radar also uses frequency agility to combat active ECM, the MTI must be compatible with frequency agility. This problem has been addressed in Section 4.7.2.1.

An estimate of the total value of EIF needed to overcome a given ECM may be determined as follows. In an air defence system let the required detection range of the associated search radar for desired target intercept point be R_D and let the actual detection range with jamming be R_J. Clearly, we must increase the detection range by 20 log R_D/R_J. In principle we could employ several 'power type' ECCMs whose total EIF would equal the above value. For example, we might increase the peak power output by using a transmitter output tube having higher peak power output, or increase the radar PRF, or increase the pulse width as Gardner did[63]. The above ratio is not the true value of total EIF needed. It will be appreciated that at the two different points P_D and P_J on the path of the attacking target corresponding to the respective ranges R_D and R_J, the target will have different aspect angles and different elevation angles. Consequently we must add delta sigma and delta G_A to the above ratio. These two factors correct for the changes of radar cross section (σ) and antenna gain (G_A), because with the target in its new position, the cross section and the antenna gain will have changed.

As a practical matter, Gardner[63] showed that in the cases he studied, his EIF_{Pavg} provided less than 10 dB of EIF. Dax[112] presented representative performance data showing typical J/S ratios in search radars of 20 dB or greater, making Gardner's transmitter power output improvements inadequate. Prior and Woodward[57] reached the conclusion for their LREW (long range early warning) radar that to increase the radar power output or antenna gain in an airborne ECM environment is inadequate. Clearly, other means of weapon system improvement must be sought other than 'power type' ECCMs.

It will be appreciated that the EIF being a power ratio in decibels is mathematically equivalent to a partial derivative. Subramanian[155] has presented the equations for the partial derivatives for a number of ECCMs. It can be readily shown that the EIF equations in Table 4.16, when taken as individual terms, are mathematically the same as the partial derivatives of Subramanian. The equations in Table 4.16 are actually total derivatives in that they include other effects, as indicated above, which were not taken into account by Subramanian.

4.8.5 THE JAMMING-TO-SIGNAL (J/S) RATIO

The J/S ratio is an important parameter in both the design and the analysis of radar performance as well as an indicator of actual

radar performance in the field. It also forms the basis for determination of radar burnthrough range, and is used by ECM system
designers in the design of various repeater jammers. J/S ratio
when expressed numerically corresponds to the reciprocal of the
well known S/N ratio in the benign environment. Since the jamming signal at the radar arrives at the radar receiver on a one-way
transmission, whereas the reflected signal from the target
involves two-way transmission, it will be appreciated that the
jamming signal is generally greater than the target signal. Hence
the use of J/S rather than S/J. This is especially true at long
ranges. Strictly speaking, one should properly use the ratio J + S/S,
where the operation J + S is performed numerically, not logarithmically. Generally J $\gg$ S, hence J + S $\doteq$ J.

Usually J/S is expressed in decibels, i.e. 10 log J/S where J and
S are both numeric power levels at an appropriate place in the
radar. A positive value of J/S in dB indicates that J > S, while a
negative dB value indicates J < S. Use of the decibel form of J/S
greatly simplifies actual J/S computation while facilitating consideration of various tradeoffs. (Note that doubling radar power
output has a very different cost than say doubling antenna gain!) It
is convenient to express the J/S ratio in a radar at the input of the IF
amplifier. Here J/S ratio may be easily measured, most of the various receiver signal processing ECCMs have still to take effect, and
the very important detection probability process is not involved.

We begin the J/S ratio computation process by determining the
magnitude at the IF amplifier input of the signal received from
the target:

$$S = P_T G_T G_R \lambda^2 \sigma / R_T^4 (4\pi)^3 L_T L_R \qquad (1)$$

Similarly, the power received from the jammer is expressed by:

$$J = P_J G_J G_{RJ} \lambda^2 B_R / R_J^2 (4\pi)^2 L_J L_R B_J \qquad (2)$$

Note that R_J in Equation 2 is not necessarily equal to R_T in
Equation 1. Similarly, G_{RJ} is not necessarily equal to G_R in
Equation 1.

Division of Equation 2 by Equation 1 and simplifying yields the
numeric expression for J/S:

$$J/S = (P_J/P_T)(G_J/G_T)(G_{RJ}/G_R)$$
$$(R_T/R_J)^2 (R_T^2/\sigma)(B_R/B_J)(4\pi)(L_T/L_J L_R) \qquad (3)$$

For purposes of comparison, similar quantities for the jammer
and the radar are shown as ratios in this equation. It applies for

standoff jamming (SOJ) in the radar antenna main lobe. For SOJ in the radar antenna sidelobes, $G_R = G_{SL}$.

For self-screening jamming (SSJ), $R_J = R_T$ and $G_{RJ} = G_R$, making Equation 3 become:

$$J/S = (P_J/P_T)(G_{RJ}/G_T)(R_T^2/\sigma)(B_R/B_J)(L_T/L_J L_R)4\pi \quad (4)$$

Crossover range, i.e. the range at which $J/S = 1$, is of interest. For ranges less than the crossover range, $J/S < 1$ or $S/J > 1$. Crossover range referenced to the IF amplifier input can be given as follows:

(a) *Self-screening*:

$$R_T^2 = (B_J/B_R)(P_T/P_J)(G_T/G_J)(L_J L_R/L_T)(\sigma/4\pi)$$

(b) *Standoff jamming off boresight axis*:

$$R_T^4/R_J^2 = (B_J/B_R)(P_T/P_J)(G_T/G_J)(G_R/G_{SL})(L_J L_R/L_T)(\sigma/4\pi)$$

(c) *Standoff jamming on boresight axis*:

$$R_T^4/R_J^2 = (B_J/B_R)(P_T/P_J)(G_T/G_J)(L_J L_R/L_T)(\sigma/4\pi)$$

As indicated previously, jammers are often used for deception purposes. Resulting J/S ratios for their use are important in determining whether the induced false target signal at the victim radar will be of sufficient strength to be detected by the radar (but not too strong to overpower the true target signal), or in the case of an inverse gain jammer, of sufficient level to cause the radar to break lock or to induce sufficient angle tracking errors. For transponder operation, the radar signal received at the transponder input must be of sufficient level to trigger the responder. Here, the well known radar beacon equation (actually Equation 2) applies with the required condition of $P_{REC} > P_{MIN}$, where the latter is the transponder triggering sensitivity. Resulting J/S ratio at the victim radar receiver IF amplifier input may be obtained from Equation 3 when the jamming is in the radar sidelobe, and from Equation 4 when the jamming is in the main lobe and the jammer is on the attacking aircraft.

There are two cases of repeater jammer operation. At close range, the repeater amplifier may be saturated, but at longer range the repeater will generally be unsaturated. In the saturated case the J/S ratio at the victim radar may be obtained from the above equations. Equation 3 applies for jamming in the antenna sidelobes, while Equation 4 applies for jamming in the radar main lobe if the jammer is located on the attacking aircraft. For unsaturated repeater operation in the radar main lobe, we must modify Equation 3 by using G_X (repeater unsaturated gain), G_{J1} (repeater receiving antenna gain), G_{J2} (repeater transmitting antenna gain), and L_X (repeater losses). The somewhat unlikely Equation 5 results[22]:

$$J/S_U = G_X G_{J1} G_{J2} W^2 / 4\pi\sigma L_X \qquad (5)$$

Note that J/S for the unsaturated repeater is not a function of range. Accordingly, we could use an appropriate missile guidance simulation to find what value of required radar angular tracking error at a specified range would be needed to cause a specified missile miss distance. From a simulation of Cikalo and Greenbaum discussed below, we could determine the J/S which would produce that tracking error. From Equation 5 the necessary repeater characteristics, such as repeater gain, could then be ascertained.

4.8.6 RADAR SIMULATION

Radar performance assessment is accomplished through simulation. Table 4.17[22] lists representative radar simulation types. The General Electric Electronic Systems Evaluator (GEESE) is an example of the use of a general purpose analogue computer such as the Electronics Associates PACE for the simulation of the interaction of ECM with a radar. Although designed to operate at d.c., many analogue computers will operate at frequencies up to about 100 Hz. Use of frequency scaling techniques permits simulation of a radar (or other electromagnetic radiating and recep-

Table 4.17[22]   Radar-ECM simulation techniques

Analogue:
  Scaled frequency (GEESE)

Digital:
  Digital model of analogue process
  Digital solution of J/S and detection
  Digital solution using waveform math models
  War games

Special:
  Oscillator with digital control

Equipment:
  Equipment modules with digital control

---

tion equipment) on a general purpose analogue computer. If the radar IF frequency is 30 MHz, a scaling factor of 10^6 results in a scaled IF frequency of 30 Hz. Various elements of the radar and the ECM such as a noise jammer, local oscillators, mixers, band pass filters, IF amplifiers, discriminators, etc., can be represented by standard apparatus in the analogue computer. In some cases this is done directly, e.g. noise sources, oscillators, and servo multipliers are available on most analogue computers. The equivalents of other radar elements may be modelled through use of integrators, summing amplifiers, coefficient potentiometers, etc., on the analogue computer.

The principal advantage of this technique is that the characteristics of a radar/ECM may be changed by a twist of knob(s) and the effect of the change may be noted by rerunning the simulation. Accordingly, it makes an excellent radar design tool. Disadvantages are the inability to include actual hardware in the loop, and that the weapon system may not be directly included. Lambert[164] described such a simulation and showed its application to an FM radio set. As he indicated, utilisation of GEESE requires only knowledge of the transfer functions of the elements of a radar; it is not necessary to have the complete schematic diagram. The GEESE technique readily permits verification of the data supplied and estimation of missing values. Unfortunately, the GEESE facility has been dismantled, but it is believed that other US firms have employed scaled frequency simulation techniques on their own facilities.

Digital techniques are widely used for radar/ECM simulation. The first such entry in Table 4.17 uses a general purpose digital computer to model an analogue process. Several digital computer programs have been written for this purpose. Cikalo and Greenbaum[41] described the simulation of an inverse gain jammer against a conventional conical scan tracking radar through the use of the IBM CSMP (Continuous System Modeling Program) on an IBM Model 1103 general purpose digital computer. Their results vividly showed that a J/S of 17 dB could cause the radar to break lock in angle tracking. Lesser values of J/S could induce significant tracking errors in both azimuth and elevation. As in the previously described GEESE, only transfer functions were used here.

This simulation apparently used a constant value of radar cross section. Additionally, the real world effects of J/S variation with range were not represented. As indicated in Section 4.8.5, the

repeater jammer would be expected to be unsaturated at long
ranges, but probably saturated at short ranges. Accordingly, in
actual situations tracking accuracy would be independent of
range until the repeater became saturated. Establishment of the
range at which break lock occurs would depend on repeater input
level required for saturation. The actual repeater input signal
level is of course a function of range squared. By proper modification, the simulation of Cikalo and Greenbaum could provide a
plot of tracking errors as a function of range, with an indication of
break lock range. Since weapon kill probability is the desired end
result, this simulation should be combined with a missile guidance
simulation to obtain the effects of actual inverse gain repeater
jamming on weapon system miss distance.

Digital simulation of the J/S equation, followed by detection
probability computation with ECCM effects included, is widely
used to determine radar detection range in an ECM environment.
It is essential that the simulation include the trajectory of the
approaching aircraft, the radar elevation angle antenna pattern,
aircraft radar cross section pattern as functions of aspect angles,
ECCM effects, and various individual radar losses. Boothe[165]
described such a simulation. His simulation is noteworthy in that
he solved the equations of Marcum and Swerling directly in the
computer program at each time step for the approaching target
computation rather than using table look-ups.

Digital simulation using waveform mathematical models have
been described by Hancock *et al.*[166] and by Gutsche *et al.*[167]. In
this technique, mathematical models are prepared for various
radar elements. In a typical radar simulation the appropriate
simulations are utilised to represent the effects of the various
radar elements. Hancock *et al.* showed the spectrum of a 15 bit
binary phase code as a function of frequency and the decoder
output waveform envelope of one radar generated by use of his
simulation models. Gutsche *et al.* showed results of standoff
jamming on the detection of aircraft flights from two different
directions on a naval aircraft search radar. In another simulation,
self-screening jamming was employed. This simulation was noteworthy in that it included aircraft radar cross section variation.
The detailed simulation models of Hancock *et al.* are available
from NTIS; however, the models of Gutsche *et al.* have not been
published.

The effects of radar(s) are also included in 'war games'. Unfortunately in most of these the radar is often represented in a very

gross way, e.g. it is unjammed, or it is jammed at specified fixed ranges. This is clearly unrealistic. Admittedly, a war game model is very complex. Even so, such gross representation does not reflect performance in the real world.

A special simulation using an oscillator under control of a digital computer has been developed by the CALSPAN Corporation. Here, the oscillator frequency and power output at various instants are determined by the associated digital computer using the J/S ratio equation. This enables representation of several jammers against several radars. It also permits employment of actual radar displays with operators.

Use of actual radar operators in a radar/ECM simulation can be very important both for target detection with 'raw' video, and for situations where the operator provides a tracking function or is the weapon systems loop. Pritsker *et al.*[168] described the simulation of a GCI (ground controlled intercept) system wherein the radar operator issues vectoring commands to the associated interceptor aircraft. This simulation is noteworthy in that the actual operator was included in the simulation and that the indicated final results were bomber probability of survival. Interceptor weapon kill probability as a function of aspect angle was also included. This simulation did not include effects of friendly ECM against bomber navigation systems or hostile ECM against friendly ground-to-air communications or against the indicated interceptor AI radar.

The importance of interactions of radar and associated weapon systems cannot be overemphasised. The case of interaction of an ARM (anti-radiation missile) in flight with a radar and its dummy transmitter is of great current importance. Barbour and Radford[169] recently presented very spectacular results of such a dynamic simulation, though for security reasons the results were presented in only very general terms. The paper gave no details of the simulation model other than stating that well known mathematical representations were used.

The last radar/ECM simulation technique of Table 4.17 uses equipment modules with digital control. This is an important technique. The associated digital computer permits inclusion of associated weapon systems effects. It also permits employment of actual ECM hardware as well as actual radar hardware elements. For maximum utility, the various radar modules should be designed with variable characteristics, e.g. the receiver IF amplifiers should have variable bandwidth and gain. These variations

Table 4.18[22]   Principal radar characteristics

GENERAL DATA					
Nomenclature:			Category:		
Functional description:					
Manufacturer and address:					
Dates of manufacture			Quantity manufactured:		

TRANSMITTER					
Primary users:			STATUS		
Freq. band:	Tuning rg. (GHz)	P_t (kW)	P_{av} (W)	τ (μs)	f_r (pps)
Waveform:					
No. of freq. and mode of use:					
Emission band (MHz)	Freq. source:	Output tube:		L_t (dB)	

ANTENNA									
Type and shape:									
Trans.	$w \times h$ or D(m)	Type of feed:	θ_a (deg)	θ_e (deg)	G_t (dB)	at E (deg)	No. of beams	Pol.	L_a (dB)
			G_s (az) (dB)	G_s (el) (dB)	G_s (dB)	No. of elem.	$d\lambda$ (hor.)	$d\lambda$ (vert.)
Rec.	$w \times h$ or D(m)	Type of feed:	θ_a (deg)	θ_e (deg)	G_r (dB)	at E (deg)	No. of beams	Pol	L_a (dB)
			G_s (az)	G_s (el)	G_s	No. of	$d\lambda$	$d\lambda$

RECEIVER-PROCESSOR

method:

						(az)	(el)	(deg)
A_m (deg)	E_m (deg)	W_a (deg/s)	W_e (deg/s)	t_s (s)	t_o (s)	f_s (Hz)	L_K (dB)	θ_k (deg)

No. of rec:

B_v (MHz)	F_n (dB)	T_e (K)	L_r (dB)	T_r (K)	T_a (K)	T_s (K)	B_n (MHz)	L_m (dB)

Type of proc:

n	n_r	τ_g (μs)	t_e (μs)	n_t	B_f (Hz)	f_e (Hz)	T_n (μs)	G_s (dB)
p	L_c (dB)	L_e (dB)	L_g (dB)		L_x (dB)	M or C_B (dB)	L_{mf} (dB)	I_m (dB)

Type of detector:

							$D_x(50)$ (dB)	SCV (dB)
							$D_t(50)$ (dB)	P_{fa}

OUTPUT

Form of output data or display:

Threshold control:

Angle f_x (Hz)	σ_A (deg)	σ_E (deg)	Range f_x (Hz)	σ_r (m)	F req. f_x (Hz)	σ_f (Hz)		
Range for unity snr (km)	Range for P_d = 0.5 (km)			Range for σ_A, σ_E (km)		INFORMATION SOURCE		DATE

MISC

Gross (kg)	Ant. (kg)	Input (V)	Input (kVA)	Input (Hz)	Input ϕ	Related types:	D_m (dB)	

could of course be accomplished by auxiliary variable bandwidth filters and attenuators.

4.8.6.1 *Radar characteristics*

In all radar simulations it is essential that the radar be properly represented, with all the necessary radar characteristics included. Table 4.18[22] is a list of the principal radar characteristics required for a radar simulation. These characteristics must be properly defined[22], and great care must be taken in selection of the values used for the various parameters, 'design goals' being clearly differentiated from production values, and accuracy figures established for each item. It is necessary to represent some items by tables of values or functions, e.g. the antenna gain patterns as functions of elevation angle in shaped beam radars.

4.8.6.2 *Target characteristics*

Similar care must be taken in representing the target characteristics. A single value of radar cross section is insufficient. RCS must be given as function(s) of aspect angle(s). Target fluctuation must also be expressed as function(s) of aspect angle(s). A statement that the target is a single Swerling fluctuation model is unrealistic. Utilisation of target characteristics as function(s) of aspect angle(s) requires that a target trajectory be employed as part of an appropriate scenario.

References

1. Price, A. *History of US Electronic Warfare*, Vol. 1, Association of Old Crows (1984).
2. Johnston, S. L. 'Radar ECCM History'. *IEEE NAECON-80 Record*, 1210–14, May (1980).
3. Johnston, S. L. 'WW-II Radar ECCM History', *IEEE RADAR-85 Conf. Rec. Supp.* S-2–S-7 (1985).
4. Neale, B. T. 'CH – The First Operational Radar', *GEC J. of Res.*, 3, 2, 73–83 (1985).
5. Johnston, S. L. 'Soviet Electronic Warfare – A Review of Published Material', *Int. Defense Rev.*, Supplement No. 2, 'Electronic Warfare', 9–14 (1985).
6. Johnston, S. L. 'Philosophy of ECCM Utilization', *Elec. Warfare Mag.*, 7, 9, 59–61, May/June, reprinted in Ref. 15 (1975).
7. 'Dictionary of Military and Associated Terms', Department of Defense, Joint Chief of Staff, *JCS Pub-1*, Sept. (1974).

8. Johnston, S. L. 'CESM, A New Category of ECCM', unpublished manuscript (1985).

9. 'Electronic Warfare Definitions', *Elec. Warfare Mag.*, **2**, 4, 29 (1970).

10. Chin, H. A. (ed.) 'Summary Technical Report of NDRC Div 15, Radio Countermeasures', *NDRC Div 15* **1**, DTIC AD 221601 (1946).

11. Ridenour, L. N. (ed.) *Massachusetts Institute of Technology Radiation Laboratory Series* (28 vols.) McGraw-Hill, New York (1946).

12. Boyd, J. A., *et al. Electronic Countermeasures*, Ann Arbor, Mich., Univ. of Michigan IST 71204 R 1961, DTIC AD 357877, republished by Peninsula Publishing Co.

13. Schlesinger, R. J. *Principles of Electronic Warfare*, Prentice-Hall, Englewood Cliffs (1961).

14. Schleher, D. C. *Introduction to Electronic Warfare*, Artech House, Dedham, Ma., in press.

15. Johnston, S. L. *Radar Electronic Counter-Countermeasures*, Artech House, Dedham, Ma. (1979); Robert E. Krieger, Melbourne, Fa. (1985).

16. Maksimov, M. V. *et al. Radar Antijamming Techniques*, Moscow (in Russian); English language translation, Artech House, Dedham, Ma. (1979).

17. Tispouras, D. *et al.* 'ECM Technique Generation: Dual Coherent Source and Offboard Expendable Techniques', *Microwave J.*, **27**, 9, 38–73, Sept. (1984).

18. 'Special Issue on Electronic Warfare', *IEE Proc., F, Comm. Radar, and Sig. Proc.*, **129**, Part F, 3, June (1982).

19. Maksimov, M. V. *et al.* 'A Soviet View of ECM and ECCM', *J. of Elec. Def.*, 53–60, Jan. (1982). (Chapter on ECM from *Radar Antijamming Techniques*, English language translation, Artech House, Dedham, Ma.)

20. Brick, D. B. and Galejs, J. 'Radar Interference and its Reduction', *The Sylvania Technologist*, **11**, 3, 96–108, July (1958), reprinted in Ref. 15.

21. Johnston, S. L. 'Radar Electronic Counter-Countermeasures', *IEEE Trans.*, **AES-14**, 1, 109–117, Jan. (1978), reprinted in Ref. 15.

22. Johnston, S. L. 'Radar/Defense Systems Electronic Counter-Countermeasures', *Course Notes*, Continuing Education Institute Course ENG 216.

23. Hartman, R. 'ESM Receiver Overview', *Proc. Mil. Microwaves Conf. (MM-78)*, 26, London (abstract only), Oct. (1978).

24. Harper, T. 'Receivers Evolve to Era of Computer Controlled Hybridization', *Microwave Syst. News*, 112–22, Aug. (1979).

25. Van Nieuwenhuizen, E. 'Wide-open and Scanning ESM Systems', *Proc. Military Microwaves Conf. (MM-80)*, 169–83, Oct. (1980).
26. Andrews, R. S. 'Design Aspects for ESM Systems', *loc. cit.* 151–156.
27. Vakin, S. A. and Shustov, L. N. *Principles of Jamming and Electronic Reconnaissance*, Vols. 1 and 2, English Language translation, Moscow (1968).
28. Wiley, R. G. *Electronic Intelligence: The Analysis of Radar Signals*, Artech House, Dedham, Ma. (1982).
29. Wiley, R. G. *Electronic Intelligence: The Interception of Radar Signals*, Artech House, Dedham, Ma. (1985).
30. Fitts, R. E., Maj. *Fundamentals of Electronic Warfare*, US Air Force Academy, March 1, 1972 edition.
31. Johnston, S. L. 'Hostile ECCM: Potential Achilles Heel for US ESM/ECM', *Microwave J.*, **27**, 6, 41–48, June (1984).
32. *Radar Antijamming*, US Air Force Manual AFM 100–4, June (1954).
33. Hoffmann-Heyden, A. E. 'Antijamming Techniques at the German AAA Radars in World War II', *RADAR-85 Supp.*, S-22–32 (1985); also IEE Seminar on History of Radar (1985).
34. Lake, J. S. 'Observable Countermeasures', *Proc. Military Microwaves Conf. (MM-84)*, 391–6 (1984).
35. Parkhomenko, A. 'Interference and Interference Suppression in Radio Equipment', Radio, JPRS 51003, Moscow (1970).
36. Steer, D. J. 'Airborne Microwave ECM', *Proc. Military Microwaves 78 (MM-78)*, 29–38 (1978), reprinted in Ref. 15
37. Pett, M. C. D. 'System Performance Trade-offs–Responsive and Repeater Jammers', *Proc. Military Microwaves (MM-80)*, 19–27, London, Oct. (1980).
38. Dodington, S. H. 'Development of "Moonshine" in World War II', *RADAR-85 Supp.*, S-19–21; also IEE Seminar on History of Radar (1985).
39. Bryant, K. O. 'Programmable 20-Bit Pseudorandom (PRF) Generator', *US Patent # 3,662,386*, May 9 (1972).
40. Grant, P. M. *et al.* 'Introduction to Electronic Warfare', *Special Issue on Electronic Warfare, IEE Proc.-F*, **129**, Part F, 113–132, June (1982).
41. Cikalo, J. and Greenbaum, M. 'Radar/ECM Computer Modeling', *IEEE NAE-CON-75 Record*, 431–7 (1975); also reprinted in Ref. 15.
42. For example, US Patents 3,852,747; 3,896,438; 4,037,227; 4,126,862, and 4,314,248. In: Johnston, S. L. 'Tracking Radar Electronic Counter-Countermeasures against Inverse Gain Jammers', *Radar-82, IEE Conf. Pub. No. 216*, 444–7; also reprinted in Ref. 15.

43. Bitters, B. C. F. 'Chaff', *Special Issue on Electronic Warfare, IEE Proc.-F*, **129**, Part F, 197–201, June (1982).

44. Johnston, S. L. 'Correspondence' (Comments on 'Chaff' in *IEE Proc.-F*, **129**, 129–201 (1982)), *IEE Proc.-F*, 4, 355–6, June (1983).

45. Mahaffey, M. 'Electrical Fundamentals of Countermeasure Chaff', in *The International Countermeasure Handbook*, 512–7, 2nd Ed., Eustace, H. F., ed., EW Communications Inc. (1976).

46. Mitchell, P. K. and Short, R. H. 'Chaff Primer', in *The International Countermeasure Handbook*, 316–24, 6th Ed., Eustace, H. F., ed., EW Communications Inc. (1980).

47. Eustace, H. F., ed. *International Countermeasures Handbook*, 115, 3rd Ed., EW Communications Inc. (1977).

48. 100*ff, loc. cit.*, 6th Ed. (1980).

49. Rhodes, J. D. 'A Review of Radar Warning Receivers', *Military Microwaves (MM-84) Conf. Proc.*, 3–12 (1984).

50. Wiseman, C. 'Raw Audio Processing For Radar Warning Receivers', *International Countermeasures Handbook*, 331–334, 10th Ed., EW Communications Inc. (1985).

51. 'Fine Resolution Angle of Arrival is the Key to Sorting Agile Threats', *loc. cit.*, 324–329.

52. Forrest, J. R. 'Techniques For Low Probability of Intercept Radar', *Proc. MSAT '83*, 496–501.

53. Wiley, R. G. 'The Interceptor's Response to LPI Radar', *Proc. MSAT-83*, Addendum.

54. Forrest, J. R. 'Some Considerations for Low Probability of Intercept Radar', *Defense Elec.*, 97–103, Aug. (1983).

55. Shenoy, R. P. 'Evolution of Radar: An Indian View Point', *Int. Conf. on Radar*, 5–8, Paris, May (1984).

56. Schleher, D. C. 'Low Probability of Intercept Radar', *RADAR-85 Rec.*, 346–9.

57. Prior, J. R. and Woodward, N. 'Performance of Current Radar Systems in an EW Environment', *Proc. Military Microwaves-78, (MM-78)*, 39–50 (1987), reprinted in Ref. 15.

58. Ewell, G. W. *Radar Transmitters*, McGraw-Hill, New York (1981).

59. Vyse, B. *et al.* 'The Use of Magnetrons in Coherent Radar Transmitters', *Proc. MM-82*, 217–222, Oct. (1982).

60. Weill, T. A. 'Applying the Amplitron and Stabilotron to MTI Radar Systems', *IRE National Conv. Rec.*, Part 5, 120–130 (1958).

61. Johnston, S. L. *Millimeter Wave Radar*, Artech House, Dedham, Ma. (1980).

62. Johnston, S. L. 'Radar Electronic Counter-Countermeasures Against Chaff', *Proc. Int. Conf. on Radar*, 517–22, Paris, France, May 21–24 (1984).

63. Gardner, W. L. 'Effect of ECCM Techniques on Transmitter Requirements', reprinted in Ref. 15.

64. Larson, R. W. 'Tuning Mechanism', *US Patent No. 2,603,744*, issued July 15 (1952).
65. Carr, P. H. 'The Application of SAW Technology to Radar ECCM', reprinted in Ref. 15.
66. Martin, J. R. *The Frequency Agile Magnetron Story*, Varian Beverly Division Brochure, undated.
67. Fuller, J. B. and Martin, J. R. *Introduction to Frequency Agile Radar Systems*, Varian Beverly Division Brochure, undated.
68. Taylor, J. W. Jr, and Sinclair, A. L. 'Dual Frequency Transmission Apparatus for Frequency-Agile Radar Systems Utilizing MTI Techniques', *US Patent No. 4,155,088,* issued May 15 (1979).
69. Petrocchi, G. *et al.* 'Anti-Clutter and ECCM Design Criteria For a Low Coverage Radar', *Proc. Int. Conf. on Radar*, 194–200, Paris, Dec. (1978), reprinted in Ref. 44.
70. Bergkvist, B. 'Jamming Frequency Agile Radars', *Defense Elec.* 75–79, Jan. (1980).
71. Klaver, L. 'Combined X/K_A-band Tracking Radar', *Proc. MM-78*, 147–156, Oct. (1978), reprinted in Ref. 15.
72. Fagen, M. D. *A History of Engineering and Science in the Bell System – National Service in War and Peace (1925–1975)*, Bell Telephone Laboratories, Inc. (1978).
73. Davis, H. M., Capt. 'History of the Signal Corps Development of Radar Equipment, Part III', *US Archives Washington, DC, RG 319*, Records of the Army Staff, Box 317, 27 March (1944).
74. Johnston, S. L. 'mm-Wave Radar: The New ECM/ECCM Frontier', *Microwave J.*, **27**, 5, 265–271, May (1984).
75. Johnston, S. L. 'Millimeter Waves Present New Opportunities For EW Techniques', *International Countermeasures Handbook*, 323–331 (1986).
76. 'Antijamming Research', *UK Public Records Office file Nos. AVIA 7*, pieces 963–966 (1938–45).
77. Starr, A. T. 'Theory of a Single Valve Multi-Frequency Generator of Closely Spaced Frequencies' (approximate title), *Experimental Wireless* (UK), Sept. (1931).
78. De Rosa, L. A. 'Random Impulse System', *US Patent No. 2,671,896,* issued March 9 (1954) (filed Dec. 18, 1942).
79. Reid, M. S. 'A Millimeter Wave Pseudorandom Coded Meteorological Radar', *IEEE Trans.*, **GE-7**, 3, 146–156, July (1969), reprinted in Ref. 44.
80. Moser, R. and Stover, J. 'Generation of Pseudo-Random Sequences for Spread Spectrum Systems', *Microwave J.*, **28**, 5, 287–295, May (1985).
81. Albanese, D. F. 'Pseudo-Random Code Waveform Design Trade-Offs for CW Radar Applications', *IEE Conf. Pub. No. 155*, RADAR-77, London, 482–487, Oct. (1977).

82. Forrest, J. R. and Meeson, D. J. 'Solid State Microwave Noise Radar', *loc. cit.* 531–534.

83. Winnberg, J. O. 'Search and Target Acquisition Radar for Short Range Air Defence Systems. A New Threat – A New Solution', *IEE Conf. Pub. No. 216*, RADAR-82, London, 120–124, Oct. (1982).

84. Fahey, M. D. and O'Reilly, G. T. 'A P–N Coded Radar', *IEEE Nat. Telecomm. Conf. (NTC 78) Conference Record*, 1, 18.4.1–3 (1978).

85. O'Reilly, G. T. *et al.* 'Track-While-Scan Quiet Radar', *IEEE EASCON-82 Record*, 369–374.

86. Gager, C. H. 'The Impact of Waveform Bandwidth Upon Tactical Radar Design', *loc. cit.*, 278–282.

87. Cross *et al.* 'TRAKX; A Dual Frequency Tracking Radar', *Microwave J.*, **19**, 9, 39–41, Sept. (1976), reprinted in Ref. 44.

88. Lidvel, U., Strom, P. and As, B. O. 'A Dual Frequency Band Antenna for a Multipurpose Search Radar for 250–1000 Ton Warships', *RADAR-85 Rec.*, 52–57.

89. Powell, N. F. 'System for Obscuring Antenna Sidelobe Signals', *US Patent No. 4 435 710*, issued March 6 (1984).

90. Bianucci, L. 'Modern Trends in Fire Control Radar', *Proc. MM-80*, London, 115–120, Oct. (1980).

91. Getting, Ivan 'SCR-584 Radar and the Mark 56 Naval Gun Fire Control System', *IEEE Trans.* **11**, 5, 922–936, Sept. (1975).

92. Alvarez, L. A. Private Communication (1985).

93. Kirkpatrick, G. M. 'Final Engineering Report on Angular Accuracy Improvements', in Barton, D. K. *Radars*, Vol. 1, *Monopulse Radar*, Artech House, Dedham, Ma. (1974).

94. Schmidt, J. D. 'Apparatus for Eliminating Amplitude Modulation Interference in Conically Scanning Radars', *US Patent No. 4 224 622*, filed April 20 (1962).

95. Valley, George, Private Communication (1985).

96. Sakamoto, H. and Peebles, P. Z., Jr. 'Conopulse Radar', *IEEE Trans.*, **AES-14**, 1, 199–208, Jan. (1978), Correction, **AES-14**, 4, July (1978), reprinted in Ref. 15.

97. Bakut, P. A. *et al. Questions of the Statistical Theory of Radar*, Vol. II, DTIC AD 654 775, June 28 (1966).

98. Woodruff, J. H. *et al.* 'An A/J Measure for Use Against Circular Polarized Jamming', *Radio Res. Lab Rep. 411–207*, DTIC ATI 15 411, June 20 (1945).

99. Guli, D., Fossi, F. and Gheradeli, M. 'A Technique for Adaptive Polarization Filtering in Radars', *RADAR-85 Rec.*, 313–319.

100. Dicken, L. W. 'The Use of Null Steering in Suppressing Main Beam Interference', *Int. Radar Sym.* (RADAR-77), London, *IEE Conf. Pub. No. 155*, 226–231, Oct. (1977).

101. Chapman, W., Huber, S. and Miller, T. 'Mainbeam Notcher', *DTIC AD A120 981,* July (1982).
102. Loomis, J. M. and Rose, J. F. 'A Digital Beamforming Prototype Array', *USAMICOM Tech. Rep. RE-83-21,* Redstone Arsenal, AL, *DTIC AD A130 015,* Nov. (1982).
103. Howard, J. E., Young, G. O. and Birgenheier, R. A. 'System Design Considerations For Decision-Theoretic Antenna Processing Systems', *AFCRL Rep. No. 70-0009, Hughes Aircraft Rep. No. P69-395, DTIC AD 864 974,* Sept. (1969).
104. Barton, P., Wong, A., Kelly, K. and Gywnn, P. 'Array Signal Processing for Tracking Targets at Low Elevation Angles', *Int. Radar Sym.* (RADAR-77), London, *IEE Conf. Pub. No. 155,* 318–322, Oct. (1977).
105. Wirth, W. D. 'Radar Signal Processing With an Active Receive Array', *loc. cit.,* 218–221.
106. Milne, K. 'Principles and Concepts of Multistatic Surveillance Radar', *loc. cit.,* 46–52.
107. Barton, P. 'Digital Beamforming For Radar', *Proc. IEE,* **127**, Part F, 266–277, Aug. (1980).
108. Hicks, R. C. 'Comparison of Arithmetic Requirements for the PFA, WFTA, SWIFT, MFFT, FFT, and DFT Algorithms', *USA-MICOM Tech. Rep. RE-83-6,* Redstone Arsenal, Al., *DTIC AD A133 087,* Nov. (1982).
109. Spaulding, W. G. 'A Dispersed Radar Concept for Air Defense', *USAMICOM Tech. Rep. RE-81-27,* Redstone Arsenal, Al., *DTIC AD A122 256,* July (1981).
110. Valentino, P. A. 'Digital Beamforming: New Technology for Tomorrow's Radars', *Defense Elec.,* 102–7, Oct. (1984).
111. Wardrop, B. 'Digital Beamforming in Radar Systems – A Review', *Proc. Military Microwaves-84 (MM-84),* London, 319–323, Oct. (1984).
112. Dax, P. R. 'Noise Jamming of Long Range Search Radars', *Micro-Waves Mag.,* **14**, 9, 54ff, Sept. (1975).
113. Rudge, A. W. and Foster, P. R. 'Low Sidelobe Radar Antennas', *Proc. MM–78,* London, 245, Oct. (1978) (abstract only), reprinted in full in Ref. 15.
114. Evans, G. E. and Schrank, H. E. 'Low Sidelobe Radar Antennas', *Microwave J.,* **26**, 7, 109–117, July (1983).
115. Hansen, R. C. 'A One Parameter Circular Aperture Distribution With Narrow Beamwidth and Low Sidelobes', *IEEE Trans.,* **AP-24**, 477, July (1976).
116. Fante, R. L. 'Tolerance Errors For Very Low Sidelobe Antennas', *RADC Tech. Rep. 77-360,* Oct. (1977) reprinted in Ref. 15.
117. Fante, R. L. 'Effect of Fresnel Zone Blockage on Very Low Sidelobe Antennas', *RADC Tech. Rep. 77-361,* Oct. (1977) reprinted in Ref. 15.

118. Cassel, E. and Lind, G. 'Considerations for Location of Antennae Aboard Warships', *Proc. Int. Nav. Technol. EXPO-78*, 88–97, June (1978).

119. Green, T. J. *et al.* 'Antenna Requirements for Naval Radars', *MM-78*, late paper (not in Conf. Proc.).

120. 'Near Field Antenna Blockage of an Ultra Low Sidelobe Antenna (ULSA)' (On Shipboard), *Westinghouse Def. and Elec. Sys., Final Report 77-1070*, Pt. 1, *DTIC AD A069 984*, Dec. (1977).

121. Applebaum, S. 'Adaptive Arrays', *IEEE Trans.*, **AP-24**, 5, 585–598, Sept. (1976), reprinted in Ref. 15.

122. Maisel, L. 'Performance of Sidelobe Blanking Systems', *IEEE Trans.*, **AES-4**, 2, 174–180, Mar. (1968).

123. Aranciba, P. O. 'A Sidelobe Blanking System Design and Demonstration', *Microwave J.*, **21**, 3, 69–73, Mar. (1978) reprinted in Ref. 15.

124. Boothe, R. R. 'Frequency Agility Technique for Frequency Scanned Antenna', *US Patent No. 4 297 705*, issued Oct. 27 (1981).

125. Galenian, J. C. 'Designing Radar Receivers to Overcome Jamming', *Elec. Mag.* **36**, 17, 50–54, May 17 (1963) reprinted in Ref. 15.

126. Hansen, F. 'Desensitization in Transistorized PM/FM Receivers', *Proc. 18th IEEE Vehicular Comm. Conf.*, 78–86 (1967) reprinted in Ref. 15.

127. Hope, W. D. 'A Broad Band Balanced Mixer For S-Band', *MIT Rad. Lab. Rep. RL-916*, Jan. 23 (1946).

128. Lamb, J. F. 'A Noise Silencing IF Circuit For Superheterodyne Receivers', *QST Mag.*, **20**, 2, 11ff, Feb. (1936).

129. Wald, M. 'Noise Suppression by Means of Amplitude Limiters', *The Wireless Eng.*, **17**, 205, 432–438, Oct. (1940).

130. Schukin, A. N., Bull. Acad. Sci., USSR, *Ser. Phys.*, **10**, 1, 49–56 (1946).

131. Taylor, J. W. Jr., Pardoe, L. W. and Johnston, S. L. 'A Monopulse Radar With MTI for Tracking Through Fixed Clutter', *IEEE Int. Radar Conf. Rec., RADAR-80*, 200–205, Apr. (1980).

132. Cartledge, L. and O'Donnell, R. M. 'Description and Performance Evaluation of the Moving Target Detector', *MIT Lincoln Lab. Tech. Rep. ATC-69*, Mar. 8 (1977) reprinted in Ref. 15.

133. Farina, A. and Studer, F. A. 'Adaptive Implementation of the Optimum Radar Signal Processor', *Proc. Int. Conf. on Radar*, 93–102, Paris, May (1984).

134. Evans, N. T. 'Constant False Alarm Rate Moving Target Indication System (CFAR-MTI)', *US Patent No 4 103 301*, issued July 25 (1978).

135. Skolnik, M. I. *Introduction to Radar Systems*, McGraw-Hill (1980).

136. Tong, P. S. and Steichen, P. E. 'Performance of CFAR Devices in ECM Environment', *DDRE Radar ECCM Sym.* (1976) reprinted in Ref. 15.
137. Turner, F. M. *et al.* 'Noise Quality Optimizes Jammer Performance', *Elec. Warf. Mag.*, **9**, 117–119 (1977), also reprinted in Ref. 15.
138. Hiner, F. P. III, 'The L 2000, A Remote Radar and Data Processor', RADAR-77, *IEE Conf. Pub. No. 155*, 168–72, London, Oct. (1977).
139. Trunk, G. V. 'Survey of Radar ADT', *Microwave J.* **26**, 7, 77–88, July (1983).
140. Northsworthy, K. H. 'Electronic Correlator For Passive Ranging', *Proc. Int. Countermeasures Conf.*, 290–320, London, Sept. (1976) reprinted in Ref. 15.
141. Hammerlie, K. J. 'Raid Count by Autocorrelation', *IEEE RADAR-85 Rec.*, 350–354.
142. Jelelian, A. V., Kawachi, D. A and Miller, C. R. 'OADARS (Optical Aids to Detection and Ranging Systems)', *IEEE ELECTRO-76 Rec., Part 30,* 30-3-1–30-3-5, reprinted in Ref. 15.
143. Jelelian, A. V. 'Laser Radar Systems', *IEEE EASCON-80 Rec.*, 546–554.
144. Friend, R. G. 'The Effect of Window on Army Radar Equipment', *A.D.R.D.E. Rep. No. 250*, Malvern, Worcs., June 6 (1944).
145. anon, 'The Use of Radar Equipment in the Presence of Window', British Air Ministry, transmitted Aug. 18 (1943) *172.4*, Apr. (1943) in *USAF Collection*, Air Force Historical Research Center (AFSHRC), Maxwell Air Force Base, Alabama, USA.
146. 'Report on Jamming and Counter-Jamming Measures', *MIT Special Rep.*, Section IV, August 14 (1941).
147. 'The Protection of Radar Cover Against Enemy R.C.M.', UK Radar Board AJ Panel Special Meeting, Dec. 7–13 (1943) *UK Public Records Office file No. ADM 116*, piece No. 5287.
148. Johnston, S. L. 'Guided Missile ECM/ECCM', *Microwave J.* **21**, 9, 20–24, Sept. (1978) reprinted in Ref. 15.
149. Johnston, S. L. 'Burnthrough Range, an Overrated Parameter', *Elec. Warfare Mag.* **6**, 6, 49–54, Nov./Dec. (1974) reprinted in Ref. 15.
150. Mitchell, O. B. 'ECCM: Effective Deployment and Employment', *Elec. Warfare Mag.,* **6**, 6, 36–38, Nov./Dec. (1974).
151. Johnston, S. L. 'ECCM Improvement Factors (EIF)', *Elec. Warfare Mag.* **6**, 3, 41ff, May/June (1974) reprinted in Ref. 15.
152. 'IEEE Standard Radar Definitions', *ANSI/IEEE Std 686-1982*.
153. Subramanian, A. K. 'ECCM Improvement Factor Considerations for a Multifunction Radar', *Int. Radar Sym.*, India (IRSI-83), 587–592, Oct. (1983).

154. Subramanian, A. K. 'Modelling for Electronic Conflict', *Int. Conf. on Comp., Sys. and Sig. Proc.*, Bangalore, India, Dec. 10–12 (1984).

155. Subramanian, A. K. 'ECCM Evaluation – Some Models', *Int. Conf. on Radar*, 523–527, Paris, May (1984).

156. Subramanian, A. K., 'Parametric Analysis for the Radar ECCM Improvement Factor (EIF), unpublished paper (1985).

157. Nengjing, Li, 'Formulas for Measuring Radar ECCM Capability', *Proc. IEE, Part F, Comm. Radar and Sig. Proc.*, **131**, 4, 417–423, July (1984).

158. Johnston, S. L., Correspondence: 'Comments Formulas for Measuring Radar ECCM Capability', *loc. cit.*, 3, 198–200, June (1985) with response by Nengjing, Li, 200–201.

159. Johnston, S. L. 'The ECCM Improvement Factor (EIF): Illustrative Examples, Applications, and Utilization in Radar ECCM Performance Assessment', unpublished paper (1985).

160. 'IEEE Standard Radar Letter Bands', *IEEE STD 521* (1984).

161. Radford, M. F. 'Radar ECCM: A European Approach', *IEEE ELECTRO-76*.

162. Toomay, J. C. *Radar Principles For the Non-Specialist*, Lifetime Learning Publications, Belmont, Ca. (1982).

163. Schrader, W. W. 'MTI Radar', Chap. 17 in: Skolnik, M. I. (ed.), *Radar Handbook*, McGraw-Hill (1970).

164. Lambert, J. 'Simulator Checks Out Radio-Radar Operation', *Space/Aero. Mag.*, **33**, 4, 157–166, April (1960) reprinted in Ref. 15.

165. Boothe, R. R. 'A Digital Computer Program for Determining the Performance of an Acquisition Radar Through Application of Radar Detection Probability Theory', *US Army Missile Command Rep. RD-TR-64-2, DTIC AD 462 473*, Dec. (1964).

166. Hancock, R. J., Krolak, P. D., Wilson, L. K. and Cleary, J. C. 'Recent Innovations in Radar Simulation', *IEEE Region III SOUTHEASTCON-75-Rec.* 6E-4-1–6E-4-9, reprinted in Ref. 15.

167. Gutsche, S. L., Bogusch, R. and Guigliano, F. W. 'Applications of Computer Simulation Techniques to the Evaluation of Radar System Performance in ECM/ECCM Environments', reprinted in Ref. 15.

168. Pritsker, A. A. B., Van Buskirk, R. C. and Wetherbee, J. W. 'Simulation to Obtain a Systems Measure of an Air Duel Environment', *IRE Trans.*, **EC-8**, 1, Mar. (1959) reprinted in Ref. 15.

169. Barbour, M. D. and Radford, M. F. 'An Anti-Radiation Missile Simulation Model', *Proc. Mil. Microwaves (MM-84)*, 544–547, London, Oct. (1984).

CHAPTER 5
Over-the-horizon Radar

E. D. R. SHEARMAN

5.1   Introduction and historical note

Although microwave radars have detected targets as far away as
Venus, their long range detection potential when located on the
earth's surface, for low altitude or surface targets, is normally
limited to within the radio horizon. Given sufficient power, the
range may be pressed somewhat beyond this into the diffraction
region, but here losses follow a punitive decibels per kilometre
law. Longer ranges are occasionally obtainable for abnormal
tropospheric refraction or ducting conditions, but such sporadic
occurrences cannot be relied upon in engineered operational
systems.

Operation in the decametric or 'high frequency' (HF) band (f
$= 3$–30 MHz, $\lambda = 100$–10 m) enables this horizon limit to be
overcome by the use of one of two propagation modes, sky-wave
or ground-wave, as illustrated in Fig. 5.1.

In sky-wave radar, a radar installation operates like an HF
communication station, radiating energy in a narrow azimuthal
beam, but with a broad vertical beam extending typically from 5°
to 25° elevation. Rays from low elevation angles up to a critical
penetration angle, related to the transmission frequency and the
electron density in the ionosphere, are reflected so that the
downcoming rays illuminate the Earth's surface (Fig. 5.2).
Avoiding steep angle rays, for which the ray reflection is very
sensitive to ionospheric density and height variations, and near-
grazing angles for which antenna radiation at HF is inefficient,
the illuminated zone for propagation by way of the F2 layer
extends typically from 900 km to 3000 km.

It is interesting to note that the first HF radar-like experiments
were carried out in Germany, Britain and the USA[1], as long ago

as 1927 in research aimed at diagnosing the long time-delayed echoes observed on the then new beamed HF communication circuits. The technique employed direction finders and measurements of the time-delay of echoes from short telegraph dots. Subsequently, in 1935 the first British radar experiments were carried out at 6 MHz (to maximise detectability by obtaining resonance with an aircraft wing), leading, by 1939, to the Chain Home radar network[2] operating at 20–40 MHz. These radars were occasionally troubled by sky-wave propagated long range back-scatter echoes from the Earth's surface and had to work at reduced pulse repetition frequencies on such occasions to avoid clutter returning at multiples of the pulse repetition interval.

It is at first surprising to realise that it took a further forty years after the Chain Home before HF sky-wave radar became a serious candidate for operational use, whereas microwave radar came of age within two or three years. The reasons for this lie in propagation, clutter and interference problems of unusual difficulty, requiring advanced antenna arrays, Doppler radar technology and computer signal processing to overcome. The problems and their solution are the subject of much of this chapter.

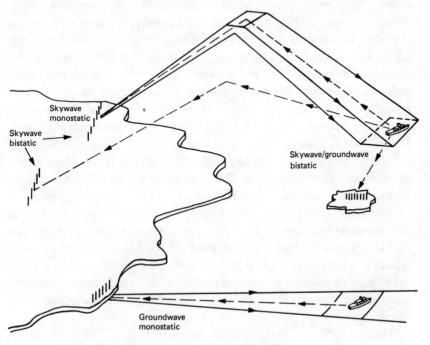

Skywave
monostatic

Skywave
bistatic

Skywave/groundwave
bistatic

Groundwave
monostatic

Fig. 5.1 HF radar configurations.

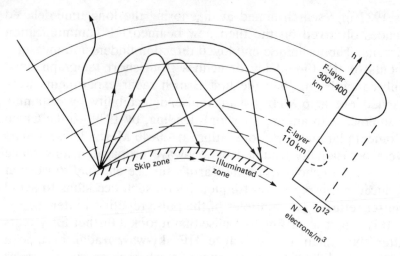

Fig. 5.2 Ray paths for refraction through a thick F-layer in absence of E-layer ionisation. Note that high angle and low angle propagation to the same ground location is possible.

Briefly, a sky-wave radar is analogous to an airborne radar looking down at the Earth's surface and trying to detect low flying or surface targets: it must identify the target echoes against a very much stronger surface return and the achievement of sub-clutter visibility by Doppler velocity discrimination is thus essential. In addition, since the long range is obtained by reflection from ionospheric layers, any movement, rippling, roughness or multiple stratifications of those layers will complicate the detection, ranging and Doppler discrimination processes. Also, other scatterers are present in the ionosphere (meteors and auroral irregularities) which have their own unique spatial distribution and velocity signatures, while the high atmospheric noise, man-made impulsive interference and communication and broadcasting transmissions add further difficulties.

As in HF communication, frequency changes are required as the ionosphere changes with time of day and season. The design of HF radars is thus a severe test of modern technology, one which has been met and largely solved, the driving force being the capability of seeing far beyond the horizon, and in military terms, countering the threat of low flying aircraft undetectable by microwave radar.

The other class of HF radar shown in Fig. 5.1 is the ground-wave (or surface-wave) radar. This avoids the use of ionospheric

refraction (with its problems), by capitalising on the low attenuation of the Norton surface wave for propagation of vertically
polarised waves over sea water at frequencies below 30 MHz.
The radar must be located on the coast, or on an island or ship, as
even a few tens of metres of overland path can cause severe
attenuation of the transmitted and received ground-wave. Overland applications are thus not feasible. The ranges for this mode
are shorter than for sky-wave systems, extending from zero to a
maximum range of 200–400 km. Compensating advantages are
freedom from ionospheric reflecting layer problems so that
Doppler velocity discrimination and tracking become more accurate, capability for avoiding long range sky-wave clutter by range
discrimination and more freedom in the choice of operating
frequency, since it is no longer required to follow the diurnal and
seasonal ionospheric variations. Sky-wave propagated noise and
interference and strong sea clutter are, however, still
experienced.

So far, we have discussed the problem of detection of discrete
targets in the presence of land and sea clutter. A very fertile field
of work, however, has centred on the use of sea echo for remote
sensing of the characteristics of ocean waves and surface currents
and also, by inference, of the winds at the sea surface. This has
been the stimulus of some ingenious radar techniques and will be
discussed later in this chapter.

Bistatic operation (see Fig. 5.1) is more common in HF radar
(where it can have considerable practical advantages), than in
microwave radar, where this practice is comparatively recent.
Another variant, potentially very useful at sea, is mixed mode
operation with sky-wave illumination and ground-wave reception, also illustrated in Fig. 5.1.

In all these variants, the unique propagation characteristics of
HF radar are of central importance and we begin by discussing
propagation factors to set the scene.

5.2 Propagation factors, sky-wave

Sky-wave propagation to beyond the horizon is made possible by
the existence in the ionosphere of approximately spherically
stratified ionised layers concentric with the Earth's surface (Fig.
5.2). The variability of the layers with time of day, season and
sunspot cycle implies that the radar operator must vary the
frequency from time to time so as to ensure that refraction in the

layers results in illumination of the target[3]. This process is known as 'frequency management'.

The lowest of these layers, the D-layer at 70–80 km height, has a density of free electrons insufficient to refract radio waves in the 3–30 MHz band, but because of the high collision rate with neutral particles, gives rise to attenuation. Except in auroral regions, this attenuation is a daylight-only effect. The attenuation, measured in decibels, is approximately inversely proportional to the square of the transmitted frequency and also increases as the sun approaches the zenith and as the maximum of the 11 year sunspot cycle is approached. The inverse square frequency variation is of crucial importance to frequency management in HF radars. For instance, an attenuation of 5 dB at 10 MHz can become 20 dB at 5 MHz, enough to convert a clearly detectable target to one well below noise level.

The expression giving the attenuation, L_{ob} for a frequency f_{ob} MHz, is given by George and Bradley[4] in terms of the angle of incidence on a layer at 100 km of the unrefracted ray, $i_{100} = $ arc sin(0.985 cos Δ), where Δ is the angle of elevation of the ray at the transmitter. They give

$$L_{ob}(f_{ob}) = \frac{A_T(R = 0, \chi = 0) \cdot (1 + 0.0067R) \cdot F(\chi) \cdot \phi_n(x) \cdot \sec i_{100}}{(f \pm f_L)^2} dB \qquad (1)$$

$A_T(R,\chi)$ represents the D-layer absorption at vertical incidence for the conditions: (i) $f = 1$ MHz; (ii) solar activity $= R$ (expressed on the Wolf sunspot number scale, or for greater accuracy, on an equivalent ionospherically derived index); (iii) solar zenith angle $= \chi$. Thus $A_T(R = 0, \chi = 0)$ represents the vertical incidence absorption for sunspot minimum and overhead sun.

George and Bradley have given a universal contour plot mapping the first factor in the numerator of Equation 1, the quantity $A(R = 0, \chi = 0)$, against season and latitude with respect to the magnetic equator ('modified dip latitude'). The second factor in the numerator then gives the solar activity variation, the third factor gives the zenith angle variation and the denominator gives the frequency variation. The term f_L in the denominator is the gyro frequency about the component of the Earth's field in the direction of propagation for vertical incidence, obtainable by $f_L = f_H \sin I$, where f_H is the gyro frequency about the total magnetic field and I is the dip angle, both obtainable from charts[3].

The term $F(\chi)$ is equated by George and Bradley to $\cos^p(0.881\chi)$ or 0.1, whichever is the larger. The authors map the index, p, (as A_T above) in terms of season and modified dip latitude. The remaining term is $\phi_n(x)$, a factor taking into account extra 'deviative' absorption occurring during refraction in the higher E-layer. This absorption is a function of the E-layer critical frequency, f_oE (the highest frequency that the layer can reflect at vertical incidence) and the frequency f_v, which would be reflected at vertical incidence at the same height as f_{ob} at oblique incidence. Thus $x = f_v/f_oE$, where f_v is given by $f_v = f_{ob} \cos i_{100}$. Deviative absorption peaks when f_v equals the critical frequency of the E-layer, for which condition $x = 1$, the enhancement of $A_T(0, 0)$ being less than 0.5 dB for $f_v < (f_oE)/2$, around 2 dB close to $f_v = f_oE$ and 0.9 dB at $f_v > 1.5f_oE$. (When multiplied by the factor sec i_{100}, whose limiting value for $\Delta = 0$ is 5.7, this can be a significant correction to the attenuation.)

With this method and data available, the prediction of iono-spheric attenuation becomes a very practical and straightforward matter, whether done by graphical or computer technique.

The next two layers, E and F_1, are capable of refracting radio waves back to Earth, their maximum electron densities occurring respectively at heights of about 110 km and 200 km. The greater the electron density, the greater the frequency which can be refracted back to Earth, a vertically travelling wave being reflected at a height where the local plasma frequency, f_p, is equal to the wave frequency ($f_p = 8.98\sqrt{N}$ Hz, where N is in electrons/m^3).

These layers are a daytime phenomenon, their electron densities varying in a regular manner with solar zenith angle χ (the angle between the sun's rays and the local vertical). For these two layers the plasma frequency at the layer maximum, $[f_p]_{max} = f_o$, known as the critical frequency, since it is the highest frequency which the layer can reflect at vertical incidence, is given approximately by[3]:

$$f_oE = 0.9\,[(180 + 1.44\,R)\cos\chi]^{0.25} \qquad (2)$$

$$f_oF_1 = (4.3 + 0.01\,R)\cos^{0.2}\chi, \chi < 90° \qquad (3)$$

More accurate expressions taking into account the influence of geomagnetic latitude are given in Ref. 5.

Although this expression would make the critical frequency f_oE zero at night-time, a small residual ionisation remains, too small to affect propagation at HF. (This ionisation is sufficient to reflect the sky-wave radiation of medium and long wave broadcasting transmissions and is responsible for their large night-time coverage. In daylight these frequencies are too heavily attenuated by D-layer attenuation for sky-wave field strengths to be significant.)

The uppermost layer is the F-layer (F_2 in daytime), the maximum electron density of which occurs at heights of 200–500 km, dependent on time of day and season. Its maximum density and height vary over the Earth in a complicated pattern influenced by the Earth's magnetic field as well as solar zenithal angle. The highest electron densities occur near the geomagnetic equator. Seasonally, the highest densities occur around noon and in winter. The F2 layer, having the greatest density and height, is capable of refracting radio waves back to Earth at distances up to 3000–4000 km in a single hop and at frequencies at times as high as 40–50 MHz.

Predictions of critical frequencies and heights for the F2 layer over the Earth are not amenable to simple formulae as for the D, E and F1 layers. However, it has been found from an analysis of measurements over several sunspot cycles that the monthly mean $f_o F_2$ for a given location, season and universal time, is linearly related to sunspot number, R. The International Radio Consultative Committee (CCIR) has accordingly published maps[5,6] (and computer compatible digital tape look-up tables) giving, for sunspot numbers $R = 0$ and $R = 100$, contours of the maximum usable frequency (MUF) for vertical incidence reflection (F2 (zero) MUF) for each month and 2 hour intervals of universal time. Linear interpolation yields values for any other sunspot number. Similar maps have been prepared for the MUF which can be reflected at oblique incidence over a ground range of 4000 km, the so-called F2 (4000) MUF. By interpolating between the zero-distance MUF and the 4000 km MUF, the MUF for any other required range may be found.

5.2.1 EARTH'S MAGNETIC FIELD EFFECTS

If there were no Earth's magnetic field, we would not have needed to use, above, different symbols for the critical frequency for vertical incidence reflection, $f_o F_2$, and for the maximum usable frequency for vertical incidence, F2 (zero) MUF. The existence of this static magnetic field renders the ionospheric medium doubly refracting, like the mineral Iceland Spa. Two characteristic waves, the ordinary (not much altered from the no-field wave) and the extraordinary propagate in the medium, each with its own polarisation, velocity and ray path. A radio wave incident on the bottom of the ionosphere couples energy into these two characteristic waves as determined by polarisation matching. Thus a linearly polarised wave incident on the iono-sphere, at a location where the characteristic waves are left hand and right hand circularly polarised, would couple half its energy into each; a left hand circularly polarised wave would couple all its energy into one wave.

The difference between the ray paths followed as the two waves are refracted by the ionosphere is not great, so that no-field theory is usually satisfactory for computing radar coverage. However, the extraordinary wave is refracted back to Earth to a slightly higher frequency, typically about 0.5 MHz. Thus the highest frequency reflected from the F2 layer at vertical incidence by the ordinary ray is termed f_oF2 and by the extraordinary ray, f_xF2. The zero distance MUF is thus f_xF2, not f_oF2 and the MUF for 4000 km is similarly that of the extraordinary ray.

If very short pulses are transmitted, say < 150 µs, the path length difference between ordinary and extraordinary rays is sufficient at some transmitted frequencies to separate them in time, so that they can be seen as individual pulses at the receiver. With longer pulses or continuous wave transmission, the signals received at a distant point overlap in time and wave interference occurs. The different polarisations of the two waves and the different phase corresponding to their distinct paths then become very significant. At a fixed point on the ground, fading will be observed as the ionospheric layer moves vertically and the phase difference between the two paths changes. In radar, we are concerned with the illumination over a large ground area, and the wave interference will result in fringes of high and low intensity being formed on the ground. A target moving through such a pattern would give rise to a fluctuating echo amplitude, this being also influenced by the varying alignment of the incident wave polarisation and the polarisation characteristic of the target echo-ing area[7].

If Fig. 5.2 (which is drawn for the no-field case) is inspected, it will be seen that even without this magneto-ionic splitting effect, it is possible for two different rays to interfere at a point on the ground. This can happen because of the thickness of the layer which produces 'high angle' and 'low angle' rays to a given point.

Such effects produce a fluctuating characteristic to sky-wave radar returns, which simplifies if the frequency is such that only one ray is possible or when the ionosphere is very stable.

The attenuation suffered by the extraordinary ray is greater than that by the ordinary ray, the former being given by the negative sign in Equation 1.

5.2.2 RAY PATH

To analyse the performance of a sky-wave radar, whether from the points of view of estimating returned echo power, Doppler shift or ray elevation angle, it is essential to have a satisfactory model for the trajectory of the rays. Three useful and well established models are available for the cases, respectively, of a thin layer, a single thick layer and multiple layers. These will be reviewed in turn. 'No-field' theory (ignoring the effect of the Earth's magnetic field) is sufficiently accurate for these purposes. First, however, we describe the data source.

The basic data from which ray paths are computed is the vertical variation of the free electron density in the ionosphere *vs.* height. The most widely available measurements are from the world-wide network of sweep-frequency pulsed vertical sounders (ionosondes), yielding 'ionograms' such as that shown in Fig. 5.3(a). These show as a function of transmitted frequency, the apparent (or 'virtual') height of reflection, h', at each frequency, assuming that the vertically travelling sounding pulses have free space velocity throughout. Since the electron density needed to reflect vertically travelling waves at frequency f Hz is $N = f^2/80.6$ electrons/m^3, the frequency tells us directly the value of N at h'.

Unfortunately, h' does not represent the true height, since the pulses do not travel at free space velocity when in the ionised layers, the group velocity being reduced. An integral equation has to be solved to correct at each frequency for the retardation of the pulse in travelling through all intermediate heights to reach the height of reflection and obtain the true height. This procedure is now automated and Fig. 5.3(b) shows the resulting deduced curve of electron concentration *vs.* height.

When the vertical variation of electron concentration, $N(h)$, is known, the refractive index, $\mu(h)$, and hence the refraction of rays in the ionospheric layers, can be computed, taking account of the earth's magnetic field and any horizontal gradients in the layers. For most purposes it is sufficient to fit simple models

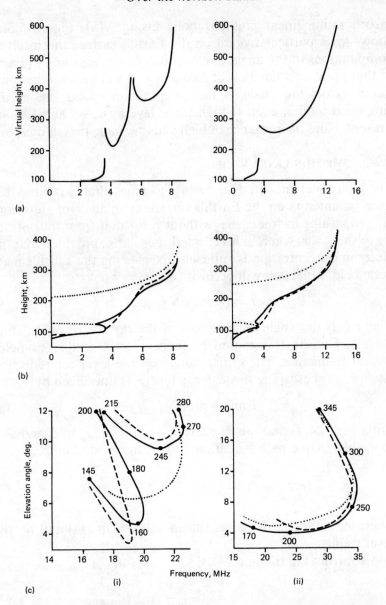

Fig. 5.3 Accuracy of electron concentration distributions and corresponding oblique propagation mode/angle plots using:
——— true height analysis, ... CCIR dual-parabolic model,
---------- Bradley-Dudeny linear/dual-parabolic model.
Column (i): ionogram showing F1 cusp. Column (ii): ionogram with no cusp present; (a) recorded ionograms; (b) vertical distributions of electron concentration (abscissa is plasma frequency, MHz); (c) mode-angle plots for propagation to a range of 3000 km as function of transmitted frequency for models as above. Numbers quoted on diagrams are ray apogees in kilometres. (*After P.A. Bradley*[10].)

incorporating linear plus parabolic fits to $N(h)$. Figure 5.3(c) shows for a particular point on the Earth's surface the result of computations of the angle of elevation of rays returning to Earth at that point as a function of frequency. It will be seen that only minor errors are made in the computation by the use of the simplified model, even though three layers (E, F1 and F2) are present. Note the presence of high and low angle rays in this plot.

5.2.3 THE THIN LAYER MODEL

The thin layer model, Fig. 5.4(a), assumes that a ray emitted from an antenna on the Earth's surface at an angle of elevation, Δ, propagates in free space without refraction from the surface up to the layer, where it is reflected specularly, provided that the electron concentration is sufficient. Neglecting the Earth's magnetic field, reflection will occur if

$$f_o \sec i_o = (8.98 \ \sqrt{N}) \cdot \sec i_o > f \qquad (4)$$

where i_o is the angle of incidence of the ray on the layer, (Fig. 5.4(a)), f is the transmitted frequency and f_o is the (no-field) critical frequency. The critical angle on the layer for reflection (steeper rays escaping through the layer), is thus given by:

$$i_o \text{min} = \text{arc } \cos(f_o/f) \qquad (5)$$

From Fig. 5.4(a) and the sine law, we can relate i_o to Δ and also to p, the oblique path length, and to D, the ground range:

$$(p/2)/\sin \theta = (r_b)/\sin\left(\frac{\pi}{2} + \Delta\right) = r_o/\sin i_o \qquad (6)$$

where r_o is the Earth radius (mean value 6370 km) and r_b, the layer radius.

Also, from the triangle TOB:

$$\theta = \frac{\pi}{2} - i_o - \Delta \qquad (7)$$

Finally, using $\theta = (D/2)/r_o$, we obtain the convenient relationships:

$$i_o = \text{arc } \sin[(r_o/r_b) \cos \Delta] \qquad (8)$$

$$D = 2r_o \left(\frac{\pi}{2} - i_o - \Delta\right) \qquad (9)$$

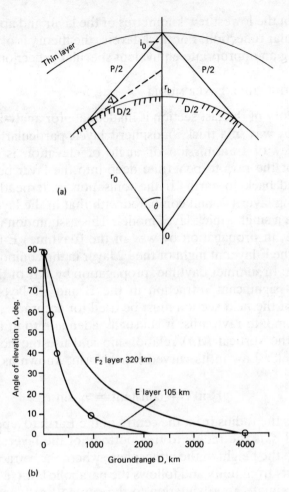

Fig. 5.4 Thin layer model; (a) geometry; (b) ground-range *D vs.* angle of elevation of ray, Δ, for typical E-layer and F2 layer heights.

$$p = (2r_o/\cos \Delta) \sin (\frac{\pi}{2} - i_o - \Delta) \qquad (10)$$

These relationships are directly applicable to propagation by way of Sporadic-E clouds (very thin sheets of ionisation at 110–120 km height, seen particularly in temperate zone summer); they are also applicable with fair accuracy to propagation by the normal E-layer, which has a semi-thickness of only 20 km at a mean height of 110 km. Fig. 5.4(b) presents the relationships graphically.

The thin layer model can also be applied to propagation by the F2 layer at frequencies well below the MUF, where refraction occurs in the lowest few kilometres of the layer and approximates to specular reflection. For thick layers, the theory is often used by choosing an appropriate equivalent specular reflection height.

5.2.4 THE THICK LAYER MODEL

The theory of the last section is inadequate for analysis of propagation by way of a thick ionospheric layer, particularly when the frequency of transmission or angle of elevation is sufficiently great for the rays to penetrate deep into the layer before being refracted back to earth. If the ionisation underneath the main refracting layer is small compared with that in the layer itself we may use a single, thick layer model. This assumption is valid, for instance, in propagation by way of the (daytime) E-layer or by way of the F-layer at night or the F2 layer in the equinox or winter daytime. In summer daytime, propagation by way of the F2 layer involves significant refraction in the E and F1 layers and the theory of the next section must be used for accuracy.

To compute ray paths, it is usually adequate to fit a parabolic law to the vertical $N(h)$ relationship and use the no-magnetic-field Snell's Law in its curved Earth form, known as Bouguer's Rule:

$$\mu r \sin i = \text{constant} = r_b \sin i_o \tag{11}$$

Here r is the radius from the centre of the Earth to a point on the ray, and r_b is the radius to the 'bottom' of the layer, that is the radius to the height in the atmosphere where the refractive index, μ, departs from unity and follows the parabolic law (see Fig. 5.2).

A legitimate approximation to the curved Earth geometry for ground ranges of up to 1000 km is a model of a plane Earth and a plane stratified ionosphere. For this model, a parabolic $N(h)$ relationship leads to simple exact expressions for the ground range and path length[8]. For a curved Earth and curved ionosphere, the approximation of neglecting second order terms in $(r - r_b)/r_b$ leads to the following solutions for the ground range, D, and the group path p' [$p' =$ (free space velocity) × (time of flight)][8]:

$$p' = p_1' + p_2'$$

$$= 2xy_m \tanh^{-1}\left[\frac{x \cos i_o}{1 - x^2 \frac{y_m}{r_b} \sin^2 i_o}\right] + \frac{2r_o \sin(\frac{\pi}{2} - \Delta - i_o)}{\sin i_o} \tag{12}$$

$$D = D_1 + D_2$$

$$= \frac{r_o}{r_b} \sin i_o \cdot p_1' + 2r_o \left(\frac{\pi}{2} - \Delta - i_o \right) \tag{13}$$

In these equations, x is the ratio f/f_o, y_m is the semi-thickness of the parabolic layer, $p_1' p_2'$ are the parts of the group path in and below the layer respectively and D_1, D_2 represent the corresponding portions of the ground range. One further quantity needed is the phase path p (p = (free space wavelength) × (number of wavelengths in path)). The latter (see below) is needed to compute Doppler shift, given by $f_d = (1/\lambda)dp/dt$ for one way transmission.

Croft[9], following a suggestion by de Voogt, has shown that a very small modification to the parabolic electron density *vs.* height law, in which the quadratic term in the electron density is weighted by $(r_b/r)^2$, makes possible exact solutions to the ray paths. Although not significant in ordinary prediction use, this is valuable in checking computer ray tracing algorithms; the algorithms may be tested on this 'quasi parabolic' $N(h)$ model and the results compared with the exact solution for the same model. Croft tabulates to seven significant figures, calculations of Δ, D, p' and p for two values of x, typical of F2 layer propagation at 20 and 29 MHz.

Figure 5.5 (after Croft[9]) shows for the same layer model the ground range D, take off angle Δ, virtual height of reflection and approximate time of flight (= p'/c one way) on a convenient diagram. Such a diagram is particularly useful for relating echo time delay, ground range and through Δ, antenna gain. The locus of the virtual reflection point, shown in Fig. 5.5, is known as the *reflectrix*.

5.2.5 THE MULTIPLE LAYER MODEL

As will be seen from Fig. 5.3(b), the concept of discrete layers in the ionosphere is an over-simplification; there is often no deep minimum between the successive ionisation maxima. Bradley and Dudeney[10] have shown that a good model for computing refraction through an ionosphere with such an $N(h)$ profile is one having parabolic maxima and linear regimes between, as shown by the dashed lines in Fig. 5.3(b). As illustrated in Fig. 5.3(c), the errors of calculations of ground range *vs.* elevation angle (mode

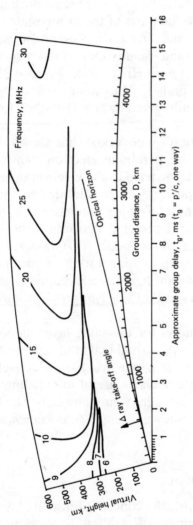

Fig. 5.5 Reflectrixes showing radio ray propagation in a representative quasi-parabolic ionospheric layer (*after Croft and Hoogasian*). From any point on a reflectrix for a selected frequency, drop a radial to the curved baseline to find the ground distance of a ray. The length of the radial is the virtual height, using the scale on the left. From the same point draw a line to the distance-height origin; the angle between this line and the optical horizon is the ray take off angle. Finally, the length of the line is (approximately) the ray group delay, using the lower scale. Quasi-parabolic ionosphere, peak electron density $10^{12}/m^3$, height of maximum $h_m = 300$ km, semi-thickness $y_m = 100$ km. (Simplified version. For full detail showing reflectrixes at 1 MHz intervals, see Ref. 9.)

plots) from explicit solutions obtained with this model relative to those for a ray trace through the accurate $N(h)$ profile are small.

This model is now recommended by the CCIR for prediction purposes and ray parameter expressions are included in that organisation's *Atlas of Ionospheric Characteristics*[5]. The inputs required are the E-layer critical frequency, f_oE, and the F2 layer MUF (zero) and MUF (4000), all obtainable from the contour maps provided, together with the minimum virtual height of the F2 layer, $h'F_2$, a quantity measured at ionospheric sounding stations and predicted. It has been very effectively used in a modified quasi-parabolic form by Pielou[11] to compute spatial coverage and multipath occurrence as a function of transmitted frequency.

5.3 The radar equation: sky wave

Having found, from ionospheric predictions for a given ground range, the ionospheric attenuation, path length and angle of elevation as described above, we are in a position to estimate the amplitude of target echoes and the back-scatter from the sea or land surface. We assume initially that a thin layer model can be used, inserting if necessary an equivalent triangular path for an ionospherically refracted path using Fig. 5.5. Putting the range R in the radar equation equal to the group path p', we obtain for the received echo power from a discrete target

$$\frac{P_r}{P_n} = \frac{P_t g_t}{4\pi R_t^2 L_t L_{it}} \cdot \frac{\sigma}{4\pi R_r^2 L_{ir}} \cdot \frac{g_r \lambda^2 t_i}{4\pi F_a k T_o} \tag{14}$$

Here P_t is the mean transmitter power, L_t the transmitter system loss, L_{it}, L_{ir} the outward and return path ionospheric attenuation due to D-layer and E-layer absorption (see Section 5.2), g_t, g_r the transmitter and receiver gains relative to an isotropic radiator as measured over ground at the corresponding ray elevation angle, and λ the radio wavelength. $P_n = F_a kT_o/t_i$ is the noise power in the coherent integration bandwidth, $1/t_i$, where F_a is the noise factor of the antenna due to atmospheric, man-made and galactic noise, which in the HF band is usually large compared with receiver noise. Measured values of F_a have been collated by the CCIR[12,6] and are available in contour maps *vs.* time of day and season. σ is the echoing area of the target as exhibited over the Earth's surface, i.e. including the effect of surface reflection.

Equation 14 is valid for a bistatic configuration, with separated transmitter and receiver sites, provided the appropriate ranges, ionospheric losses, antenna gains and echoing area are inserted. For a common transmit and receive site (monostatic operation), the expression simplifies to:

$$\frac{P_r}{P_n} = \left(\frac{P_t g_t g_r t_i}{L_t}\right) \cdot \frac{\lambda^2}{(4\pi)^3 R^4} \cdot \frac{1}{L_i} \cdot \frac{\sigma}{F_a k T_o} \tag{15}$$

The ionospheric loss, Li, is now the two-way loss, so that $L_i = L_{it} + L_{ir}$. It is useful to note that the first term on the right-hand side of Equation 15 represents the total effective isotropic radiated energy in the direction of the target during the coherent integration time t_i. This quantity is often used as a measure of radar performance; measured in dB, it may vary from 50 to 120 dBJ (dB greater than 1 J), depending on the transmitter power and antenna aperture.

As an example of the orders of magnitude involved in Equation 15, we give the parameters for a feasibility study carried out at the University of Birmingham to assess the use of sky wave radar for monitoring the accuracy of station keeping of civil airliners on the North Atlantic air routes. Figures are given in Table 5.1 for ionospheric loss and atmospheric noise for summer and winter conditions to illustrate the dominant influence of propagation phenomena on such systems. A broadcast transmitter ($P_t = 200$ kW or 23 dBW) and antenna were available, together with a wide aperture steerable beam antenna array designed for back-scatter ionospheric sounding experiments. The transmitting array had two side-by-side bays, each of four vertically stacked horizontal $\lambda/2$ dipole elements, all with reflectors, the lowest being 1 wavelength above ground (HR 2/4/1). This configuration gives a

Table 5.1 Signal-to-noise ratio budget expressed in terms of Equation 15. The bottom line gives the negative of the system energy required to give signal equal to noise for a 200 m² target at 2100 km in the North Atlantic. (After M.D. Moorhead, 1982, private communication.)

Factor	Dimension	Night 7 MHz	Day 25 MHz
$\lambda^2/(4\pi)^3 R^4$	dBm^{-2}	−253	−264
$1/L_i$	dB	−22	−8
σ	dBm^2	28	28
$1/kT_0$	−dBJ	204	204
$1/Fa$	dB	−40	−20
Total	−dBJ	−83	−60

9° vertical by 50° horizontal beam at 26 MHz and a gain of 19.2 dB[13]. The receive antenna consisted of 49 vertical tilted fan monopole wideband elements in front of a reflecting screen, giving a 4° horizontal by 10° vertical beam and a gain of 22 dB. Both antennas had a peak radiation at an elevation angle of 8°, for which the ground range was about 2200 km. The receive antenna beam could be steered azimuthally within the transmit beam, the sector viewed being governed by the receive beam position. The radar performance figure, $P_t g_t g_r \ t_i/L_i$, for this system at 26 MHz was 94.5 dBJ at 5° to 12° elevation angle.

If the average echoing area for a large airliner is estimated as 160 m^2, or 22 dBm^2 (dB greater than 1 m^2), and a maximum enhancement of 6 dB due to constructive interference of direct and sea-reflected rays is allowed for, σ becomes 28 dBm^2. We may then find the required radar performance figure for a signal-to-noise ratio of 0 dB under given ionospheric attenuation and atmospheric noise conditions. Table 5.1 gives such results for winter propagation at appropriate frequencies for propagation to 2100 km. For winter daytime conditions at 25 MHz, an effective isotropic radiated energy of 60 dBJ is required, so that for a signal-to-noise ratio of 10 dB, the figure becomes 70 dBJ. For winter night, however, the operating frequency drops to 7 MHz and the energy for 0 dB S/N is 83 dBJ, leading to 93 dBJ for a 10 dB S/N. This latter result may seem to contradict the earlier assertion that D-layer absorption falls to near-zero at night; the answer lies in the radar beam trajectory, which was directed westwards across the Atlantic from the UK and, therefore, skirted the auroral zone, incurring auroral absorption.[14]

5.4 Clutter

The calculations of the previous section have concerned only the limitation set on target detection by atmospheric and man-made noise; clutter and interference have not been taken into account. The significant scatterers giving rise to clutter in HF radars are irregularities on the land and sea surface, transient ionisation trails left by meteors, and auroral and equatorial field-aligned irregularities. We review each of these briefly below.

The dominant source of clutter is the Earth's surface, as illustrated in Fig. 5.6. This shows a range/amplitude display with multihop backscatter observed at night on a southerly beam from the south of England. Surface returns can be seen at ranges up to

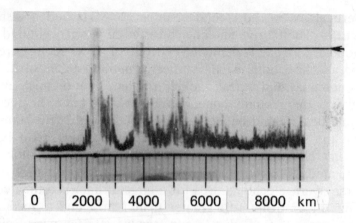

0   2000   4000   6000   8000   km

Fig. 5.6 Range/amplitude display of Earth's surface backscatter from slant ranges up to 9000 km by multi-hop F-layer propagation. Frequency 15.4 MHz 0330 GMT, 18 March 1957. Azimuth 207°, peak pulse power 100 kW, pulse length 120 μs. Receiver input corresponding to horizontal line: −101 dBW, linear amplitude scale. (*After Shearman*[15].)

9000 km[15]. The skip distance phenomenon and the zones illuminated by the main vertical beam of the radar antenna after successive ionospheric reflections can be clearly seen.

5.4.1 LAND CLUTTER

The land surface exhibits roughness at many scales, but those of importance here are those of size comparable with a wavelength. Irregularities of size small compared with a wavelength (say of centimetric scale) will appear smooth to metric radio waves. Gently undulating hills having slopes changing only on a kilometric scale will reflect downcoming sky waves onwards like light reflected from a slightly corrugated mirror so that an incident wave will suffer near-specular reflection, with the emergent rays exhibiting angular spreading over a cone of half-angle twice the typical slope of the surface. The important irregularities, giving rise to backscatter returning to the radar, are such features as trees and undergrowth, rocky outcrops, buildings, power lines, towers and other artifacts. Most developed countries or natural landscapes other than featureless plains, provide a variety of such targets. Shearman[8] took a simple model for such scatterers of hemispherical conducting bosses of 0.1λ radius on the Earth's surface; he showed that the observed backscatter intensity in a particular experiment could have arisen if bosses only 1.7 m in radius had been spaced an average distance of 30 m apart (a density of 1000 bosses per square km).

An interesting report by Basler and Scott[16] shows a range-azimuth scan of the central United States obtained with a radar of high range resolution (10–50 μs). The cities of Tulsa, Kansas City, Omaha and Oklahoma City gave enhanced echoes, 10–20 dB above the background terrain clutter. Similar results were obtained for islands in the Carribean. A useful review of ground scatter has been given by Hayden[17].

The observed Doppler spread of land clutter is due only to ionospheric motion; the Doppler wander of the ground return has been used to monitor ionospheric motion due to diurnal effects and travelling ionospheric disturbances.

5.4.2 SEA CLUTTER

The ocean surface, except under the rare conditions of a flat calm, exhibits waves of a variety of scales extending from capillary waves of millimetric scale to swell from distant storms of wavelength up to 300 m. The wave field can best be characterised by a directional wavenumber or frequency spectrum, which quantifies the amount of wave energy per unit area of surface per increment of azimuth per increment of wavenumber or frequency. This description, favoured by oceanographers, is also ideally matched to the analysis of radio wave scattering from the surface, since incident waves are selectively backscattered by sinusoidal surface irregularities, those which satisfy the Bragg condition

$$L \cos \Delta = \lambda/2 \qquad (16)$$

Here, L is the ocean wavelength, λ the radio wavelength and Δ the grazing angle of the incident radio ray. The radar thus acts as a spectrum analyser, selecting two only from the total spectrum of ocean waves. These are the approaching and receding waves whose wavelength satisfies Equation 16. These waves, from the dispersion relationship for gravity waves on deep water, have velocity $v = \pm(gL/2\pi)^{1/2}$ and give a Doppler shift $((2v/\lambda) \cos \Delta)$ of:

$$f_B = \pm[(g/\pi\lambda) \cos \Delta]^{1/2} = \pm 0.102(f_{MHz} \cos \Delta)^{1/2} \qquad (17)$$

The Doppler spectrum of ocean backscatter thus has a dominant feature, two spectral lines at $\pm f_B$ (the frequencies related to the transmitted frequency and grazing angle at the surface rather than to the sea-state), the lines respectively measuring the energy in approaching and receding waves (see Fig. 5.7). For a 10 MHz radar and a grazing angle less than 15°, these 'Bragg lines' would be at ±0.3 Hz.

The power of the clutter return from land or sea is given, as for an airborne radar, by the area of surface simultaneously illuminated by the transmitted pulse, times the backscatter coefficient, σ_o (echoing area per unit ground area):

$$P_r = \frac{P_t g_t g_r}{L_t} \cdot \frac{\lambda^2}{(4\pi)^3 R^4 L_i} \cdot \frac{c\tau}{2} \sec \Delta \cdot R\theta_B \sigma_o \qquad (18)$$

Here θ_B is the horizontal beamwidth of the radar antenna.

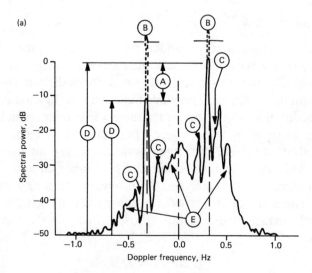

Fig. 5.7 Sea-echo Doppler spectra; (a) features of spectra permitting sea parameter measurement:

A: Ratio of advance to recede first-order Bragg line amplitude: mean direction of wind sea and hence surface wind.

B: Doppler shift of Bragg lines from expected symmetry: radial component of surface current.

C: Separation of inner edge of second-order structure from Bragg lines: low frequency cut-off of ocean waveheight spectrum. (Spectral peaks identify swell components.)

D: Magnitude of first-order Bragg lines: ocean waveheight spectral values for one wavelength and reciprocal directions.)

E: Magnitude and shape of second-order structure: ocean waveheight spectrum for all wave frequencies and directions. Ground-wave data for 1245 UT, 25 February 1982, frequency 9.25 MHz, bearing 245° from Angle, Pembroke, UK, range 37.5 km. Average of 13 four-minute spectra with 50% overlap.

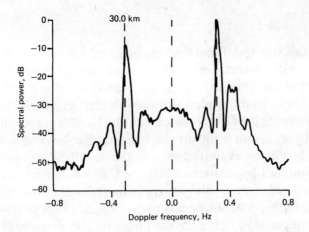

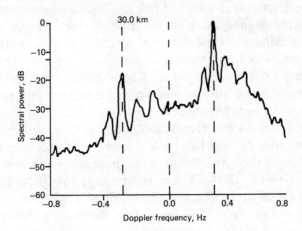

(b) Effect of sea-state on level of second-order continuum relative to Bragg lines. (9.25 MHz spectra from Angle, as for (a): above – wind speed 4 m/s; below – wind speed 20 m/s.

Barrick[18] has derived σ_o for ocean surface scatter in the case of a fully developed wind sea, having components at the Bragg matched wavelength and a semi-omnidirectional angular distribution. He obtains the value as -17 dB relative to 1 m^2/m^2, independent of the radio wavelength.

The sea clutter has a second order structure in the form of a Doppler continuum some 20–40 dB below the 'Bragg' lines discussed here (Fig. 5.7). This is important in remote sensing and ship tracking and will be returned to later.

5.4.3 METEOR CLUTTER

Meteoroids are small material particles or assemblages of particles in orbit around the sun, some in clearly defined streams observed each year at the same period as the Earth passes through their orbits, while the direction and occurrence of others are sporadic. Those intercepted by the Earth's atmosphere are heated by collision with atmospheric molecules and ions. The heating produces evaporation and the resulting expanding gas cloud produces by further collision a trail of ionised gas behind the meteoroid, which can give rise to a transient echo on an HF radar. The phenomenon occurs over a height range of 80–140 km with a typical trail being 25 km long. As the meteoroid orbital velocity is comparable with that of the Earth, the number swept up by the Earth on its forward side as it travels around the sun is considerably higher than on its trailing side. There is thus a marked maximum of meteor trail formation in the period midnight to noon and a minimum in the afternoon/evening hours, a four to one variation being seen. There is also a marked seasonal variation, with the July/August sporadic meteor flux rate being 4–5 times the February/March rate.

As observed on the range/amplitude (A scope) display of an HF pulse radar of >10 kW peak power, meteor echoes are seen at the range of the intersection of the main antenna beam with the E-layer, typically 200–500 km slant range. A pulse-like echo peaks up rapidly to maximum amplitude in a fraction of a second and either dies away rapidly with a fluctuating decay over a second or so (underdense trail) or persists for many seconds or even minutes, then decaying rapidly (overdense trail). The overdense trails are those for which the plasma frequency in the trail exceeds the radar frequency so that total reflection occurs.

As observed on a Doppler radar, the effect varies with the coherent integration time. With a response time of a fraction of a second, the falling Doppler shift of the approaching meteor head as it travels towards the point of nearest approach may be detected. The simplest apparatus needed is a receiver with a beat frequency oscillator located within the skip distance from a high power transmitter; audible descending whistles will be heard, followed by large amplitude non-Doppler shifted signals after the trail has embraced the central Fresnel zones around the point of minimum path length needed for specular reflection. Finally the fluctuating decay is noted, as the linear trail is distorted by

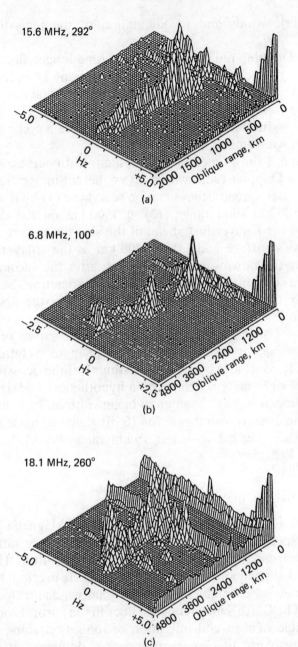

Fig. 5.8 Range-Doppler-amplitude plots for sky-wave pulse radar. Range bins 0.5 ms/75 km, coherent integration 50 s. Amplitude staircase 10 dB steps; (a) land-sea transition (change over from single peak to Bragg pair at 750 km); (b) E- and F-propagated modes with different Doppler shifts; (c) meteor returns (large spectral spread) at short and long range penetrations of E-layer. (*After Humphrey and Gibson*[19].)

ionospheric winds and recombination of the ionisation takes place.

On a Doppler radar of integration time longer than the trail duration, the echo response will overlap many Doppler velocity cells and an offset may be noticed due to the radial motion of the complete trail in the prevailing ionospheric wind. This last effect will have a diurnal variation as the winds have a cyclic azimuthal variation with time of day.

Figure 5.8 shows meteor echoes along with surface clutter as seen on a Doppler radar with a 50 s coherent integration time[19]. The Doppler spread echoes can be seen here (1) by line-of-sight at 200–500 km slant range, (2) at 1500 km on the downward transit of the E-layer just ahead of the skip distance return from the Earth's surface and (3) at 3400 km as the E-layer is penetrated by the downward travelling ray after the second F-layer reflection. (Additional meteor returns are sometimes seen as the radio ray travels up through the E-layer after the first ground reflection.)

Milsom[20] has published a useful up-to-date survey of the properties of meteor trails and the effect of meteor clutter on HF radars. He concludes by giving an estimate of the occurrence rate of line-of-sight meteor echoes on a hypothetical 7 MHz radar of 300 kW mean power, 2° antenna beamwidth and 2 s integration time. The average count rate for 16 dB signal-to-noise ratio was predicted as 450 echoes/h per 10 km range bin in August and 100/h in February.

5.4.4 AURORAL CLUTTER

When an HF radar is directed towards the Magnetic North, a highly aspect-sensitive type of echo is seen, very different in character from any of the foregoing classes of clutter. This arises from field aligned ionisation caused by particle precipitation from the magnetosphere influenced by the solar wind and electric field effects. The Earth's magnetic field lines in the auroral zone have a steep angle of dip, and migration of ionisation along the field from ionosphere to magnetosphere is a dominant effect. This results in near-vertical tubes of ionisation persisting as entities, forming linear features from which aspect-sensitive echoes arise. The electric fields associated with current systems in the E-layer drive these near-vertical tubes of ionisation laterally along complex-shaped trajectories around the pole, so that the tubes are in motion relative to the radar. Some success in modelling this complicated situation has been achieved by Elkins[21].

Much information on the phenomena has been acquired from VHF and UHF radars, but an added complication with HF radars is that ray refraction in the E- and F-layers influences the otherwise simpler geometry governing the location of the small regions where orthogonality takes place between the radio ray and the ionisation tubes. An example of a calculation including these refraction effects by Villain, Greenwald and Vickrey is shown in Fig. 5.9. The importance of such calculations may be realised from the aspect sensitivity figure generally accepted, namely a 10 dB decrease in backscattered power per degree off-perpendicular. The Doppler spread associated with auroral clutter may extend to greater than 10 Hz.

5.5 Propagation factors: ground wave

HF ground wave radar operation over the sea to beyond the horizon makes use of the low attenuation over salt water at HF of vertically polarised waves. This attenuation is very low at 2 MHz,

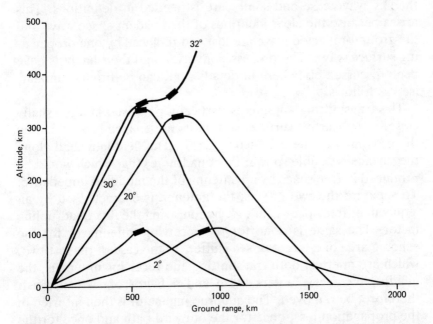

Fig. 5.9 Ray tracing in a geomagnetic meridian plane for an HF radar located at Anchorage, Alaska. The rectangles on the rays indicate that the ray is within 1° of normal to the Earth's magnetic field. (*Simplified form of: Villain, J.P., Greenwald, B.A. and Vickrey, J.F., Radio Science, 19, 359 (1984).*)

only 4 dB more than over a perfectly conducting plane for a one way path over a smooth sea to 200 km, but rises with frequency until at 30 MHz for the same distance the attenuation is 53 dB. There is also additional loss for propagation over a rough sea[23], the loss over a 200 km one way path at 10 MHz rising by 10 dB between the conditions of smooth sea and sea state 6 (surface wind 30 knots).

The lower frequencies, 2–4 MHz, initially seem attractive for such systems because of the low ground wave attenuation, but balancing disadvantages are the large antenna aperture needed for a narrow beam (4 km for a 2° beam at 2 MHz) and the high night-time noise and interference level. Frequencies between 20 and 30 MHz have the attraction of low noise level and freedom from spectral congestion, but are only suitable for short range because of the high attenuation. This band has found application for short range sea-surface current mapping radars, where the interest is in estuarial tidal streams and currents at ranges up to 30 km or so. For most applications where ranges up to 200 km are sought, operation in the band 5–15 MHz is logical.

The radar equation for the ground wave mode is different from the sky wave case and some care is needed in definitions. This arises because the clear identities of the incident space wave and the ground-reflected wave are lost and replaced by one propagating surface wave. The processes involved and their analysis have been discussed elsewhere in detail[24], but can be briefly summarised as follows.

The transmitting antenna is vertically polarised and is usually close to the Earth's surface, so that its impedance is modified by the proximity of the conducting Earth. The field launched along the surface is double (power flux quadruple) that which would be produced in free space by an antenna of the modified impedance. To separate the two effects, the antenna is characterised by an 'equivalent free space gain', g', by removing the flux quadrupling factor. The same is done for the receiving antenna or for the echoing area of a target or sea clutter. In the case of the last two, which are in effect both transmitting and receiving antennas, the quadrupling factor enters twice and a factor of sixteen must, therefore, be removed. The quadrupling factor is then inserted in the propagation loss, once for the outward path and once for the return. This concept, first introduced by Norton, eliminates the awkward necessity for making the effective apertures of transmitting and receiving antennas different.

The final radar equation thus takes the form

$$P_r = \frac{P_t g_t{}'}{4\pi R^2} \cdot 4 \cdot \frac{\sigma'}{4\pi R^2} \cdot 4 \cdot \frac{g_r{}' \lambda^2}{4\pi} \tag{19}$$

Note that the quadrupling factor now enters once only on the outward path and once on the return path. If the echoing area, as measured in free space, of a target such as an aircraft is inserted, the equation will correctly account for the over-sea propagation terms. Unfortunately, the definitions chosen for clutter have led to some confusion due to the adoption of two different conventions. Barrick, in his derivation of the normalised backscattering cross section of sea clutter, has used the form discussed in Section 5.4.1, in which irradiation is by an identifiable incident plane wave, a convention quite logical for sky wave illumination. For a directional sea wave spectrum, which is fully developed at the Bragg resonance sea wavelength for the incident radio wavelength, and which has a semi-isotropic directional pattern, this model leads to a backscattering cross section of -17 dB relative to 1 m^2 per square metre of sea surface. As explained above, to put this cross section in terms of the total field at the surface for insertion in Equation 19, it is necessary to extract a factor of sixteen, or 12 dB, leading to a value of -29 dB > 1 m^2/m^2. Barrick, however, leaves the value at -17 dB and modifies Equation 19. This procedure has led to confusion when measurements are compared with the two different theoretical approaches.

A procedure avoiding the difference between ground wave and sky wave treatments (which is behind these difficulties) is to remove the flux enhancing factor from σ_o in the sky wave equation in a similar fashion to the ground wave analysis. A difference is that this factor is then elevation-angle dependent. The sky wave backscattering coefficient then becomes:

$$\sigma_o = \sigma_o{}' \cdot F(\Delta) \tag{20}$$

In this equation, σ_o is the value used in the sky wave analysis of Equation 15, σ'_o is the equivalent free space cross section and is a factor of 16 less that σ_o, while $F(\Delta)$ gives the elevation angle dependance. For ground wave propagation and small elevation angle sky wave propagation, $F(\Delta)$ will be 16 ($+12$ dB), but at higher angles would constitute the vertical reradiation pattern factor. Adoption of this convention might usefully form the basis of a new standard. An illustration of the application of this ground wave theory is given in the section on remote sensing.

5.6 HF radar systems

Two features required by HF radar systems will have become clear from the discussion of propagation factors. First, the operating wavelengths are in the dekametric band, so that to obtain narrow beams, antenna apertures of hundreds to thousands of metres will be required. Secondly, sky wave systems require to operate over a 4:1 frequency band and (for many requirements) ground wave systems also require at least 2:1. These two features have a dominant effect on transmitter, antenna and receiver design and make the discipline different in kind from microwave radar, where antenna apertures greater than 10 m and bandwidths greater than 10% are rare.

Other features identified are the high noise level (20–40 dB above kTB), the congested radio spectrum, which particularly at night can make clear channel identification a major problem, the high clutter-to-signal ratio and the variable path attenuation in sky wave propagation.

In the space available here, it is possible only to illustrate with various examples the solutions which have been adopted in various sky wave and ground wave applications. Figures 5.10, 5.11 and 5.12 show some of the antenna systems which have been used.

5.6.1 SKY WAVE SYSTEMS, EXPERIMENTAL

Early sky wave radar systems in the 1950s were principally aimed at ionospheric propagation assessment, either by multi-frequency observations in a given direction using rhombic or broadside array antennas[16,25], or by the use of a rotating antenna and plan position indicator. In the latter type, Yagi antennas of three or four elements were used, giving, for common transmit-receive operation, beamwidths of 30°–40°. In the IGY Backscatter Sounder[26], three such antennas, each for a different frequency, were mounted on a common rotatable pole, each antenna being at the same height in wavelengths to give identical vertical radiation patterns. A peak power of 1 kW and a pulse length of 1 ms (corresponding to a range gate width of 150 km) was employed. The clutter amplitude received at this low power was enhanced by the spatial integration provided by the 1 ms pulse for a tolerable price in range resolution for the purpose in hand.

No Doppler capability was incorporated in these 'Scatter Sounders', the aim being to locate skip distance contours and the

Fig. 5.10 The Wide Aperture Research Facility (WARF) of SRI International at Los Banos, California, used for sky-wave radar and remote sensing experiments. The 2.5 km wide antenna is the receiving array of a bistatic FMCW radar and has 256 twin-whip doublets which can be phased to look east or west and achieves a beamwidth of 0.5° at 15 MHz. (*Photograph courtesy of SRI International.*)

location of sporadic E clouds by the presence or absence of sky wave propagated ground backscatter. Such information is also a vital requirement of modern HF radar installations to permit good frequency management. Figure 5.13 shows how much useful information on coverage such sounding can yield, in spite of the poor azimuthal resolution. The radar[1] operated at 17 MHz, using

Fig. 5.11 A 49-element 300 m wide transmit-receive steerable antenna array located in the United Kingdom and used by the University of Birmingham and Rutherford-Appleton Laboratory for remote sensing of sea-state and ionospheric conditions (see Fig. 5.8). The tall central poles support a reflector curtain with 49 tilted fan monopoles (westward looking) strung between them and the shorter poles to the right. A further 49 elements (eastward looking) are strung to the left of the reflector. (*RSRE photograph, British Crown Copyright 1982.*)

Fig. 5.12 Part of the multiple beam receive array of active vertical loop/monopole elements used in ground-wave radar sea-state sensing and ship-tracking experiments by the University of Birmingham. UK. (See Fig. 5.7.) Two nested 15-element arrays of length 150 m and 300 m cover the frequency range 4–18 MHz and are used in conjunction with a nearby Log. Periodic transmitting array. (*Photograph E.D.R. Shearman.*)

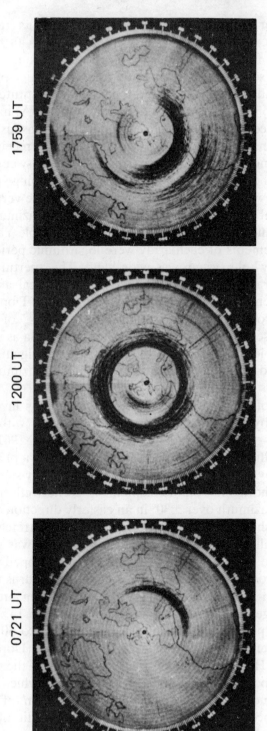

1759 UT

1200 UT

0721 UT

Fig. 5.13 Sequence of 17 MHz backscatter sounder PPI displays recorded at Slough, UK, showing (a) F2 propagation opening up to eastern Europe at dawn; (b) complete 1 hop F2 propagation azimuthal coverage at noon with sporadic-E clouds to NW and SW; (c) 1 and 2 hop F-propagation to SW at dusk. The fuzzy echoes to the north are fast-fading auroral echoes. (*After Wilkins and Shearman*[1].)

a peak pulse power of 150 kW and a pulse length of 140 μs (range resolution 20 km). The 4-element Yagi antenna had a 40° half-power beamwidth for common transmit-receive operation.

All these early 'sounders' used common transmit-receive operation, but the 'Table Mesa' radar developed at the Institute for Telecommunication Sciences at Boulder, Colorado, USA, in the late 1950s introduced a new principle. This used for transmission a floodlighting transmitter and one of two phased array receiving systems, one giving an azimuthally narrow fan beam sweeping horizontally and the other a vertically narrow fan sweeping vertically. This system was capable of some resolution of the vertical mode structure of the returns and of mapping the azimuthal structure with a much finer grain than possible with simple Yagis. The individual elements of each array were logarithmic periodic antennas, so the whole system was wide band. The aperture of the horizontal array was 450 m and that of the vertical array, 160 m. This system was later equipped with a pulse-Doppler capability and produced the first published example[16] of the mapping of land–sea boundaries (the coastline of Florida as seen from Boulder, Colorado) using the different Doppler signatures of sea- and land-echo in conjunction with high azimuthal resolution.

The detection of ships and aircraft by HF radar was investigated intensively by the US Naval Research Laboratory with the MADRE pulse – Doppler radar, operational from 1961 as described by Headrick and Skolnik[27]. The antenna was a phased array 98 m wide by 43 m high consisting of two vertically stacked rows, each of 10 horizontal dipole elements in corner reflectors. Beam steering in azimuth over ±30° in an easterly direction over sea was accomplished by mechanically actuated beam stretchers. In addition a smaller, rotatable corner reflector array was used for observations in other azimuths. This radar was equipped with Doppler signal processing which filtered out clutter returns with velocities less than 100 knots and displayed the remaining aircraft returns on a range/velocity format as shown in Fig. 5.14. The radar operated typically with average powers from 5 to 50 kW and with a coherent integration time of 10 s, giving a Doppler resolution of 0.1 Hz. The dynamic range displayed in the processed Doppler spectra was 60 dB. It was this radar which was used by Long and Trizna in the first demonstration of the measurement of ocean surface wind direction by the ratio of the approach and recede Bragg spectral lines in the sea clutter echo[27].

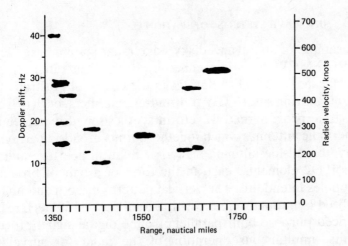

Fig. 5.14 Format of aircraft echoes on range/Doppler record obtained with Madre radar looking west across USA showing resolution by velocity of equi-range targets. (*After Headrick and Skolnik*[27].)

A pioneering system of considerable potential, illustrated in Fig. 5.10, which has led to new applications and to derivative systems, is the Wide Aperture Research Facility (WARF) at Los Banos, California, USA, designed and constructed by the Ionospheric Dynamics Laboratory, then part of Stanford University and now operated by SRI International. This is a bistatic radar using FMCW, the transmitter being 185 km distant. CW operation is possible, since the receiver is out of overland ground wave range and within the skip distance for the frequencies used for long range radar. The radar employs a steerable transmit beam to floodlight a sector within which the much wider receive array forms a similarly steerable group of eight simultaneous 0.5° beams. The receive array consists of 256 end fire doublets spaced 10 m apart. The doublets can be phased so as to beam west across the Pacific or east across the Caribbean. Sweep-frequency backscatter soundings are made to assist frequency management. The installation has been used intensively for remote sensing of ocean surface winds and wave height and for tracking of ships, as described by Maresca *et al.* and Barnum[28].

Other experimental radars in the UK, Australia, the USA and France are described in the survey papers by Shearman[29] and Croft[16] and recent work by the University of Paris by Parent and Gaffard[28].

5.6.2 SKY WAVE SYSTEMS, OPERATIONAL

An example of an advanced sky wave radar system based on the WARF FMCW bistatic technology is the Australian Jindalee radar located near Alice Springs in the centre of Australia[28]. At the transmitting site 16 CW transmitter amplifiers, each driven by a separate programmed waveform synthesiser, drive 16 end fire log periodic antennas which together form a broadside array. The receive broadside antenna array is 2.8 km in aperture and consists of 492 elements, each in the form of a pair of broadband monopoles in end fire. The vertical patterns of both antennas are stabilised by ground screens with a total area of 50 hectares. An advanced purpose built parallel/pipeline digital signal processor permits simultaneous operation of the radar for surveillance operations and for routine acquisition of sea state and propagation data.

In addition to operation at the full capability of the transmitters and receiving system, the installation can operate in sweep frequency backscatter, vertical or oblique sounding modes with no Doppler capability, or as a low power frequency agile 'mini radar'. In this last mode a repetitive narrow band sweep is dedicated to the gathering of range/Doppler scattering function plots for propagation assessment. These are presented in colour contour displays, analogous to the 'mountain range' plots obtained by the UK experimental installation and shown in Fig. 5.8.

The above sounding data provides the propagation and field strength data needed for efficient frequency management of the radar, but a different function provides the other essential information, the occupancy of the frequency channels available. This data is presented in a display of signal level *vs.* frequency and is also put together with the sweep frequency sounding data to provide a contour display of signal-to-noise ratio *vs.* frequency and slant range (group path). With these powerful aids, the Jindalee radar is provided with an enviable frequency management capability, a vital function which has been notably ill provided for in some earlier systems.

Defence journals suggest that major sky wave radar systems are now being installed in the continental United States.

A system which has not been described by its designers, but about which much has been learnt by radio reception and reported in the technical press, is the USSR 'Woodpecker', generally assumed to be a long range sky wave surveillance radar located in the Ukraine. The name comes from the characteristic 10 Hz pulse repetition frequency, a frequent source of irritation to short wave broadcast listeners. The effective radiated power during the pulse is very much larger than any other transmission heard in the HF band, including broadcasting. Although frequency agile, in that it frequently jumps in frequency after a dwell of several seconds, its power is such that the average receiver will indicate an output if tuned to within 1 MHz of the centre frequency. Its strength relative to high power broadcasters indicates an effective radiated power in the multi-gigawatt range. Another obvious feature is that the bandwidth is much wider than the inverse of the pulse width, suggesting that a spread spectrum modulation is employed, presumably to combine good range resolution with high average power. It would be interesting to see an engineering account of this installation, but in the absence of this, these speculations must suffice.

5.6.3 REMOTE SENSING AND SHIP TRACKING SYSTEM CONSIDERATIONS

In the above account of aircraft tracking with the MADRE radar, the 'MTI' technique of filtering out the ground or sea clutter was described. This approach is not available if the clutter itself is the concern, as in remote sensing, or if ships having velocities comparable with sea wave velocities are to be tracked.

In remote sensing, the aim is to process the sea echo so as to obtain high quality Doppler spectra, such as shown in Fig. 5.7. The process of extraction of sea wave information from such spectra would require a treatment of its own (for a survey see Ref. 29), but the features of the spectrum which yield wind wave, swell, and surface current magnitudes and directions are indicated in the legend of Fig. 5.7(a). It is important to realise that the observed Doppler spectrum is that of a noise-like process, reflecting the random nature of the sea wave directional/wavelength power spectrum. If one isolated spectrum is derived from a coherent integration period of, say, 240 s, this will constitute one estimate of this noise-like process with a resolution of 4 millihertz. A second or a third such spectrum would yield estimates with significant differences. To reduce the variance of the derived spectra, we must average N power spectra at a time to obtain resulting spectral estimates with a variance of $1/N$ of the individual spectra. It is this process which yields high quality data such as that of Fig. 5.7 (an average of 13 spectra), which show good consistency between adjacent range cells and time periods, for which the sea parameters would be expected to be substantially constant. Figure 5.7(b) shows the effect of increasing sea state on the second order continuum in the spectra. This continuum in sea-state sensing is inverted to derive the ocean wave directional spectrum; in ship tracking, it constitutes the clutter background which sets a limit to sensitivity.

To record faithfully the spectral features with a dynamic range of 60–70 dB, the quadrature samples of the baseband data from a given range gate over the coherent integration period must be digitised to at least 12 bit accuracy and weighted by a function which reduces the sidelobes in the frequency domain to the desired extent. When this is done, the integration periods may be overlapped by up to 50% with substantial independence of the weighted data, reducing the total time needed to acquire one averaged spectrum. Averaging over adjacent range or azimuth bins may also be used.

Although this spectral averaging technique has been introduced in the connotation of remote sensing, the same arguments apply to ship tracking. Ship echoes appear as discrete spectral peaks at a frequency offset from zero corresponding to the Doppler shift $(2v/\lambda)$ for the radial component, v, of the ship velocity. The spectral peak is distinguished from features in the sea echo spectrum by its localisation to one or two range cells and azimuths. It is, therefore, important to have as good an estimate as possible of the sea clutter spectrum to act as a stable comparison threshold; this may be obtained by averaging over spectra in adjacent range and azimuth cells not containing the ship echo and also carrying out temporal averages of both classes of cell. Beam, range cell and Doppler cell comparison techniques are used to increase the accuracy of target plots.

Ship-tracking results have been described for ground wave radar by Shearman *et al.*[21] and sky wave techniques and results with the WARF have been comprehensively reviewed by Barnum[28].

Ground wave radar systems for remote sensing of sea state, surface current mapping and iceberg detection and tracking are all reviewed in Ref. 28, which provides a good conspectus of the technology at the time of writing.

A technique not so far mentioned, but which is of considerable interest, is that of spectral processing before directional determination. It is clearly useful for discrete targets, but has also been used for surface current mapping in the CODAR system[28,29]. Pulsed sea echoes from four closely spaced whip antennas in a square are separately range-gated, the spectrum for each range gate derived and the four antenna outputs at each Doppler frequency processed to determine the direction of origin. Not more than two echo sources in the same range and Doppler cells may be resolved, which limits the complexity of surface current field which can be mapped. Nevertheless, considerable success in mapping has been achieved, claimed to approach the accuracies obtained with narrow beam systems without the large antenna arrays needed with the latter.

Another technique of interest is that used to acquire the data of Fig. 5.7. In order to avoid the disadvantages of pulse radar systems for use in the HF band (low duty ratio to avoid sky-wave clutter leading to the use of high peak powers with interference potential, wide pulse sideband spread and high output data rate) the FMCW scheme has been adopted. An interrupted format, FMICW, is used to permit common-site working. This scheme[30] is considered to have much potential for use in the HF band.

Figure 5.15 shows the sea echo/noise ratio achievable with a ground wave radar for different operating frequencies and for a mean power of 250 W.

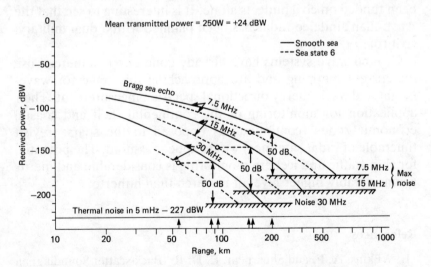

Fig. 5.15 Computed received powers for reception of Bragg sea returns and atmospheric/cosmic noise with 250 W mean transmitted power from ground wave radar installation of Ref. 24. The dotted lines show result of extra attenuation over ocean with sea state 6.

5.6.4 GROUND WAVE SYSTEMS

Although much has been published on ground wave radar systems associated with remote sensing and ship tracking, as already discussed in Section 5.6.2, no information has appeared on the use of ground wave radar for aircraft tracking. However, a feasibility study of such systems for use in the North Atlantic area has been presented by Millman and Nelson[31]. Using reasonable models for aircraft echoing area and atmospheric noise, together with feasible transmitter and antenna parameters, they conclude that such systems would be cost effective for detection of low flying aircraft out to 150 nautical miles.

5.7 Concluding remarks

Sky wave radar systems have now achieved a high degree of sophistication and have been demonstrated in the roles of aircraft tracking, ship tracking and sea-surface wind and waveheight mapping, with particularly spectacular results in hurricane tracking. An essential part of such systems is a comprehensive propagation and interference monitoring capability for frequency management. To date the expense of operational systems has meant that the progression from experimental to operational radars has not been funded on civil budgets alone. It is interesting to see that the Australian Jindalee radar has been planned with a dual military/ civil role.

Ground wave systems have already gone into commercial use for current mapping and are approaching this stage for waveheight and wave energy directional spectrum measurement. Their application for monitoring of the continental shelf and coastal economic zones (continuous as opposed to the sparse revisit timetable of radar satellites) would appear assured. The potential for ship traffic and iceberg monitoring is considerable and merits a considerably higher level of research than hitherto.

References

1. Wilkins, A. F. and Shearman, E. D. R. 'Back-scatter Sounding: an Aid to Radio Propagation Studies', *J. Brit. IRE*, **17**, 601–616 (1957).
2. Neale, B. T. 'CH – the First Operational Radar', *GEC J. of Res.*, **3**, 73–78 (1985).

3. Davies, K. *Ionospheric Radio Propagation*, New York, Dover (1966).
4. George, P. L. and Bradley, P. A. 'A New Method of Predicting the Ionospheric Absorption of High Frequency Waves at Oblique Incidence', *ITU Telecomm. J.*, May (1974).
5. CCIR *Atlas of Ionospheric Characteristics, Report 340*, ITU, Geneva (1983).
6. Braun, G. *Planning and Engineering of Shortwave Links*, London, Heyden (1982).
7. Barnum, J. R. 'Skywave Polarization Rotation in Sweep Frequency Sea Backscatter', *Radio Sc.*, **8**, 411–422 (1973).
8. Shearman, E. D. R. 'The Technique of Ionospheric Investigation Using Ground Backscatter', *Proc. IEE*, **103**, Part B, 210–223 (1956).
9. Croft, T. A. and Hoogasien, H. 'Exact Ray Calculations in a Quasiparabolic Ionosphere with no Magnetic Field', *Radio Sc.*, **3**, (Special Issue on ray tracing), 69–79 (1968).
10. Bradley, P. A. 'Long-term H.F. Predictions for Radio-circuit Planning', *Radio and Elec. Eng.*, **45**, 31–41 (1975).
11. Pielou, J. M. 'Sky-wave Radar Propagation Predictions for HF Radar System Planning', *IEE Proc. Int. Conf. Ant. and Prop.*, CP 248, London 510–514, (1985).
12. CCIR *Characteristics and Applications of Atmospheric Radio Noise Data*, Report 322-2 Geneva, ITU (1983).
13. CCIR *Antenna Diagrams: Arrays of Horizontal Dipoles, Horizontal Rhombics*, Geneva, ITU (1984).
14. Foppiano, A. J. and Bradley, P. A. 'Prediction of Auroral Absorption of High Frequency Waves at Oblique Incidence', *ITU Telecomm. J.*, **50**, 547–560 (1983).
15. Shearman, E. D. R. 'An Investigation of the Usefulness of Backscatter Sounding in the Operation of HF Broadcast Services', *Proc. IEE*, **108**, Part B, 361–374 (1961).
16. Croft, T. A. 'Sky-wave Backscatter: a Means for Observing our Environment at Great Distances', *Rev. of geophysics and space physics*, **10**, 73–155, (1972).
17. Hayden, E. E. 'Ground Scatter in Review', paper 1 Thrane, E. (ed.) *Proc. Conf. Scatter Prop. Radio Waves*, AGARD Conf. Proc. **37**, Part 1 (1968).
18. Barrick, D. E. 'Remote Sensing of Sea State by Radar', Chapter 12, 1–46, in *Remote Sensing of the Troposphere*, Derr, V. E. (ed.), US Govt. Printing Office (1972).
19. Humphrey, J. A. and Gibson, A. J. 'Doppler Analysis of Backscatter Radar Returns for High Frequency Propagation Studies', *Int. Conf. Ant. and Prop.*, IEE Conf. Pub. 248, 505–509 (1985).
20. *Ibid*, Milsom, J. D. 'Meteor Trail Detection Rates Using a Monostatic Pulse-Doppler HF Radar', 515–519.

21. Elkins, T. J. 'Recent Advances in HF Propagation Simulation', Paper 21, 1–17; Shearman, E. D. R., Sandham, W. A., Bramley, E. N. and Bradley, P. A. 'Ground-wave and Sky-wave Sea-state Sensing Experiments in the U.K.', Paper 30, 1–11 Coyne, V. J. (ed.) *Conf. Special Topics in HF Prop.* AGARD Conf. Proc. No. 263 (1979).
22. Rotheram, S. 'Ground-wave Propagation, Part I: Theory for Short Distances, Part II: Theory for Medium and Long Distances and Reference Propagation Curves', *Proc. IEE*, **128**, 275–295 (1981).
23. Barrick, D. E. 'Theory of HF and VHF Propagation Across the Rough Sea; 1. The Effective Surface Impedance For a Slightly Rough Highly Conducting Medium at Grazing Incidence; 2. Application to HF and VHF Propagation Across the Sea', *Radio Sc.*, **6**, 517–526 (1971).
24. Shearman, E. D. R. 'Propagation and Scattering in MF/HF Groundwave Radar', *Proc. IEE*, **130**, Part F, 579–590 (1983).
25. Shearman, E. D. R. 'A Study of Ionospheric Propagation by Means of Ground Back-scatter', *Proc. IEE*, **103**, Part B, 203–209 (1956).
26. Peterson, A. M., Egan, R. D. and Pratt, D. S. 'The IGY Three-frequency Backscatter Sounder', *Proc. IRE*, **47**, 300–314 (1959).
27. *Proc. IEEE*, Special number on 'Modern Radio Technology and Applications', **62**, 660–687 (1974).
28. *IEEE J. Oceanic Eng.*, Special issue on 'High Frequency Radar for Ocean and Ice Mapping and Ship Location', **OE-11**, 145–332 (1986).
29. Shearman, E. D. R. 'Radio Science and Oceanography', *Radio Sc.*, **18**, 299–320 (1983).
30. Wyatt, L. R., Burrows, G. D. and Moorhead, M. D. 'An Assessment of a FMICW Ground-wave Radar System for Ocean Wave Studies', *Int. J. of Remote Sensing*, **6**, 275–282 (1985).
31. Millman, G. H. and Nelson G. R. 'Surface Wave HF Radar for Over-the-horizon Detection', *IEEE Proc.*, IEEE Int. Radar Conf., Washington, 106–112 (1980).

CHAPTER 6
Secondary Surveillance Radar Techniques

H. W. COLE

As compared to primary radar, SSR has had very little concentrated academic treatment. Few books have been written on the subject. Those seeking fundamental data are commended to Refs. 1 and 2. SSR has a history as long as primary radar, and indeed it can be argued that they share the same birthday, the date of the Watson-Watt memorandum to the Air Ministry in 1935. In this, it was pointed out that if aircraft were to be attacked by radio means, it would first be necessary to identify them as 'friendly or hostile'. Thus came the name of such systems – 'IFF', identification, friend or foe. Numerous techniques were tried, including re-transmission of received primary radar signals by crude amplification in the aircraft. This was abandoned when primary radar frequencies moved into the 10 cm band; during the early 1940s, it was difficult to maintain stability of 10 cm transponders.

During World War II, very many people were involuntarily given the experience of flying. The realisation came that provided aircraft were not being shot at, they were a quick and reasonably safe method of travel. This, together with a vast stock of redundant airframes at the end of World War II, propelled the world into Civil Aviation. At this time, IFF had developed up to Mark 10 with its technique of pulse position coded interrogation and replies. It was seen by PICAO (The Provisional International Civil Aviation Organisation, established in 1944) as a near-ideal means of generating air traffic control data and work began on standardising performance parameters for SSR.

From the formation of ICAO in 1947 up to 1953 there were many bitter wrangles over which of two different interrogation standards to use[3].

As more and more civil aviation authorities operated SSR stations, the system's inherent problems became more widely known and solutions to all of them found[4]. However, a radical new approach was proposed in 1972 by Ullyat[5]. Called the 'Address Selectable (ADSEL) System', it quickly stimulated parallel work in the US (The Direct Addressed Beacon System, DABS). In 1983, ICAO published a rationalisation of these two companion schemes, both of which retained the existing SSR frequencies of 1030 MHz and 1090 MHz for interrogation and reply respectively. The rationalised system is known as Mode S and avoids the fundamental 'self-inflicted' wounds of the SSR Systems. It also massively increases data capacity.

A summary of important dates and events is shown in Fig. 6.1. Because SSR has relatively little collected literature, a brief introduction to its basic principles is given below.

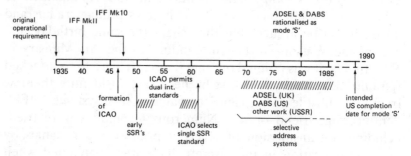

Fig. 6.1 A guide to significant dates in SSR.

6.1 Basic principles of SSR

Regular transmission of pairs of position coded pulses are made from the ground station at a frequency of 1030 MHz via a rotating aerial with a beam shape narrow in azimuth and wider in elevation, as in normal primary radar systems.

A pulse pair constitutes an interrogation and modes of interrogation are characterised by coding of the separation of the pair, internationally designated P_1 and P_3. Vehicles, commonly aircraft, using the system carry transponders which detect and decode interrogations by sensing pulse spacing. In the following text, the transponder will be assumed to be in an aircraft. When certain criteria are met, the transponders transmit a pulse position coded train of pulses at 1090 MHz, i.e. 60 MHz above that of the ground transmission, via an omni-directional aerial. The ground station receives these replies and decodes them to extract the data contained. This process of interrogation and reply is illustrated in Fig. 6.2.

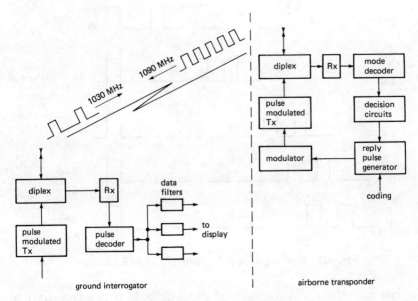

Fig. **6.2** Basic SSR system.

6.1.1 MODES OF INTERROGATION

These are shown in Fig. 6.3. Through the agency of the International Civil Aviation Organisation (ICAO) there is internationally agreed spacing and connotation for the civil modes. Various military agencies treat the military modes in similar fashion.

Military Modes Request:
  via Mode 1 – Secure data
  via Mode 2 – Secure data
  via Mode 3 – Joint military and civil identity data.

Civil Modes Request:
  via Mode A – Joint military and civil identity data (same as Mode 3)
  via Mode B – Civil identity data
  via Mode C – Altitude data
    Mode D – Is reserved for systems expansion (unassigned).

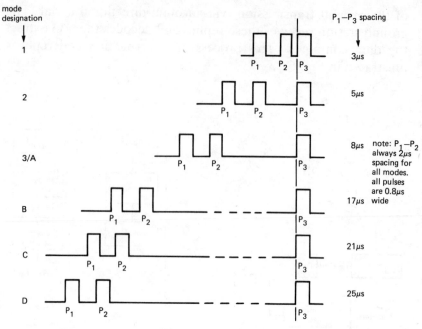

Fig. 6.3 Interrogation pulse structure in SSR systems.

Because there is a standarised small delay between receipt of a valid interrogation pair and the subsequent reply train (also standardised), the round trip time of interrogation and reply between a ground station and given aircraft allows range to be accurately measured as in primary radar systems. The dwell-time of the ground station's beam on target is generally of the order of 30 ms, dependent upon aerial beamwidth, rotation rate and interrogation rate (p.r.f.). There is thus time enough in general to make some 15 to 20 interrogations of a given target.

Advantage is taken of this to execute repetition of different modes by mode interlacing. Repetition confers the necessary redundancy of data in the system so that data accuracy is brought to a high level. By this means, for example, the range, bearing, altitude and identity of an aircraft can be accurately known during each and every passage of the beam across the target. Hence in one aerial revolution this data is gathered on all targets in the radar cover.

6.1.2 REPLIES

Aircraft fitted with transponders will receive interrogation during the dwell-time of the interrogation beam. The transponder carries out logic checks on the interrogations received. When relative pulse amplitudes, pulsewidth and spacing criteria are met, replies are made in the format shown in Fig. 6.4 within 3 μs of the receipt of the second pulse (P_3) of the interrogation pair. They are transmitted at a frequency of 1090 MHz, 60 MHz higher than the interrogation frequency. In air traffic control terms this confers an important advantage over primary radar, as can be seen from Fig. 6.5, illustrating the freedom from clutter of the SSR System. The pulse train of a reply is constructed according to internationally agreed standards, and allows configuration of any or all of the 12 information pulses contained between two bracket or framing pulses, designated F_1 and F_2 which are always present. The pulse structures possible may be deduced from Fig. 6.4.

The code is octal based; the four groups of three digits are designated in order of significance as groups A, B, C and D. Of the 4096 possible codes, ICAO specifies that code 7700 is reserved for signalling 'Emergencies', code 7600 to signal 'Communication Failure' and code 7500 to signal 'Unlawful Interference with the Aircraft', i.e. 'skyjacking'. Altitude is signalled by a Gilham code pattern giving increments of 100 ft. The tabulation can be found in the ICAO document Annex 10[7] and covers altitudes from − 1000 ft to +100 000 ft.

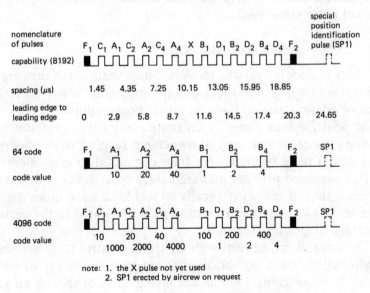

Fig. 6.4 The ICAO reply format in SSR.

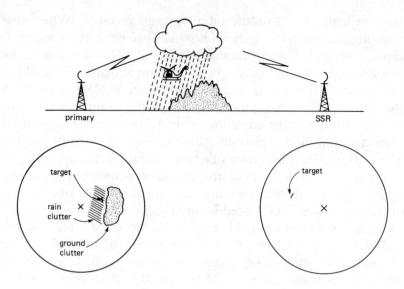

Fig. 6.5 The clutter-freedom of SSR.

It will be necessary in the following text to distinguish between two types of SSR, defined as

Traditional SSR (non-monopulse).
Monopulse SSR.

The latter is almost always specified nowadays, having been in the market place since 1980.

6.1.3 OPERATIONAL REQUIREMENTS

In order to understand why modern equipments are as they are, it is helpful to appreciate the user's requirements. Many air traffic control administrations have, in recent years, adopted a policy of using SSR for long range or en-route coverage in preference to primary radar, whose cost of ownership (capital costs plus running costs) have become very high compared to equivalents in SSR. Combined primary and secondary radar cover is called for at much shorter ranges (typically 80 to 120 nautical miles dependent upon local needs). This strategy is illustrated in the vertical coverage diagram in Fig. 6.6.

The operational objective in air traffic control is to maximise controlled airspace utilisation after ensuring the safety of traffic within it. Since control entails the laying down of specific airways and 'advisory routes' for air traffic, aircraft separation standards

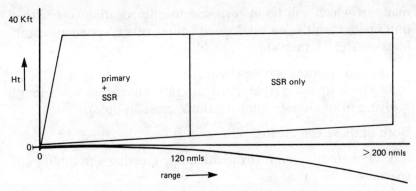

Fig. 6.6 Modern A.T.C. radar strategy.

for safety have to be maintained. Altitude encoding and calibration allow automatic height reporting to 100 ft increments
with an accuracy of 500 ft for all airspeeds. This is entirely
satisfactory for en-route operations where lateral separations are
more naturally sought. (Modern aircraft usually seek the same
altitudes for minimum fuel consumption and maintain them for as
long as possible. It is worth observing that those with the same
destination also seek the same final altitude – that of the runway.)
Thus if the SSR is to be used as a means of ensuring safe
separation standards, its range and azimuth resolution must be
consistent with these standards.

At present the procedural method of air traffic control[6] calls for
10 nautical miles separation between craft at the same altitude.
Some SSR systems designed in the past 15 years have 2.5 degrees
beamwidth and so produce this discrimination up to 230 nautical
miles. But many systems have much greater beamwidth. Thus
unless the effective beamwidth is reduced, the radar is merely
capable of monitoring current separation standards and not
improving them.

Modern systems, using monopulse direction finding techniques
for azimuth data have improved this resolving power by a significant margin, by evading the time-honoured relationship between
beamwidth and azimuth resolution, as will be shown later.

SSR range resolution is also now a complex parameter since it
depends upon the processing power brought to bear upon reply
signal pulses arriving simultaneously in the system.

Because SSR transponders all use one radiating frequency and
a standard set of pulse positions and durations, various ambiguities can arise from receipt of concurrent reply pulse trains,

many of which will be in response to interrogations other than one's own ('fruit'). As catalogued among other 'systematic problems' in Ref. 2, they are:

1. Asynchronous garble (by fruit).
2. Synchronous garble (two aircraft on the same azimuth replying to one's own interrogations, close in time).

Both of these can create:

3. 'Phantom' aircraft (by accidentally erecting unwanted pulse spacings of 20.3 μs).
4. Code corruption (by unwanted insertion of pulses at valid positions where none were intended).

Synchronous garble is illustrated in Fig. 6.7.

If we consider range resolution to be that corresponding to an 'aircraft in the clear', i.e. with no concurrent ambiguity – creating replies, then it has a limit of that range equivalent to 24.65 μs or 1.99 nautical miles – a value of 2 will be taken hereafter. Because ambiguities can be created by unwanted replies arriving either early or late relative to the wanted reply, the resolution cell has a range dimension of 4 nautical miles.

It is usual to find reply processors which have at least two simultaneously operated decoding channels. Using fast sampling rates and the foreknowledge of pulse durations and spacings, a commutating clock establishes coherent reply trains in either channel for subsequent validation. By this means 'garble by interleaved pulses' is resolved. The range resolving power of such a system is therefore enhanced until pulses of garbled replies begin to overlap.

Thus it can be appreciated that in order to provide more effective air traffic control (A.T.C.), modern SSR systems need improvements in both azimuth and range resolution capability. The development of monopulse techniques and processing extra data (which traditional SSRs did not generate) have achieved this improvement.

6.2 Systematic effects creating problems

The following is a short resume of the systematic problems in SSR and their causes, presented to clarify understanding of the modern solutions.

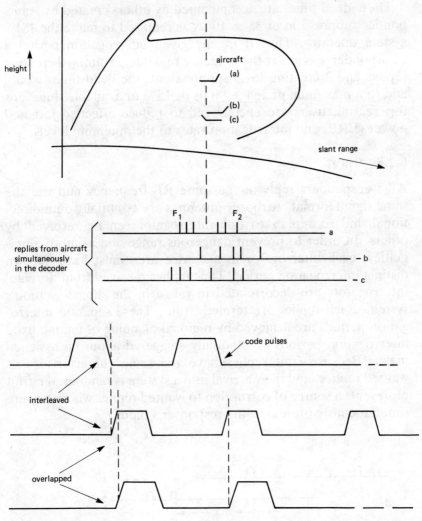

Fig. 6.7 Garbling.

6.2.1 'DEAD TIME'

When transponders are making reply to valid interrogations, their receivers must be inhibited for at least the reply duration. The ICAO specification permits this reply dead time to grow to 127 μs. Thus during these dead times created by one interrogator, other interrogators are denied a service. If the interrogation rate was the maximum permitted (450 per second) each reply dead time represents about 6% of active time.

These dead times are accompanied by others created by transponder suppression of 35 ± 10 μs as required to make the ISLS system operate[2]. Thus if in any given interrogation period a transponder was under the influence of 4 interrogators, 2 creating replies and 2 creating ISLS suppressions, the dead times would add to a maximum of $254 + 90$ μs or 15% of available time. For this reason, users are encouraged to reduce effective radiated power (ERP) and interrogation rates to the minimum levels.

6.2.2 'FRUIT'

All transponders reply at the same RF frequency and use the same signal format. Airborne antennas are essentially omnidirectional and so replies to one interrogator can be received by others. In order to prevent dangerous range and azimuth ambiguities, each interrogator in a service area must have its own distinct interrogation period. Thus replies received from 'foreign' interrogators are decorrelated in range in the 'home' station's system. Such replies are termed 'fruit'. These separate interrogation periods are achieved by regional planning of unique fixed interrogation periods or randomly staggered about an assigned mean. Because fruit replies have the same characteristics as wanted replies, and their arrival into a system is random, the fruit represents a source of corruption to wanted replies when they are simultaneously present at the responser's input.

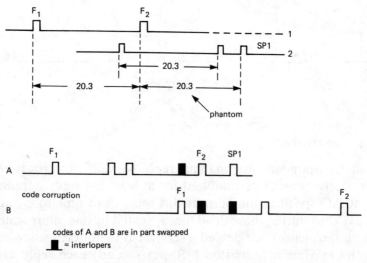

Fig. 6.8 Consequences of garbling.

Apart from minimising ERP and interrogation rates, two other means of reducing fruit are interrogation sidelobe suppression (ISLS), and receiver sidelobe suppression (RSLS). The latter uses two antenna patterns in much the same manner as for ISLS, but simultaneously in the receive mode[8].

6.2.3 CAPTURE

If transponders are bombarded with requests to reply, their transmission output stages can be overloaded. To prevent this, transponders sense the reply rate demands and when these grow to 1200 per second and above, their receivers are automatically reduced in sensitivity. Under these desensitised conditions the transponder will not respond to distant interrogators; the nearer ones will have 'captured' it from others at greater range.

6.2.4 GARBLE

Garble is a condition where two or more replies enter the system in the same time frame; i.e. within 20.3 μs of each other (24.65 μs if the SPI is included). Two classes may be identified:

1. Synchronous.
2. Asynchronous.

In the former, two aircraft at the same slant range ±1.64 nautical miles and within the same interrogator's beamwidth will issue replies synchronous to the interrogator if they respond to the same mode. In the latter, fruit replies arrive in the system at the same time as a wanted reply ±20.3 μs.

Both these classes have a further two-part distinction (see Fig. 6.7): those wherein the pulses of one reply lie within the spaces between the other and those wherein pulses of each reply overlap. These are known as 'garble by interleaving' and 'garble by overlap'. As will be seen later, modern signal processing can resolve almost any garbled situation.

6.2.5 'PHANTOM REPLIES'

A code train is declared 'valid' whenever the two framing pulses F_1 and F_2 are sensed to be 20.3 μs apart. Two garbled replies should yield two such instances. However, it is possible to find more conjunctions of code pulses within the two garbled trains which are also 20.3 μs apart. These pseudo F_1/F_2 pairs will appear as 'phantom' replies, as indicated in Fig. 6.8.

6.2.6 CODE CORRUPTION

Figure 6.8 also illustrates how corrupt codes can be present through garbling. In the case of synchronous garble this can be very troublesome, particularly if the wanted code is an altitude response: its corruption into false values could be dangerous.

6.2.7 FALSE REPLIES

It is possible (and is frequently found in practice) that valid interrogations are reflected by large vertical surfaces in the inter-rogation path into azimuths different from the antenna boresight. Any replies stimulated by these reflected interrogations will be returned by the same path. Thus valid reply trains appear in the system from completely erroneous bearings. The mechanism is described in Ref. 9, which also includes data on successful means of overcoming the problem.

6.2.8 BROKEN VERTICAL COVERAGE

This is not so much a systematic problem as one created by adopting the simplest design in antennas. Since most SSR systems are operated in conjunction with primary radars, it was custom-ary to mount the SSR on top of the primary radar antenna. To minimise the mechanical load (dead weight and windage) on the host turning gear, the SSR antennas were made in the form of linear arrays of small vertical aperture (typically 1.5 wave-lengths). The resultant wide elevation beam directs an inordinate amount of power into the ground surrounding the antenna, cre-ating deep nulls and extensive lobes in the radiated pattern in the elevation plane. Because of the high position of the antenna above the reflecting plane, the lobes and nulls are commonly numerous. Their position is given by the formula

$$\sin \theta_n = n\lambda/4h$$

where λ = wavelength in metres
h = height of the phase centre above the reflecting surface
θ_n = the elevation angle of the nth lobe or gap in the elevation domain
n = an integer (odd values represent lobes, even values represent nulls).

As a practical example, an antenna at a height of 27 m will produce a first lobe at 0.143 degrees elevation, a first null at 0.286 degrees, a second lobe at 0.429 degrees, etc. As a result, aircraft flying at a constant height will have their signal strengths modulated (both interrogations and replies) by the wildly fluctuating vertical polar diagram. At long ranges (where the SSR is used to provide en-route cover) the modulation can cause complete fading and so track discontinuities.

6.2.9 POOR AZIMUTH DATA

In traditional SSRs it is usual to find the aircraft azimuth is derived by seeking the 'centre of gravity' of the group of replies created as the interrogator's beam sweeps across the transponder, i.e. if the aircraft issues 21 replies per beamwidth, logic circuits seek the azimuth at which the eleventh reply is made. In general if there are n replies in a given beamwidth, the azimuth of $n/2$ is sought. This is usually done by storing the range and azimuth values of valid replies for a number of successive interrogation periods.

When n out of m successive replies correlate in range the presumption is made that a transponder has begun to be illuminated by the antenna beam and a 'leading edge' of a series which will form a target plot is declared. Correlation is continued until there are p failures of correlation out of q successive trials. This is held to represent the 'trailing edge' of the series. The azimuth of the leading and trailing edges are called from store and their mid point calculated, taking into account the small angles represented by n and p. The system is illustrated in Fig. 6.9.

Through the combined effects of 'dead' times, vertical polar diagram fading, failures to respond to interrogation, reply corruption, false alarms, etc., the declaration of plot leading and trailing edges can be in error. Sometimes false trailing edges are declared which, if near the true trailing edge azimuth, will not be discovered. These effects create azimuth jitter or 'track wander'. Naturally the azimuth errors are magnified at great range and can falsely indicate turns. The calculation of speed is also subjected to error. An example of the effect is shown in Fig. 6.10.

6.2.10 POOR AZIMUTH RESOLUTION

In the circumstances of two aircraft at the same range, they can be resolved provided their azimuth difference is greater than one

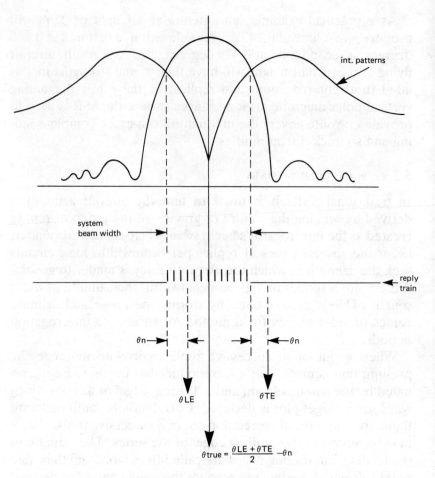

Fig. 6.9 'Sliding window' azimuth detection.

beamwidth. In many modern traditional SSR systems this is about 3 degrees, representing 12 nautical miles at 240 nautical miles range. As noted above, this is not adequate for maintenance of the required separation standard in A.T.C.

6.3   Modern solutions to SSR system problems
6.3.1   ANTENNAS

A number of the problems described above are solved by the use of modern antennas, with much larger vertical apertures and vertical distributions designed to produce a much better match to the operational requirements. These new large vertical aperture

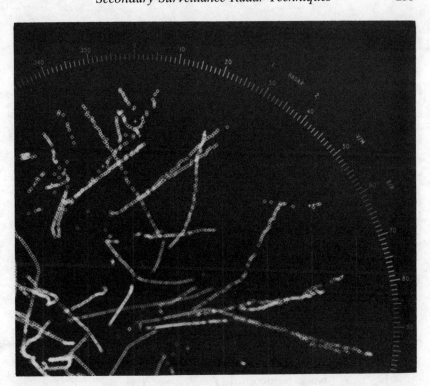

Fig. 6.10 Time exposure showing SSR plots derived by 'sliding window' detection process. Track jitter is obvious. Display range is 120 nm radius. (*Photo courtesy of Marconi Radar Systems Ltd.*)

(LVA) arrays are exemplified by that shown in Fig. 6.11. It consists of 35 identical radiator sets symmetrically disposed about its middle element. Each radiator has 10 vertically stacked dipoles fed by a strip line network within each element. The power distribution, designed by a special beam synthesising programme ('SYNF'), produces an extremely good fit to the specified ideal. Its main features are a very sharp bottom cut-off to the elevation pattern, dramatically reducing ground directed energy and hence reducing lobing, a very good fit to the 'cosecant squared' pattern desired for efficient radar coverage, and very low sidelobes in both horizontal and vertical planes.

Gains among the types currently available range from 19 dB to 29 dB, the common requirement being 24 dB. The antenna illustrated in Fig. 6.11 has gain of 29 dB, resulting from the high efficiency (85%) of the 'SYNF' design technique. The measured elevation pattern, relative to that of a typical 'hogtrough' antenna, is shown in Fig. 6.12.

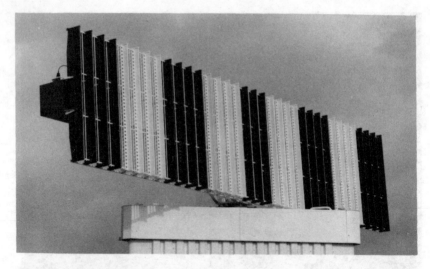

Fig. 6.11 MRSL LVA Type S1095. (*Photo courtesy of Marconi Radar Systems Ltd.*)

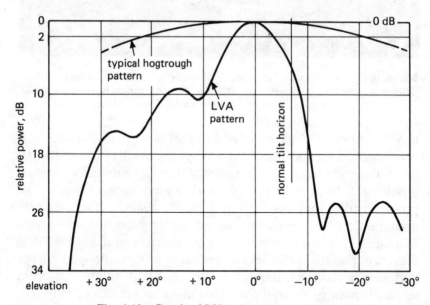

Fig. 6.12 Graph of LVA elevation pattern.

The horizontal polar patterns are suitable for both traditional and monopulse SSR systems. In the former it is possible to use either the difference or the control patterns for ISLS. The patterns are shown in Fig. 6.13.

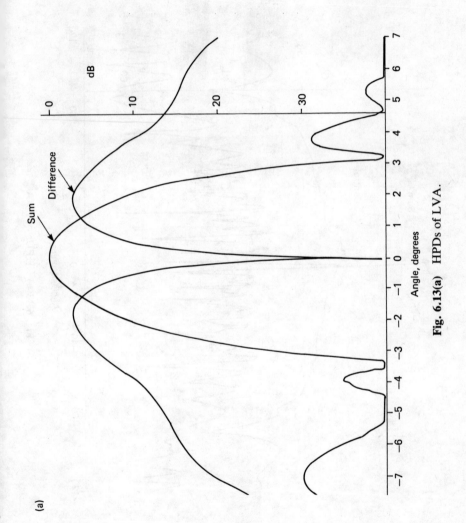

Fig. 6.13(a) HPDs of LVA.

(b)

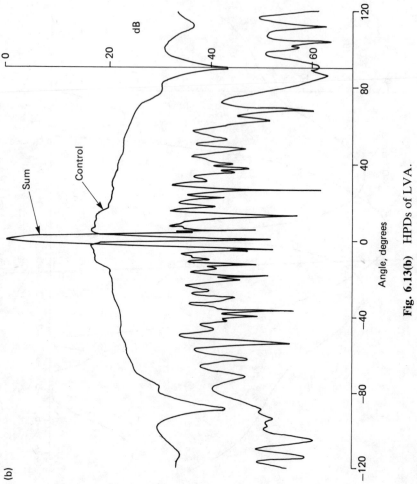

Fig. 6.13(b)   HPDs of LVA.

6.3.1.1 *Integrated primary/secondary antennas*

A small number of designs have emerged wherein the primary reflector is used for both primary and secondary radar systems, there being an 'integrated' primary/secondary radar feed system. The technique is not favoured because the feed arrangements force compromise in performance on either the primary or secondary radar system (sometimes both). This compromise is usually unacceptable. In the S.712 radar, the SSR beams are formed by a row of dipoles at the base of the main reflector. For this radar the compromise (in SSR vertical pattern shaping and primary radar antenna 'blockage') is acceptable.

The LVA overcomes problems created by the use of a small vertical aperture. It is particularly helpful in reducing reflections to a marked degree. This is illustrated in Fig. 6.14(a) and (b), which shows results achieved in a test carried out by the UK Civil Aviation Authority (CAA). Figure 6.14(a) shows plot extracted outputs from a system using a 'hogtrough' antenna. The dots represent true extracted plots from an aircraft flown orbitally at 15 nautical miles at 8000 ft. The crosses are plots derived from reflections – the site was deliberately chosen for its propensity to generate false plots by reflection. Figure 6.14(b) shows the same data but with a Marconi Radar S1095 LVA in place of the hogtrough when the same aircraft repeated the orbital flight at the same height. In both cases no reflection suppression techniques were used; the improvement shown is produced purely by the antenna characteristics. Using the 'hogtrough', 60% of plots resulted in false companions. The LVA reduced this to 3.5%.

Another desirable virtue of the LVA is that all patterns used in both up and down link regimes share the same phase centre. Thus, if ground reflection effects are present, the patterns retain their relationships throughout the elevation range despite any modulation away from the free space values.

6.3.2 MONOPULSE TECHNIQUES

As its name implies, monopulse technique allows the azimuth of each and every pulse entering the system to be measured with high accuracy. Most monopulse systems also preserve the pulse input amplitude data. In traditional SSRs, this data was almost always dispensed with at the earliest possible stage, to create purely digital signals. The availability of this extra data for subsequent processing has enabled the monopulse system to overcome some

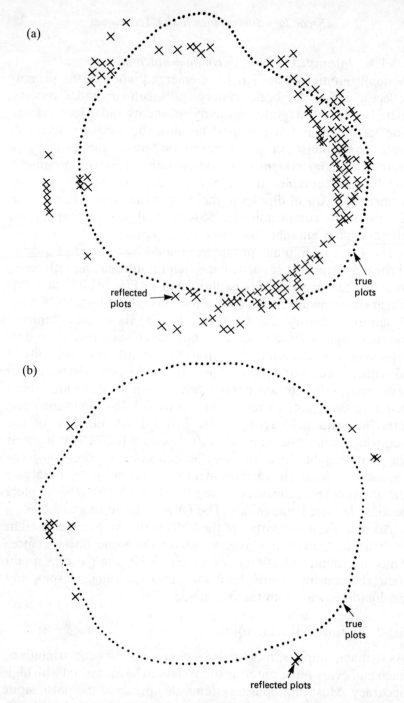

(a)

(b)

true plots

reflected plots

true plots

reflected plots

Fig. 6.14 (a) and (b) Results of comparison between 'hogtrough' and LVA antennas showing the vast improvement by LVAs in protection from reflected interrogation effects. False replies reduce from 60% to 3½%. Flight and site conditions were kept constant. The aircraft flew an orbit of 15 nautical miles radius at 8000 ft height. (*Reproduced by kind permission of UK CAA.*)

of the SSR systematic problems and to reduce greatly the impact of others. There are two classes of monopulse direction finding technique, both using 'sum and difference' antenna patterns, simultaneously feeding parallel receiver chains. One class uses the amplitude and the other the phase differences found at the output of the two parallel channels from a common signal input. In essence the two schemes are illustrated in Fig. 6.15(a) and (b). A classic analysis is to be found in Ref. 10.

6.3.2.1 *Amplitude comparison monopulse – Fig. 6.15(a)*
The use of logarithmic amplifiers for the sum and difference channel inputs allows the ratio of the two to be derived. This ratio detection scheme permits a greater part of the sum and difference beamwidth to be used than if simple amplitude difference were sought. In the latter case, ambiguity at azimuths greater than the sum and difference pattern cross-over points could not be resolved.

The azimuth patterns are symmetrical about boresight. Left–right ambiguity is resolved by a phase sensitive detector which senses reversal of the phase of the difference signal relative to the sum signal as it assumes bearings either side of boresight. A common design aim is for the logarithmic receivers to have in excess of 70 dB dynamic range and to 'track' within 0.5 dB across this range. Such systems have direction finding errors (for the whole system including antenna twist) of typically 6 minutes of arc rms. There is a limitation set to accuracy about boresight where system noise clouds the difference signal and the left–right ambiguity bit (the difference pattern has a very deep null on boresight and reverses sign there). For this reason some systems inhibit the use of 'off boresight azimuth' (OBA) when these are ±0.5 degree or less.

6.3.2.2 *Phase comparison monopulse – Fig 6.15(b)*
The most elegant forms of phase comparison monopulse use dual phase detection (sometimes referred to as 'half-angle' detection). Such devices have the distinct advantage of greater immunity to noise and the ability to cancel small differential phase errors up to the point where IF signals are generated.

6.3.2.3 *OBA derivation*
In both amplitude and phase comparison systems the OBA is generated by use of a 'look-up' table. In the former the table

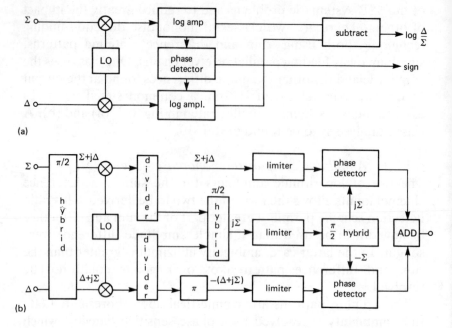

Fig. 6.15 Monopulse direction finding schemes; (a) amplitude processing; (b) phase processing.

takes the form of the sum to difference ratio expected from foreknowledge of the antenna horizontal polar diagrams in the main sum beam region. In the phase comparison system the function is sinusoidal, crossing zero at boresight.

In both cases, to obtain the looked for sensitivity in OBA measurement and to maximise accuracy, the systems need to be calibrated upon installation. During this process the 'look-up' tables are linearised – usually by corrections applied to the A to D converters forming the final OBA output to subsequent processors as a multi-bit digital word.

6.3.2.4 *Comparison of monopulse techniques*
Both amplitude and phase direction finding techniques can take various engineering forms. The output signals from the antenna's two symmetrical halves can be combined by hybrid circuits to produce various signals for subsequent processing. These are generally representative of the sum and difference of the antenna's outputs and their orthogonal components.

Thus Σ, Δ, $\pm j\Sigma$, and $\pm j\Delta$ signals can be made available. Figure 6.16 shows different processing methods of using these signals

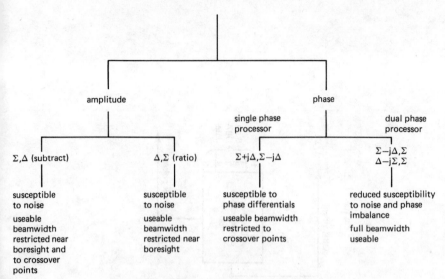

amplitude   phase

single phase processor   dual phase processor

Σ,Δ (subtract)	Δ,Σ (ratio)	Σ+jΔ,Σ−jΔ	Σ−jΔ,Σ Δ−jΣ,Σ
susceptible to noise	susceptible to noise	susceptible to phase differentials	reduced susceptibility to noise and phase imbalance
useable beamwidth restricted near boresight and to crossover points	useable beamwidth restricted near boresight	useable beamwidth restricted to crossover points	full beamwidth useable

Fig. 6.16 OBA processing review chart.

with important features noted. All methods are susceptible to errors created by the difference signal's diminished strength in its deep null and any differential phase. However, the dual phase processing scheme has greater noise immunity and has self-cancelling of small phase differentials of Σ and Δ inputs.

A practical modern form of dual phase processor is shown in Fig. 6.17. Its performance against a fixed transponder at an accurately known position is shown in Fig. 6.18. The OBA is expressed as an 8-bit word (7 bits + 1 bit signal left or right boresight). Thus, for an effective OBA aperture of 5°, the OBA increment is 1.17 minutes of arc.

6.3.2.5 *Azimuth position reporting*
Such high discretion of direction finding demands an azimuth reporting system whose discretion and stability is equally high, requiring extreme rigidity in antennas and their support structures. It is common to find system error contributions from such sources limited to not greater than 2 minutes of arc.

The azimuth reporting elements themselves must be directly coupled mechanically to the antenna's final turning shaft; any gear train coupling would be virtually impossible to design to the required limits of back-lash and wear. Various forms of digital shaft encoder are available, and for total system errors of around 6 minutes of arc a 14-bit structure is called for (1.3 minutes of arc

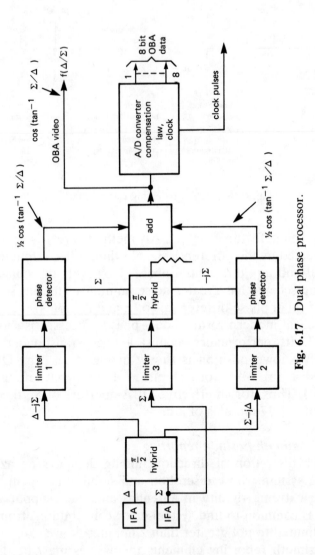

Fig. 6.17 Dual phase processor.

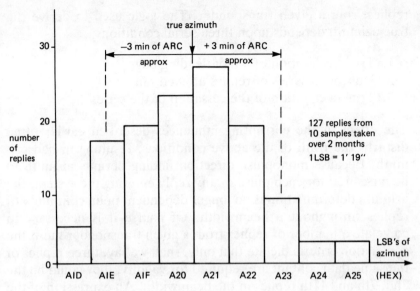

Fig. 6.18 Reply azimuth spread – fixed transponder.

per least significant bit). Again, rigidity, robustness and extreme reliability are demanded. A modern system with these properties uses an encoder based upon the rotary transformer principle (the inductosyn). In this, a stator forming the primary windings of the transformer is concentrically mounted around the antenna turning shaft and fixed to the stationary part of the antenna turning mechanism. The rotor, incorporating the secondary windings, is mechanically fixed to the turning shaft with a small air gap of about 0.01 in between the stator and rotor assemblies. The primary windings are excited by a 10 kHz source. The secondary windings' outputs are combined to express the shaft angle in a 'course, fine' system each of 8 bits. The total discretion can thus be a 16-bit word. In monopulse systems the target's true bearing is given by the sum of the OBA and the simultaneously reported boresight azimuth.

6.4 Monopulse contributions to solutions
6.4.1 AZIMUTH DATA

The foremost of monopulse contributions to solutions is the dramatic improvement in track smoothness. As described above, traditional SSR relies upon a complete beamwidth's history of replies from a given transponder. The logic used to derive the true azimuth depends upon three serial conditions:

1. True declaration of a plot 'leading edge'.
2. Unbroken series of replies at fixed range.
3. True declaration of the cessation of the series.

The effect of the corrupting influences described earlier often disturbs the truth of the above conditions, resulting in bad azimuth. Because monopulse direction finding permits azimuth to be measured for each pulse of any reply entering the system, the azimuth determination is no longer dependent upon continuity of replies throughout a beamwidth. Of course it is necessary to correlate a number of replies from a given transponder but if the correlation criteria dictate that only, shall we say, three replies of the same data content are required for validity, they could be the 2nd, 7th and 11th replies in the beamwidth. An expression of the power of monopulse in this respect is given by Fig. 6.21, which is a theoretical consideration wherein 'correct' azimuth discounts noise or quantisation errors and is based purely upon the logic of the two systems.

6.4.2   DEGARBLING

Modern semiconductor devices can operate at great speed, so that sampling times of 50 ns are now practicable. Secondary radar reply pulses have rise times of 50 ns and durations of 450 ns, so that it is possible to obtain the complete history of a standard pulse in about 10 samples; its true amplitude and OBA value can be sampled 7 times in the pulse duration at this speed. It is immediately obvious that interleaved pulses can be distinguished in a monopulse system with greater clarity than in traditional SSRs because not only are the time events of the interleaving pulses able to be measured; their accompanying OBA and amplitude differences can be called out also. The usually large number of pulses in a reply (average 8) allows considerable averging to be done as well. This serves further to improve azimuth data.

Garbling by overlapped pulses can also be much better resolved, because there will be portions of each overlapped pulse, at the edges, which are uncorrupted. With such fast sampling rates, the data contained in these uncorrupted regions is perfectly valid.

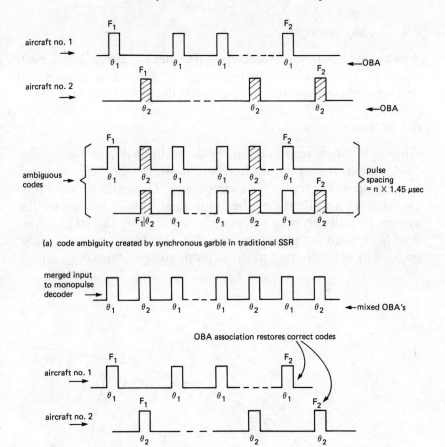

(a) code ambiguity created by synchronous garble in traditional SSR

(b) code ambiguity resolved by monopulse SSR

Fig. 6.19 (a) Code ambiguity created by synchronous garble in traditional SSR; (b) code ambiguity resolved by monopulse SSR.

6.4.3 PHANTOM REJECTION

In traditional SSR systems the reply data sought is almost exclusively restricted to the time at which pulse leading and trailing edges occur. Earlier, it was seen how synchronous replies can lead to unwanted conjunctions of pulses spaced 20.3 μs apart. This leads to generation of 'phantom' replies. In monopulse systems, OBA association can completely obviate such false detections within the azimuth discretion of the system. That is, provided the OBA values of the two pulses forming the phantom are different by more than the system azimuth error, phantoms can be rejected.

6.4.4 CODE CORRUPTION

Again, using both amplitude and OBA data associated with each pulse of two synchronously garbled replies, it is possible to resolve code ambiguities. The point is illustrated in Fig. 6.19.

6.4.5 RESOLUTION

Although range resolution in both traditional and monopulse SSR systems is very good, there will inevitably be times at which two transponders reply at the same range. Under these conditions the azimuth resolution of the traditional SSR is limited by the system beamwidth plus the margin required by the sliding window logic used for plot determination (establishing the 'leading' edge of its neighbouring plot). In monopulse systems the azimuth

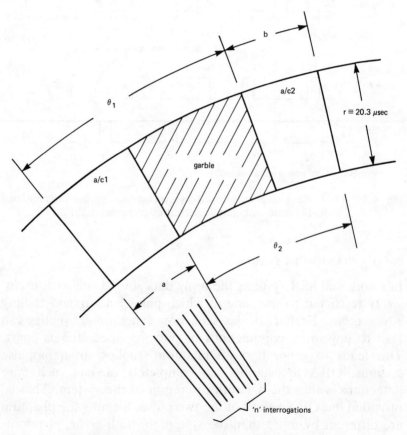

Fig. 6.20 Two aircraft in overlapped garble situation.

resolution is no longer a pure function of azimuth beamwidth but the time available to gather data 'in the clear' at the beginning and end of two synchronous reply trains. The situation is represented in Fig. 6.20. The two aircraft replies are shown with part of their azimuth history in overlapped garble. There will be times equivalent to *n* interrogations over the arcs a and b wherein incorrupt data on both aircraft can be gathered. The azimuth resolution now becomes limited to a much smaller angle than a beamwidth and depends upon the minimum permissible value of *n* and the time taken to execute it.

6.4.6 FRUIT

Although not essentially a property of monopulse systems *per se*, the technique of receiver sidelobe suppression (RSLS) comes as an almost automatic by-product of having the two simultaneous receiver channels required by monopulse. The two receivers are fed by a sum and difference pattern of the antenna. By ensuring that within the sum beam's sidelobe regions a signal from the difference channel is always superior to that simultaneously emerging from the sum channel, all signals other than in the main beam region can be inhibited. A great deal of fruit enters the system via sidelobes and so RSLS reduces this. Typical values of reduction are from 3 to 5 times, dependent upon antenna beamwidths and sidelobe levels.

There is a disadvantage in using RSLS purely as an inhibitor since there is always a possibility that a fruit pulse entering via a

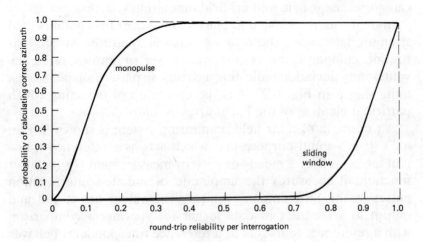

Fig. 6.21

sidelobe will be superior in amplitude to, and simultaneous with, a weak wanted signal in the main beam. In this case, wanted data would be inhibited. This disadvantage is overcome by replacing the inhibition function by one which labels a reply pulse with a 'flag' indicating it as emanating from a sidelobe or the main beam. Subsequent processing will then allow it to be used or disregarded as appropriate without wasting wanted data.

6.4.7 REDUCED INTERROGATION RATES

The increase in data integrity conferred by monopulse processing coupled with the freedom from the need for continuous reply history throughout a beamwidth allows monopulse systems to operate at lower interrogation rates. This, when applied to a community of interrogators, reduces the impact of transponder dead times and simultaneously delays the onset of capture effects, as well as reducing fruit densities.

6.5 Modern engineering forms
6.5.1 ANTENNAS

Enough has already been said to appreciate the forms of antenna currently being used. Not so widely appreciated is the fact that because monopulse systems use the antenna patterns as part of the measuring system, the patterns need monitoring as well as the electronic equipment serving them. A number of methods and equipments are used for this purpose. They fall into two categories, near field and far field measuring systems.

In the former, a small unit placed in the near field gathers field strength data across the rotating antenna aperture. An analysis routine compares the results with a set of known reference values, any deviation indicating a change in pattern shape. Such a unit, shown in Fig. 6.22, has the capability of detecting which particular element of the linear array is faulty.

An example of a far field monitoring system is shown in Fig. 6.23. It is a multi-purpose unit which acts as a reference transponder as well as a means of pattern measurement. In its latter function, it measures the amplitude of radiated interrogation pulses as the SSR antenna rotates. The values are stored and output to a recorder or data logger for viewing or comparison with a reference. In its role as a reference transponder it behaves exactly as does any other, to ICAO standards.

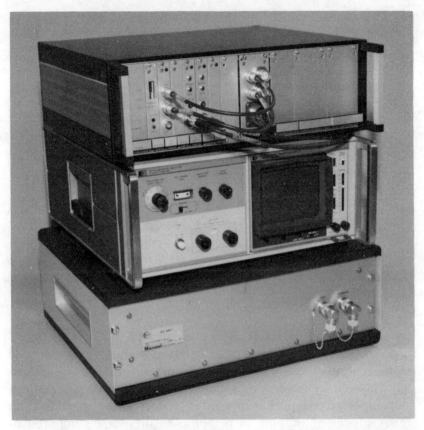

Fig. 6.22   Near field test set. (*Photo courtesy of Marconi Research Centre.*)

Its reply trains can be delayed so that it appears at any desired range. This enables it to be located on the interrogator site whilst appearing to be at great range. Garbled reply scenarios can also be created.

6.5.2   INTERROGATORS

Despite the proven reliability of modern L-band vacuum tubes of the low peak power required by SSR, many modern interrogators have solid state output stages. Because the antennas usually have high gain and the permitted ERP is restricted to 52.5 dbW, output peak powers of 2 kW and less are commonly found. As required by ICAO specifications and following the fast increasing desire of users for automatic BITE (built-in test equipment), interrogator performance is extensively monitored. In monopulse systems of high azimuth accuracy and processing power, the need

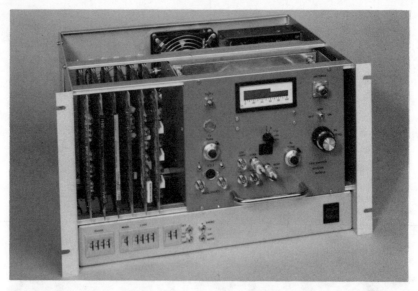

Fig. 6.23 Far field monitor. (*Photo courtesy of Marconi Radar Systems Ltd.*)

for constant internal checking is even greater. The interrogators' main parameters are automatically monitored, 'go/no go' signals being generated as a result. The OBA measuring system is internally checked by generating signals in the known phase relationship expected of inputs at specific OBAs across the aperture. The OBA processor outputs in response to these are compared to internal reference values, any differences indicating a failure. The decoding functions are automatically checked by test reply trains generated internally and injected at the decoder's input as real-time video signals. Simultaneously the reference transponder replies are passed right through the system. The plot extractor also has self-generated test routines and thus the total system has the means of detecting short-fall in performance and isolating the faulty area.

The requirement for remote computer controlled monitoring is met by signalling all the results of self-checking as a composite digital word incorporated into the plot extractor output data stream. Indications can be called out at the remote point from a VDU menu.

6.5.3 DECODING, PLOT FORMING AND DATA EXTRACTION

In monopulse systems a very great deal of data is generated. With 20 MHz sampling rate, each reply involves 9 bits of time data, 8 bits of OBA data, 7 bits to express amplitude plus a few more to express the confidence to be placed in the outputs. It is usual to design for over 256 wanted targets per antenna revolution, with peak densities of over 20 wanted targets per beamwidth: this with an unwanted fruit rate of more than 20 000 per second.

The techniques for decoding, plot forming and data extraction are many, but most share the common chain of:

1. Detecting valid code trains.
2. Forming partial plots (rejecting replies which do not correlate in range as 'fruit').
3. Forming valid plots.
4. Formatting code data associated with valid plots.
5. Output of full plot data (R·θ, code/altitude, confidence, system status).

Most systems have architectures which cater for varying target densities and incidence of multi-target garble. It is usual to have separate decoding channels to ensure pulses of garbled replies are associated into valid reply trains. Two channels are necessary to ensure continuity of code detection throughout the range continuum to effect correct decoding of a dual reply garble. Other channels (usually up to a maximum of four) can be added to cater for higher target densities, which could lead to more complex garbles.

With so much data available for use, it is possible to construct algorithms which seek to enhance output data integrity to a high maximum by the exercise of 'confidence' or 'validation' rules. By this means, data need be processed only for the time necessary to achieve this maximum, while data for plots with less than maximum integrity can be further processed in order to achieve the highest integrity possible.

Modern techniques of fast real-time decoding involve the use of either parallel microprocessors or bit/slice processors. The latter are faster, reduce component count and hence improve reliability and space requirements. Because decoding and plot forming are so closely interlinked, they are often combined in one unit, as in Fig. 6.24, a photograph of a four-channel decoder and plot extractor. Space is still available for the process of primary radar plot extraction and their combining with concurrent SSR plots. In common with many modern equipments, the processors mounted on signal printed circuitboards are interconnected by a

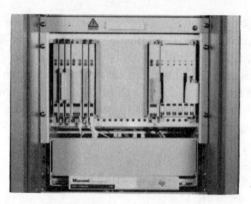

Fig. 6.24 'Messenger' decoder/plot extractor.
(*Photo courtesy of Marconi Radar Systems Ltd.*)

fast multi-bus highway at the back-plane, while services to the outside world are connected at the front end of the board.

6.6 Performance – range

The range performance of an SSR system is determined by the lesser of two separate range equations, corresponding to the up-link interrogation and the down-link reply.

6.6.1 THE UP-LINK RANGE

This is calculated from:

$$R_{i(max)} = \frac{\lambda_i}{4\pi \times 10^3} \left[\frac{p_i \cdot G_i \cdot G_t}{S_r \cdot L_i \cdot L_a} \right]^{\frac{1}{2}} \tag{1}$$

where

$R_{i(max)}$ = peak interrogation range (km)
λ_i = wavelength of interrogation radiation (m)
p_i = peak interrogation power at source (W)
S_r = transponder input required (W)
L_i = total loss from interrogator source to antenna terminals
G_t = transponder antenna gain, and
L_a = atmospheric attenuation in the up-link path.

It should be noted that:

1. The product of P_i G_i (the ERP) must never be greater than 52.5 dbW for systems conforming to the ICAO Specification for SSR.

2. Although airborne antennas usually have about 3 dB gain, this is off-set by a like value of attenuation between the antenna and the transponder. Thus it is common to find a value of unity ascribed to G_t.

3. The practical value for the up-link range is less than its peak for the obvious reason that repeated replies on given modes of interrogation must be stimulated. A minimum of two per mode is required by reply processors and since reply probability is never 100%, three interrogations per mode must be made. Thus for a triple mode interlace, nine interrogations per beamwidth must be provided. The usual considerations of interrogation rate, antenna beamshape, and antenna rotation rate will reveal how much $R_{i(max)}$ will reduce to the useable value.

4. The equation is modified by the effect of ground reflections. The up and down link wavelengths differ by 5.8%. In systems with a very great antenna height above ground, the resultant lobes and gaps in the vertical polar diagram will be closely spaced and very numerous. As elevation increases, the mismatch in space between lobes and gaps at the two different wavelengths can affect performance, since the up- and down-link wavelengths differ by 5.8%.

6.6.2 THE DOWN-LINK RANGE

This is given by:

$$R_{rep(max)} = \frac{\lambda_r}{4\pi \times 10^3} \left[\frac{P_t \cdot G_t \cdot G_r}{S_i \cdot L_i \cdot L_t \cdot L_a} \right]^{\frac{1}{2}} \qquad (2)$$

where

$R_{rep(max)}$ = peak reply range (km)
λ_r = wavelength of reply radiation (m)
P_t = transponder peak output (W)
G_t = transponder antenna gain
S_i = signal input required by the responser
L_i = losses between antenna and responser input
L_t = loss between transponder and airborne antenna, and
L_a = atmospheric attenuation in the down-link path.

6.6.3 ROUND TRIP RELIABILITY

System specifications commonly require a level of 'round trip reliability' (r.t.r.) to be achieved, meaning the probability that a valid interrogation will result in detection of a useable reply. Call this probability $P(\text{rtr})$; then:

$$\text{rtr}\% = P(\text{rtr}) \times 100$$

and

$$P(\text{rtr}) = P_i \times Pd_{(i)} \times P_r \times Pd_{(r)}$$

where P_i = probability that a valid interrogation is received at the aircraft

$Pd_{(i)}$ = probability that the valid interrogation is detected

P_r = probability that a valid reply is transmitted after successful interrogation detection, and

$Pd_{(r)}$ = probability that a reply is useably detected.

A number of effects conspire to reduce r.t.r. from 100%, despite the usually high signal-to-noise ratios at either end of up and down links. Among these are:

1. Multipath effects (in both vertical and horizontal planes) which can corrupt interrogations as seen at the aircraft. This influences P_i.

2. The ISLS and airborne receiver suppression reply logic. Its action will reduce $Pd_{(i)}$ and P_r.

3. Multipath effects and the presence of corrupting fruit will reduce $Pd_{(r)}$.

Nevertheless, repeated interrogation on given modes during the passage of the beam across the transponder raises the value of r.t.r. to very high levels. If the r.t.r. per beamwidth is P_o and the r.t.r. per interrogation per mode is P_m then:

$$P_o = \sqrt[4]{P_m}$$

where n is the number of interrogations per mode within the beamwidth.

Thus if the number of repetitions of an interrogation in a beamwidth was 4 and the r.t.r. per interrogation was 0.8 then:

$$P_o = \sqrt[4]{0.8} = 0.946 \text{ or } 94.6\%$$

6.7 Performance – positional data

Monopulse SSR dramatically improves positional data above that provided by traditional SSR. This is largely because of the azimuth data improvement. Traditional SSR azimuth data using 'sliding window' or equivalent logic has a standard deviation, typically, of 12 minutes of arc. Some monopulse systems have cut this to a quarter, i.e. 3 minutes of arc. Results from a monopulse system with dual phase direction finding with 14-bit discretion are shown in Figs 6.25 and 6.26.

6.8 Future extensions to SSR – mode 'S'

The ability of mode 'S', a selective address system, to overcome SSR's problems is largely the result of avoiding (apart from infrequently gathering new target data) the need to broadcast interrogations.

The interrogation and reply phases are exactly the same as in SSR, using the same up- and down-link frequencies. The differences are largely in:

1. Message format.
2. Type of modulation.
3. Data integrity checking.

Both interrogator and transponder equipment in mode 'S' are organised to be totally compatible with current SSR standards.

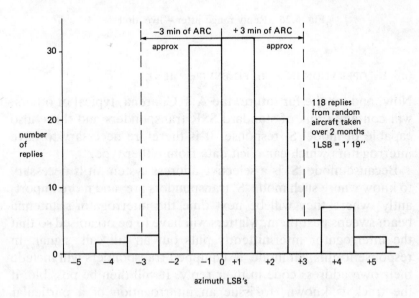

Fig. 6.25 Reply azimuth spread – live aircraft.

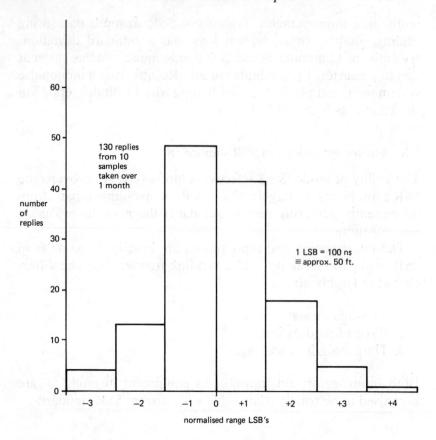

Fig. 6.26 Reply range jitter – live aircraft.

6.8.1 OPERATION IN A MIXED ENVIRONMENT

Now, and for the far future, the A.T.C. arena, typical of others, will contain a mix of standard SSR transponders and those also capable of mode 'S' response. It is therefore necessary to have interrogators which can elicit data from either type.

Because mode 'S' is a selective address system, it is necessary to know where such mode 'S' transponders are, and more importantly, where they will be next time the interrogator's antenna beam sweeps past them. Matters will have to be organised so that the interrogator intermittently puts out an 'all call' signal. In response to this, all mode 'S' equipped transponders will include their own address code in their reply. It will then be possible, if the track is known, to issue an interrogation of a particular transponder on the next antenna revolution at the appropriate time, i.e. when the interrogating beam is illuminating it. In the meantime the interrogator will issue normal SSR interrogations in the broadcast manner.

In the fullness of time, as more and more transponders are raised to mode 'S' standards in the international sphere, the full benefits of the system will be felt. Until that time (the author suggests it will be decades) the up- and down-link equipments must be of dual standard. Moreover, because the 'broadcast' mode of operating must still be maintained and the intermittent use of mode 'S' interrogations disrupts contiguous replies from normal transponders, the sliding window azimuth detection system will produce yet more errors. Such errors can be corrected by monopulse technique, which incidentially must be used in mode 'S'.

6.8.2 MESSAGE FORMAT AND MODULATION IN MODE 'S'

Message formats and types of modulation in mode 'S' are radically different from the current ICAO modes. The mode 'S' up-link format is shown in Fig. 6.27(a) and (b). As already mentioned, it is necessary to have an interrogation regime wherein new mode 'S' targets are acquired. The 'all call' format is used for this. It is like the normal SSR up-link pulse train but with the addition of a fourth pulse (P_4) which can be of either 0.8 or 1.6 µs duration. The former duration is used for obtaining normal mode A or C SSR transponder replies (the position and duration of P_4 does not affect their reply capability). Mode 'S' transponders will not reply to this. However, if P_4 is of 1.6 µs duration they will recognise it and reply with their unique addresses in mode 'S' format. Thus the position and address of all mode 'S' transponders can be down-loaded to an 'interrogation scheduler' for subsequent use.

The mode 'S' interrogation proper is shown in Fig. 6.27(b). It consists now of four pulses; P_1 and P_2 are of equal amplitude in the main interrogation beam and are construed by normal transponders as a suppression pair. The mode 'S' transponders will then seek the presence of the start of P_6 (P_3 and P_4 are only involved in normal SSR and 'all call' interrogations). It consists of a long pulse of 1030 MHz ± 0.02 MHz and its duration is either 16.25 or 30.25 µs. The increased frequency stability is required because the modulations throughout its duration are of the 'differential phase shift keyed' type (DPSK). In this, binary 1 is signalled by changing the phase by 180°.

By dividing the pulse duration into 'chips' of 0.25 μs and sampling the pulse at these intervals, phase reversals sensed between samples mean 'ones' and absence of reversal, zeros. Such modulation has high immunity from noise and interference. Thus P_6 can form a 56- or 112-bit word, dependent upon the duration chosen. To establish a reference by which the phase reversals can be sensed, the binary message begins 1.25 μs after the P_6 leading edge. The phase of the interrogation's RF during this period is used within the transponder as a reference.

A phase sensitive detector uses the sustained reference oscillation as one input and the DPSK signals as the other. Phase reversals detected generate digital outputs of 'ones' and zeros

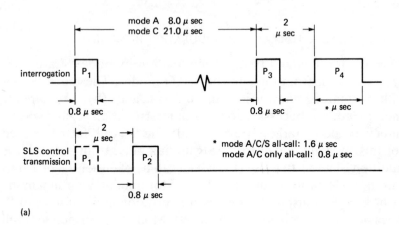

(a)

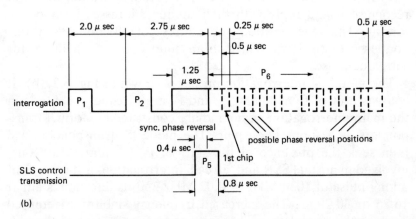

(b)

Fig. 6.27 (a) Mode 'S' all-call interrogation formats; (b) mode 'S' interrogation format P_6 can be 16.25 or 30.5 μs duration and uses differential phase shift keying (DPSK) modulation.

from the detector for subsequent decoding and reaction within the transponder. As in normal SSR an ISLS pulse, P_5, is transmitted by an interrogator 'control' pattern. This is to obviate any replies from normal SSR transponders, should they mistake part of P_6 as a normal P_3.

The mode 'S' reply format is shown in Fig. 6.28. After a 4-pulse preamble, it can express either a 56- or a 112-bit binary word using pulse position coding, as does normal SSR, but with greater economy and integrity. Each 1 μs time slot contains a 0.5 μs pulse. This occupies either the first half of the one microsecond period to signal 1 or the second to signal a 0. Thus both binary states are indicated by the presence of a pulse; in the current ICAO SSR reply format, a zero is signalled by the absence of a pulse.

6.8.3 THE USE OF MODE 'S' DATA

It is already obvious that the data capacity of mode 'S' is vastly greater than that of SSR as it currently stands. When used in its data link role, mode 'S' messages can be yet further extended by repetitions of its standard form in what are termed 'extended length messages' (ELMs). Up to sixteen blocks of eighty bits can be strung together, giving a total message content of 1280 bits. The formats, protocols, identifying bit patterns, etc., are all described in Ref. 11.

Down-link messages signalling aircraft rate of turn, heading, rate of altitude change, etc., will aid tracking algorithms, resulting in better turn detection with fewer false turn indications and

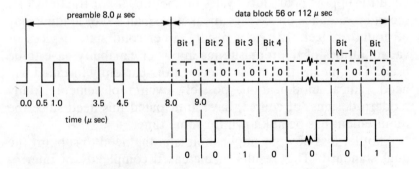

example: reply data block waveform corresponding
to bit sequence 0010.....001

Fig. 6.28 Mode 'S' transponder reply format. Note that a 0 is transmitted as a signal and not as *absence* of a signal.

quicker reaction time. The potential use of the data link in collision avoidance is anticipated.

6.8.4 TECHNICAL IMPLICATIONS OF MODE 'S'

6.8.4.1 *Transponders*
The technical implications in airborne transponder design will already have been realised. Obviously they have to cater for the dual standards of mode 'S' and the current SSR for as long as the latter is part of the ICAO Annex 10 specification. Another implication is concerned with interfacing between the aircraft's (or vehicle's) existing sensor system and providing such data as speed, heading, fuel state, rate of turn, etc., as input to the new transponders – a difficult and expensive exercise. The USA has taken a firm stance in insisting that all new transponders to be fitted in airframes operated in the USA after 1987 shall be of the required dual standard.

6.8.4.2 *Interrogators*
The transmitter output stages of current SSR interrogators need have only a very small mean power output capability, of the order of 2 W typically. This is because peak power of less than 2000 W can be employed at repetition rates of not more than 450 per second for three short pulses. The duty cycle is very low, being not more than 0.001 (0.1%). In mode 'S' systems, the output pulse duration grows from three pulses of 0.8 µs duration to just over a total of 30 µs. These must be able to be repeated sixteen times with very short spacing between bursts, resulting in the need to support peak duty cycles of about 60% for fractions of a second. Guidance on average, peak and small sector loading may be found in Ref. 12. As a result, either solid state devices or vacuum tubes of the requisite mean power capability have to be used. This means that most interrogators currently installed will need radical modification, possibly even replacement. Many modern designs, of course, have anticipated this need since the requirement has been known for some time.

Another less obvious implication is in the need to support the dual standard. This results in increased complexity of interrogators and provision of the means of 'scheduling' interrogations, to establish their priority, and to sort, format, queue and route the two sorts of reply data for transmission back to the user who demanded it.

Such arrangements are still under discussion and no internationally agreed standard has yet been published.

References

1. Honold, P. *Secondary Radar*, Heyden & Son (1971).
2. Cole, H. W. *Understanding Radar*, Collins, p. 165 (1985).
3. Cole, H. W. 'SECAR – A Modern SSR Ground Interrogator and Decoding Equipment', *J. IERE,* 33, 1 (1967).
4. Cole, H. W. 'The Future for SSR', *ICAO Bull.*, Sept. (1980).
5. Ullyatt, C. 'Sensors for the ATC Environment with Special Reference to SSR', *UK Symp. on Elec. for Civ. Av.*, Paper No. 1, Cat. 1, Sect. C, Savoy Place, London (1969).
6. *Rules of the Air & Air Traffic Services*, Doc. No. 4444-RAC/501/12, ICAO, Montreal (1985).
7. Annex 10 to the *Convention on International Civil Aviation*, (Int. Standards & Recommended Practices – Aeron. Telecomms.), HMSO, London 2 (1968).
8. Gordon, J. 'Monopulse Technique Applied to Current SSR', *GEC J. of Sc. & Tech.*, **7**, 3, Feb. (1982).
9. Cole, H. W. 'The Suppression of Reflected Interrogation in SSR', *Marconi Review*, **43**, 217, 2nd Qtr. (1980).
10 Cohen, W. and Steinmetz, C. M. 'Amplitude and Phase Sensing Monopulse System Parameters', Part I and II, *Microw. J.*, Oct. and Nov. (1959).
11. 'Secondary Surveillance Radar Mode 'S' Advisory Circular', *ICAO Circ. No. 174-AN/110*, ICAO, Montreal (1983).
12. Dept. of Transportation, Federal Aviation Administration Specification, 'Mode Select Beacon System Sensor', Draft FAA-E-2716, 2 Sept. (1982).

Index

Acronyms

A/D, ADC	analogue to digital (converter)
ADSEL	address selectable system
AJ	anti-jamming
ARM	anti-radiation missile
ATC	air traffic control
BFN	beam forming network
BITE	built-in test equipment
BWO	backward wave oscillator
CAA	Civil Aviation Authority (UK)
CCIR	International Radio Consultative Committee
CESM	counter electronic support measure
CFA	crossed field amplifier
COSRO	conical scan receive only
CW	continuous wave
D/A, DAC	digital to analogue (converter)
DABS	direct addressed beam system
DINA	direct noise amplification
DMI	direct matrix inversion
DPSK	differential phase shift keying
ECCM	electronic counter-counter measures
ECM	electronic counter measures
EFIE	electric field integral equations
ELINT	electronic intelligence
EMC	electromagnetic compatibility
EMCON	emission control
ERP	effective radiated power
ESJ	escort jamming
ESM	electronic support measures
EW	electronic warfare
FET	field effect transistor
FFT	fast Fourier transform
FMCW	frequency modulated continuous wave
FMICW	frequency modulated interrupted continuous wave
GaAs	gallium arsenide
GEESE	General Electric Electronic Systems Evaluator
GTD	geometric theory of diffraction
HEMT	high electron mobility transistor
HF	high frequency
HOJ	home-on-jam
ICAO	International Civil Aviation Organisation
ICBM	intercontinental ballistic missile
IF	intermediate frequency
IFF	identification friend or foe
IGY	International Geophysical Year
LNA	low noise amplifier
LO	local oscillator
LOCM	low observable counter measures
LPIn	low probability of intercept
LPId	low probability of identification
MEM	maximum entropy method

MFIE	magnetic field integral equations
MIT	Massachusetts Institute of Technology (US)
MM	method of moments
MMIC	monolithic microwave integrated circuit
MOE	measure of effectiveness
MOM	method of moments
MOPA	master oscillator power amplifier
MTD	moving target detection
MTI	moving target indication
MUF	maximum usable frequency
NRL	Naval Research Lab. (US)
OTH	over-the-horizon
PE	parametric estimator
PIN	semiconductor diode, with intrinsic layer between p-doped and n-doped layers
PN	pseudo-noise
PPI	plan position indicator
PRF	pulse recurrence frequency
Q	quadrature (component)
RAM	radar absorbing material
REC	radio electronic warfare (USSR)
RF	radio frequency
RGPO	range gate pull off
RSRE	Royal Signals and Radar Establishment (UK)
SRI	Stanford Research Institute (US)
SOJ	stand-off jamming
SSJ	self-screening jamming
SSR	secondary surveillance radar
TAS	track and search
TOJ	track-on-jam
TWS	track while scan
TWT	travelling wave tube
UHF	ultra high frequency
UTD	uniform theory of diffraction
VCO	voltage controlled oscillator
VGPO	velocity gate pull off
VHF	very high frequency
VLSI	very large scale integration
VTM	voltage tuned magnetron
WARF	wide aperture research facility